60 YEARS

OF

UNIVERSITY CHALLENGE

60 YEARS

OF

UNIVERSITY CHALLENGE

CASSELL

First published in Great Britain in 2022 by Cassell, an imprint of
Octopus Publishing Group Ltd
Carmelite House
50 Victoria Embankment
London EC4Y 0DZ
www.octopusbooks.co.uk

An Hachette UK Company
www.hachette.co.uk

ISBN 978-1-78840-406-8

A CIP catalogue record for this book is available from the British Library.

Printed and bound in the UK.

10 9 8 7 6 5 4 3 2 1

University Challenge™ is produced by ITV Studios
in association with The College Bowl Company.

Designed, compiled and packaged by Steve Tribe
Feature text by Abigail Kemp

Publisher: Trevor Davies
Senior Editor: Pollyanna Poulter
Senior Production Manager: Katherine Hockley
Transcribing: Lorraine Hartnoll

Contents

Foreword

Peter Gwyn
(Executive Producer)

Sixty years of *University Challenge*? The title invites the question – how on earth did it get to be 60 years old? First seen in 1962 in the flickering black-and-white television world of *Z Cars*, *Andy Pandy* and Dickie Valentine, somehow it has managed to survive to sit alongside *Strictly*, *Love Island* and everything by Russell T Davies.

It seems an unlikely survivor, because on paper the format is so minimal. There's a presenter, two teams of students, and several dozen rather difficult questions, and that's it. And when it comes to the questions, the one remark we hear from viewers more than any other is that they congratulate themselves if they can get two right per episode; only one would not be quite enough, but two right answers will leave them feeling very pleased with themselves. But those three elements – the presenter, the teams, the questions – are the keys to the programme's survival.

For a programme celebrating its 60th birthday, it's remarkable that it has only ever had two presenters, and it has been immensely fortunate in both of them.

In 1962, Bamber Gascoigne was unlike anyone else on television. With an unmistakably donnish demeanour, displaying extraordinary erudition and immense charm, he gave the impression that he had briefly stepped out of the ivory tower of academia to conquer the world of television with effortless ease. He came from a privileged and influential family who had been central to British public life since they settled in England in the 13th century from the French region of Gascony. His sprawling family tree featured a seventeenth Lord Mayor of London, a couple of MPs, and a three-time prime minister, Lord Salisbury. Bamber presented the programme for twenty-five years, his tenure only ending when, in 1987, the programme lost its place in the ITV television schedules and was cancelled. By then, his name and the title of the programme were so deeply intertwined it was difficult to imagine anyone else in the role.

Enter Jeremy Paxman. After the programme had been absent from our screens for seven years – a time the programme's production team still refer to as the Interregnum – the idea emerged to resurrect it, still produced as always by ITV, but now to transmit on the BBC, and with Jeremy Paxman at the helm. Having established himself as the *Newsnight* presenter that politicians would least like to come up against, he was an inspired choice for the presenter's chair, reflecting the continuing evolution of university education from the entitlement of the privileged few to an aspiration within the grasp of many. He brought an inquisitorial tone to the programme, much relished by the student teams who were thrilled to come up against the Mighty Paxo, and wanted more than anything to have him shout at them for any perceived lapse. Jeremy, for his part, has a genuine fondness and respect for the student population, which he does everything within his power to hide.

The questions undoubtedly take their share of the credit for the programme's longevity, managing a difficult balance between material that might be taken from a university syllabus to more general questioning about the wider world that reflects the priorities of a traditional, liberal education. Devised by both members of the programme's production team and a group of freelance question-setters before being submitted to a tenacious team of verifiers, each question has to earn its place in the programme by fulfilling one or more of a number of criteria. Is it inherently interesting? If teams do not know the answer, does it give them enough information for them to make an educated guess? Is it fair to suggest that someone on either team might be expected to know to answer? If Paxman suspects the answer to the last of these is 'no', he's been known to toss the question card over his shoulder with a contemptuous remark such as, 'Why you should be expected to know that, I have no idea!'

The main reason for the programme's success, though, lies with the student teams who entertain us with what they know – and sometimes horrify us with what they don't know – about pretty much everything. Their tightly structured, brief introductions at the top of each episode tell us nothing more than name, place of birth and subject studied, but it's during the following half an hour that we begin to get to know them, and to know how they work as a team. How do they deal with their nerves? Are they confident? Or overconfident? Which team has a bolder approach to the buzzer, which team is better at pulling the right answer out of their conferrals?

The more we see the successful foursomes progress through the competition, the more we get to know and appreciate them, and root for them all, perhaps never more so than when the final credits roll and we see the teams applaud each other in a heart-warming display of sporting good humour – all the more impressive given that the losing team may well be feeling as gutted as a row of kippers.

The programme has been now been running so long that we're accustomed to players telling us that their parents appeared on it in the past; we don't believe it's happened yet that the grandchild of a previous contestant has appeared, but that day cannot be far off, and we look forward to celebrating when it does.

We sincerely hope you enjoy celebrating the programme's 60th birthday as you test yourself on the questions that follow.

Leeds

Manchester
(1962)

It all began in 1962.

No record exists of Leeds's match-up with Reading University, but they won and went on to defeat Exeter in the second edition.

The third show – the earliest for which we have records – was described by Bamber Gascoigne as 'virtually a War of the Roses' between Leeds and Manchester. Leeds would have to retire after three shows, but would they do so undefeated?

Leeds

M. Murphy from Cheshire, doing Geography research

P. Hall (captain) from Nottinghamshire, reading English

M. Bonney from Lancashire, reading English and Philosophy

I. Channell from Kent, reading Psychology and Sociology

Manchester

S. Baddeley from Surrey, doing Botany research

H. Haste from Bristol, reading General Arts

T. Boyd (captain) from Manchester,
reading Politics and Modern History

M. Evans from Lancashire,
doing a postgraduate diploma in Education

Part One

Your starter for ten:

1   Thursday is named after the Anglo-Saxon god Thor. After whom is
    Wednesday named?

Bonus question:
(a) Five men were chiefly responsible for the revolution of the modern view of
the solar system which replaced that of Ptolemy and Aristotle. Ten points each
for any four that you name.

Your starter for ten:

2   I want you to quote the sentence which immediately precedes these lines
    of Shakespeare. 'It is twice blest: It blesseth him that gives and him that
    takes.'

Bonus questions:
By what names are the following Beethoven Symphonies known?
(a) The Third
(b) The Sixth
(c) The Ninth

Your starter for ten:

3   Identify the man who maybe was described as 'organ builder', 'organist',
    'architect', 'philosopher', 'author', 'theologian' and 'doctor'?

Bonus questions:
We call George Washington the father of his country. Other men have played
similar parts in other countries and, for five points apiece, who was the similar
man in each of these countries?
(a) Modern Turkey
(b) Columbia
(c) Post-Imperial China
(d) Haiti

Your starter for ten:

4   1776 was the date of a revolution in the study of economics. Who
    produced this revolution?

Bonus questions:
(a) How many people were found guilty of offences of all kinds in England and Wales in 1961, and I will accept anything to the nearest 100,000?
(b) What proportion of these were traffic offences, and I will accept 5 per cent either way?

Your starter for ten:
5   [The teams were played a recording of Ernest Bevin speaking in Washington in 1948]
    An important political alliance had been declared. What was it?

Bonus questions:
The following exchange of dialogue takes place in a famous play.
    First character: 'That passed the time.'
    Second character: 'It would have passed in any case.'
    First character: 'Yes, but not so rapidly.'
(a) For ten points, what is the name of the play?
(b) For a further five points each, who were the two characters?

Your starter for ten:
6   Who was the last Tsar of Russia?

Bonus question:
(a) The Witches' Sabbath in Gogol's story 'St John's Eve' is the inspiration for which of Mussorgsky's works?

Your starter for ten:
7   Solomon Grundy was born on Monday. When did he die?

Bonus questions:
In which wars did the following battles take place?
(a) Edge Hill
(b) Matapan
(c) Bunker Hill
(d) Zama?

End of Part One

Part Two

Your starter for ten:

8 Who was the South African who received the Nobel Peace Prize in December 1961?

Bonus questions:
[The bonus questions were pieces of modern music that were derived from a classical source. Teams had to name the original piece and the composer. Leeds scored a maximum by naming pieces derived from Borodin, Bizet and Prokofiev]

Your starter for ten:

9 In what modern country would you be if you visited a city which Wordsworth described as 'The eldest child of liberty'?

Bonus question:
The equation of the physical universe is said to be $E=mc^2$.
(a) Who propounded it?
(b) What do the symbols mean?

Your starter for ten:

10 Who created the famous cartoon character Colonel Blimp?
[Neither side answered, so a further starter was asked]

Your starter for ten:

11 What, according to a famous child's poem, 'sometimes shoots up taller like an Indian rubber ball'?

Bonus questions:
The art of formal mime is often used in ballet to express emotions or actions. Can you show us how to express the following?
(a) To ask something
(b) What suggests love
(c) What suggests seeing
(d) What suggests swearing (swearing loyalty, that is)

Your starter for ten:

12 According to the Bible who were Dan, Gad, Asher, Reuben, Judah—
[This question was successfully interrupted]

Bonus questions:
According to Greek mythology, Zeus had a very full sex life and a very imaginative one. For ten points each, I want you to tell me in what form he seduced the following ladies:
(a) Leda
(b) Danae
(c) Io
(d) Alkemene

Your starter for ten:
13 In 1834, six Dorset labourers—
[The question was successfully interrupted]

Bonus questions:
Dying speeches are often apocryphal, but the following are genuine. Four such speeches follow, and I want to know who said them.
(a) 'Thy necessity is yet greater than mine?'
(b) 'Let not poor Nelly starve'?
(c) 'Now, God be praised, I will die in Peace'?
(d) 'All my possessions for a moment of time'?

Your starter for ten:
14 An Oedipus complex is a term used to denote a boy's affection being being centred on his mother. What is the name for the corresponding fixation that a girl could have for her father?

Bonus question:
(a) Name the eight SEATO countries that signed the Manila treaty.

Your starter for ten:
15 [The Starter was a piece of music which neither team could identify as Honegger's *Pacific 231*, so another starter was asked]

Your starter for ten:
16 This great composer was commissioned to compose the music for a requiem mass and he said he felt he was writing his own requiem and in fact died at 35. What was his name?
[Neither team could answer correctly, so another starter was asked]

Your starter for ten:
17 How much did Great Britain spend on defence last year?

Bonus question:

(a) Who wrote a book consisting of a discourse between characters such as Piscator and Venator?

Your starter for ten:

18 His father was the West Wind and his mother was Wenonah. Who was he?

[Again, neither team could answer, so another starter was asked]

Your starter for ten:

19 Give us the name of the only continent that is south of the—

[The question was successfully interrupted]

Bonus questions:

Two of Shaw's plays have been turned into successful musical operettas or musical comedies, one by Oscar Straus and one by Frederick Loewe. What were the two plays called and what were the musical versions called?

The buzzer sounds

The game ended with Leeds retiring from the series undefeated, having beaten Manchester by 250 points to 155.

The Answers

1   Woden
    (a) (Nicolaus) Copernicus; Galileo (Galilei); (Johannes) Kepler; (Isaac) Newton;
    Tycho Brahe

2   'The quality of mercy is not strained, / It droppeth as the gentle rain from heaven / Upon
    the place beneath. / It is twice blest...'
    (Spoken by Portia in *The Merchant of Venice* Act 4, Scene 1)
    (a) The Eroica
    (b) The Pastoral
    (c) The Choral

3   Albert Schweitzer
    (a) (Mustafa Kemal) Atatürk
    (b) Simón Bolívar
    (c) Sun Yat-sen
    (d) Toussaint Louverture

4   Adam Smith
    (a) 1,152,397
    (b) 61 per cent

5   The North Atlantic Pact
    (a) *Waiting for Godot*
    (b) Vladimir and Estragon

6   Nicholas II
    (a) *Night on the Bald* [or *Bare*] *Mountain*

7   Saturday
    (a) Civil War
    (b) Second World War
    (c) American War of Independence
    (d) Second Punic War

8   (Albert) Luthuli (the Prize was actually awarded in 1960)

9   Italy (Venice)
    (a) (Albert) Einstein
    (b) Energy; mass; and speed of light

10 David Lowe

11   My shadow (from the poem 'My Shadow' by RL Stevenson)
     (a) Hands together – like praying
     (b) Hand on heart
     (c) Two hands on two eyes
     (d) Left hand on heart and right hand raised over head with fingers straight

12   Twelve sons of Jacob
     (a) Swan
     (b) Shower of gold
     (c) Cloud
     (d) Shape of her husband (Amphitryon)

13   The Tolpuddle Martyrs
     (a) Sir Philip Sydney offering water to a wounded soldier
     (b) King Charles II to Nell Gwynne
     (c) General Wolfe
     (d) Queen Elizabeth I

14   Electra complex
     (a) Pakistan; USA; Siam; Australia; New Zealand; Great Britain; France; Philippines

15   [Music round]

16   (Wolfgang Amadeus) Mozart

17   £1,656 million
     (a) Izaak Walton (*The Compleat Angler*)

18   Hiawatha

19   Australia
     (a) *Arms and the Man – The Chocolate Soldier* (Straus)
     (b) *Pygmalion – My Fair Lady* (Loewe)

Try Your Luck
Match

Your starter for ten:

1 Beijing is one of four cities traditionally known as the 'Four Great Ancient Capitals of China'. Name two of the others.

Your bonuses are on English words taken from indigenous languages of the Americas. In each case, identify the word from the description:
(a) From an Algonquian language, a seven-letter word meaning 'snow shoveller' that refers to several species of reindeer.
(b) From the Tupi-Guarani for 'squeeze out' and 'dregs', a seven-letter word for hard white grains obtained from cassava starch and used in cooking.
(c) Meaning 'he dreams', a six-letter word for a conference or a Native American ceremony involving feasting, singing and dancing.

Your starter for ten:

2 What six-letter word links all of the following? Frederick, the Elector Palatine, who briefly occupied the Bohemian throne; a former imperial residence in St Petersburg that is now part of the Hermitage Museum; and a play by Shakespeare in which a statue appears to come to life.

Your bonuses are on winners of the Booker Prize. In each case, give the name of the book from its year of publication and its first words:
(a) From 2009: '"So now get up." Felled, dazed, silent, he has fallen; knocked full length on the cobbles of the yard.'
(b) From 2013: 'The twelve men congregated in the smoking room of the Crown hotel gave the impression of a party accidentally met.'
(c) From 2014: 'Listen. Dead people never stop talking. Maybe because death is not death at all, just a detention after school.'

Your starter for ten:

3 'He rode / On a white horse, splashed with blood; / He was pale even to his lips, / Like death in the apocalypse.' These words refer to what

personification, named in the title of a work written by Shelley in response to the Peterloo Massacre?

Three questions on European rodents:
(a) Living at heights above 600 metres, Alpine is a European species of which large ground squirrel? It is in the same genus as the North American groundhog.
(b) Norway, Brown and Collared are species of which mouse-like rodent? Its numbers fluctuate widely, with high populations leading to mass migrations.
(c) The genus *Hystrix* comprises large rodents known by what common name, partly derived from the Latin for 'pig'? The crested species may be seen in Italy.

Your starter for ten:
4   I need a two-word term here. Often used in weather reports, what physical quantity is defined as 'the water content of the air expressed as a percentage relative to the vapour pressure of the same air, saturated, and at the same temperature'? The term has the abreviation RH.

Three questions on a 20th-century movement in science:
(a) Coined in 1942, the term 'modern synthesis' refers to the reconciliation of the ideas of Darwin with those of which other biologist, whose work was rediscovered in the early 20th century?
(b) A leading figure of the modern synthesis, which Ukraine-born scientist published *Genetics and the Origin of Species* and the essay 'Nothing in Biology Makes Sense, Except in the Light of Evolution'?
(c) The term 'modern synthesis' was coined in a work by which scientist, the grandson of the biologist nicknamed 'Darwin's bulldog'? I just need a surname.

Your starter for ten:
5   Subtitled *An Optical Revolution*, an exhibition at the Museum of Fine Arts in Ghent in 2020 was dedicated to which artist of the 15th century, the creator of *The Adoration of the Mystic Lamb*, otherwise known as the *Ghent Altarpiece*?

Your bonuses are on English cities and US states that share the same two-letter postcode, for example Carlisle and California. In each case, give both the English city and the US state from the descriptions:
(a) The English city associated with the artist Joseph Wright, and the US state that appears in the title of a painting by Emanuel Leutze, depicting a military action of December 1776.
(b) The third-largest, and most recent, city of the ceremonial county of West Midlands, and a US state admitted to the union in 1863.

(c) An English city on the River Lune, and a US state named after the Sun King.

Your starter for ten:

6 Which city was founded in 762 as the capital of the Abbasid dynasty? It became the capital of a modern state after the First World War, following the break-up of the Ottoman Empire.

Your bonuses are on astronomy. In each case, name the planet that the following moons orbit:
(a) First, for five points: Proteus.
(b) Second: Hyperion.
(c) Finally: Callisto.

Your starter for ten:

7 Olympic sports, Dr Johnson's *Dictionary*, Squirrel Nutkin and the 150th anniversary of the Public Libraries Act have all been depicted on coins of what denomination produced by the Royal Mint?

Your bonuses are on infectious particles. In each case, identify the particle from the description:
(a) First, an agent of certain plant diseases, a particle consisting only of a small circular RNA molecule, and no protein coat.
(b) Any of the viruses that infect bacteria or archaea, for instance, the T1 to T7 varieties used in laboratory research.
(c) What five-letter term denotes abnormally folded proteins that cause neurodegenerative conditions such as Creutzfeldt-Jakob disease?

Your starter for ten:

8 The Belgian cosmologist and priest George Lemaître is usually credited with first formulating which theory, stating that the universe began at a finite time in the past, and is expanding? Its name comes from Fred Hoyle's scornful description of the theory in a radio broadcast.

Your bonuses are on literary works. In each case, give the book of the Bible from which the following derive their titles:
(a) *A Time to Kill* by John Grisham and *The Sun Also Rises* by Ernest Hemingway.
(b) *Absalom, Absalom!* by William Faulkner; the title is taken from a book named after which biblical figure?
(c) *East of Eden* by John Steinbeck and *Sodom and Gomorrah* by Marcel Proust.

Your starter for ten:

9 Meridian, Gulfport and Biloxi are among cities in which US state, the birthplace of the civil rights campaigner Medgar Evers and the author William Faulkner?

Three questions on a year in videogames:
(a) 1991 saw the release of the first in which long-running series of strategy games, in which players build an empire across several millennia? I need a single-word title, which is often preceded by the name of its creator, Sid Meier.
(b) Which instalment in the *Legend of Zelda* series was first released in 1991? It was the first to feature a structural device that is now a series trademark, with gameplay moving between two parallel worlds. I need a five-word title.
(c) June of the same year also saw the release of the first *Sonic the Hedgehog* game – on which game console?

Your starter for ten:

10 From the Latin for 'tent', what name is given to: a multi-purpose religious building used by Mormons; an ornamented receptacle or cabinet for the consecrated host in Catholic churches; and the tent used to house the Ark of the Covenant between the Exodus and the building of the Temple of Solomon?

Three questions on visual defects:
(a) Kalnienk vision is a loss of enhanced peripheral vision more commonly known by what two-word expression?
(b) A childhood condition in which vision does not develop properly has the medical name amblyopia, but is more usually given what two-word name?
(c) Colour blindness in which all colours appear as shades of grey is known by what precise term, from the Greek for 'one' and 'colour'?

Your starter for ten:

11 What seven-letter name links the UK prime minister in 1910 and the US president in 1930?

Your bonuses are on words and expressions that have gained more widespread currency since March 2020. In each case, identify the word or phrase from references in the Oxford English Dictionary:
(a) In the OED, the first citation of what word dates to 1641 and refers to the 'pious example' of Charles I that 'will give you, for the House of Commons, and all the world, cause to rest confident'?
(b) What three-word phrase referring to a graph or chart does a 2010 citation describe with the words 'minimise transmission'?

(c) What often-hyphenated term was first defined in the OED as 'an instrument which at regular intervals interrupts an electric current'?

Your starter for ten:

12 Who is the title figure of the nursery rhyme that includes the lines, 'But when she got there / The cupboard was bare'?

Your bonuses are on the UNESCO list of Intangible Cultural Heritage. In each case, identify the landlocked country that is cited for all of the named customs:
(a) The Andean Cosmovision of the Kallawaya ethnic group; ritual journeys during the Festival of Alasita; and the carnival of the city of Oruro.
(b) The music of the two-stringed horsehair fiddle known as the morin khuur; knuckle-bone shooting; and the coaxing ritual for camels.
(c) Avalanche risk management; Holy Week processions in Mendrisio; and the Winegrowers' Festival in Vevey.

Your starter for ten:

13 Computer programs that attack a network by flooding it with messages, thereby rendering it inoperable, and people involved in money-laundering share a name with which blue cartoon characters created by the Belgian illustrator Pierre 'Peyo' Culliford?

Your bonuses are on the films of Doris Day. In each case, name the film in which the following lines appear:
(a) 'This town ain't big enough! Not for me and that frilled-up, flirtin', man-rustlin' petticoat, it ain't!'
(b) 'Mr Allen, this may come as a surprise to you, but there are some men who don't end every sentence with a proposition.'
(c) And finally: 'Que sera, sera / Whatever will be, will be.'

Your starter for ten:

14 The possessive form of what animal name comes before 'letter', 'mercury' and 'dinner' to describe, respectively: the letter 'R'; a poisonous, carpet-forming perennial plant; and a confused or jumbled mess?

Three questions on particle colliders at CERN, the European Organization for Nuclear Research:
(a) Which two subatomic particles appear in the name of the former particle collider known by the abbreviation LEP?
(b) For what subatomic particle does the letter 'P' stand in the super synchrotron known by the abbreviation SPS?
(c) For what subatomic particle does 'H' stand in the abbreviation LHC?

Your starter for ten:

15 In geology, the weathering or disintegration of rock as a result of the action of what substance is denoted by the term 'haloclasty'?

Three questions on British India:
(a) Named after a major port, which presidency of British India, until the 1930s, covered territory of present-day states and provinces including Gujarat, Maharashtra and Sindh?
(b) Also named after a seaport, which territory on the Arabian Peninsula became a dependency of the Bombay Presidency when first annexed by Britain in 1839?
(c) Which European power ceded Bombay to Britain in the 1660s?

Your starter for ten:

16 In nautical terms, what seven-letter word is the opposite of windward?

Three questions on anthropologists:
(a) Burned by the Nazis, *The Mind of Primitive Man* was a 1911 work by which German-born US anthropologist, a teacher of Edward Sapir and Zora Neale Hurston?
(b) A student of Boas, which US anthropologist's works include *Zuni Mythology*, *Patterns of Culture* and *The Chrysanthemum and the Sword*?
(c) Which student of Boas wrote *Growing Up in New Guinea* and *Coming of Age in Samoa*?

Your starter for ten:

17 The narrowest point of a major peninsula, the Kra Isthmus takes its name from a settlement in which country? The Andaman Sea lies west of the isthmus, while Singapore is more than a thousand kilometres southeast.

Three questions on chemistry:
(a) Derived from the Greek for 'other turning', what name did the Swedish chemist Berzelius suggest when he considered the possible existence of an element in two or more forms with differing chemical and physical properties?
(b) Born in 1903, the Irish-born crystallographer Kathleen Lonsdale gives her name to an allotrope of what common element, found naturally in meteorites?
(c) With the formula C60, which allotrope of carbon was discovered in 1985 and named after a US architect noted for the design of geodesic domes?

Your starter for ten:

18 The song 'Rudolf the Red-Nosed Reindeer', first recorded in 1949, includes what word, derived from Old Norse, which is now used for a

college society formed for the practice and performance of popular songs, or to mean a lively feeling of delight?

Your bonuses are on mathematics. In each case, name the method of mathematical proof being described:
(a) To show a statement is true for any natural number 'n': first show it is true for n = 1, then assume it is true for n = some value 'k', and show that it is also true for n = k = 1.
(b) To show that proposition 'p' implies proposition 'q': show instead that the negative proposition 'not q' implies the negative proposition 'not p'.
(c) Also called proof by case analysis or the brute force method, what method involves testing to see if a statement is true for all possible values in a set?

Your starter for ten:

19 Meanings of what term include: the increase in the amount of an enzyme due to a stimulus; a method of reasoning where a general law is inferred from particular instances; and the production of electric current in a circuit by varying the magnetic field applied to that circuit?

Three questions on writers on popular culture:
(a) *Kiss Kiss Bang Bang* and *State of the Art* are among the publications of which US critic? She was the *New Yorker* film critic between 1968 and 1991.
(b) Which prolific British critic wrote for the *New Musical Express* between the ages of 17 and 19, and later published *Ambition* and *Sugar Rush*?
(c) *Cultural Amnesia* and *Fame in the Twentieth Century* are among the works of which Australian writer and broadcaster, a television critic at *The Observer* in the 1970s?

Your starter for ten:

20 In contrast to virtual reality, technology that allows information to be overlaid on top of the real world is known by what two-word term, often abbreviated to AR?

Three questions on carbonate minerals:
(a) Having a value of 3 on the Mohs scale, which mineral is found in the crystal formation known as dogtooth spar? You may give the common name, or the chemical name of the corresponding carbonate compound.
(b) A son of the first Duke of Northumberland, which chemist gave his name to both the mineral form of zinc carbonate and a scientific establishment that opened in Washington, DC in 1855?
(c) Named after the Greek word for the element of which it is a minor ore, the mineral siderite is the carbonate of which common metal?

Your starter for ten:

21 What weather condition connects: Ded Moroz, the Russian equivalent of
Father Christmas; the US poet who wrote 'The Road Not Taken'; and a
British broadcaster who interviewed Richard Nixon in 1977?

Your bonuses are on cave systems:
(a) Discovered by teenage boys in 1940, what cave system in the Dordogne is
the location of a series of Palaeolithic paintings, chiefly of large animals?
(b) Said to be capable of holding forty Boeing 747 aircraft, the Sarawak
Chamber is part of the Mulu cave system on which large island?
(c) The Witch's Kitchen is a chamber in which series of limestone caves,
named after a village near Wells, in Somerset?

Your starter for ten:

22 What is the SI-derived unit of dynamic viscosity? In its abbreviated form
it spells a French word frequently used in negative sentences.

Your bonuses are on areas of outstanding natural beauty (AONB). All three answers
have two-word names in which the second word is 'coast':
(a) Which AONB is the location of Warkworth Castle, Dunstanburgh Castle
and the RNLI Grace Darling Museum?
(b) Named after a large inlet, which AONB includes the western terminus of
Hadrian's Wall?
(c) Castle Rising, Wells-next-the-Sea and Sheringham are locations within, or
close to, which AONB?

Your starter for ten:

23 In Norse mythology, Valhalla was believed to be part of which realm,
connected to Midgard by the Bifrost Bridge?

Three questions on medieval history:
(a) Henry Percy, known as Hotspur, rebelled against Henry IV and was killed
at which battle of 1403?
(b) Hotspur's son, the second Earl of Northumberland, died fighting for
Henry VI at which battle of 1455, fought about twenty miles north of
London?
(c) Fought in a snowstorm on Palm Sunday, which major battle of 1461 saw
the death of Henry Percy, the third Earl of Northumberland?

Your starter for ten:

24 Taken from the socio-cultural theories of the Russian psychologist Lev
Vygotsky, what four-word term describes the stage in the learning process

where expert guidance can make the greatest difference in the acquisition of skills and knowledge? It is sometimes abbreviated to ZPD.

Your bonuses are on vegetables of the parsley family. Identify each plant from its description:

(a) *Foeniculum vulgare*, a perennial herb whose bulb-like stem base and blanched shoots are eaten as a vegetable. Its seeds have an aroma and taste similar to anise and are used as a spice.

(b) *Apium graveolens*, which is cooked as a vegetable or in stocks and soups. It is also served raw with dips or in salads.

(c) *Pastinaca sativa*, cultivated for its fleshy off-white root which is not damaged by the freezing of soil. The root is sweet and usually served cooked.

Your starter for ten:

25 What five-letter word links the largest lake of Italy with the nationwide law enforcement body that in 1922 replaced the Royal Irish Constabulary?

Your bonuses are on Shakespeare's *Julius Caesar*:

(a) What four words spoken by Mark Antony in Act Three, Scene One gave Frederick Forsyth the title of his novel set in the fictional African country of Zangaro?

(b) What two words spoken by Brutus in Act Two, Scene One appear in the title of the only Hollywood film of Ingmar Bergman?

(c) What five-word title did the US author and vlogger John Green give to his novel of 2012, adapted from words spoken by Cassius to Brutus in Act One, Scene Two?

The Answers

1   Xi'an (pr: Shee-an; accept Chang'an) / Nanjing / Luoyang
    (a) Caribou (from the Mi'kmac: *yalipu*, 'snow shoveller')
    (b) Tapioca (Tupi-Gurani: *tipi*, 'dregs'; *ok / og*, 'squeeze out')
    (c) Powwow (Narragansett: *powah, powaw*, magician, 'he dreams')

2   Winter (Winter King, Winter Palace, *The Winter's Tale*)
    (a) *Wolf Hall* (Hilary Mantel)
    (b) *The Luminaries* (Eleanor Catton)
    (c) *A Brief History of Seven Killings* (Marlon James)

3   Anarchy (i.e. *The Masque of Anarchy*)
    (a) Marmot
    (b) Lemming
    (c) Porcupine (Latin: *porcus*, 'pig')

4   Relative humidity
    (a) (Gregor) Mendel
    (b) (Theodosius) Dobzhansky (published 1937 and 1973 respectively)
    (c) (Julian) Huxley (grandson of Thomas Henry Huxley)

5   (Jan) van Eyck
    (a) Derby and Delaware (DE)
    (b) Wolverhampton and West Virginia (WV)
    (c) Lancaster and Louisiana (LA)

6   Baghdad
    (a) Neptune
    (b) Saturn
    (c) Jupiter

7   Fifty pence
    (a) Viroid
    (b) Bacteriophage (accept and correct 'phage', a common abbreviation)
    (c) Prion

8   Big Bang (theory)
    (a) Ecclesiastes
    (b) Samuel
    (c) Genesis

9   Mississippi
    (a) *Civilization*
    (b) *A Link to the Past*
    (c) (Sega) Mega Drive / (Sega) Genesis.

10 Tabernacle (Latin: *tabernaculum*)
    (a) Tunnel vision
    (b) Lazy eye
    (c) Monochromacy / monochromatism / monochromasia

11 Herbert (Asquith and Hoover, of course)
    (a) Unprecedented ('pious example unpresidented by a king')
    (b) Flatten(ing) the curve
    (c) Circuit-breaker

12 (Old Mother) Hubbard
    (a) Bolivia
    (b) Mongolia
    (c) Switzerland

13 Smurfs
    (a) *Calamity Jane*
    (b) *Pillow Talk* (to Rock Hudson, of course)
    (c) *The Man Who Knew Too Much*

14 Dog (i.e. dog's)
    (a) Electron and positron (Large Electron-Positron collider)
    (b) Proton (Super Proton Synchrotron)
    (c) Hadron (Large Hadron Collider)

15 Salt(s)
    (a) Bombay (accept Mumbai, giving the historical name)
    (b) Aden
    (c) Portugal

16 Leeward (windward means facing the wind, or on the side facing the wind; leeward is the side sheltered from the wind, or downwind)
    (a) (Frank) Boas
    (b) (Ruth) Benedict
    (c) (Margaret) Mead

17 Thailand
    (a) Allotrope (Greek: *allo*, 'other'; *trepein*, 'to turn')
    (b) Carbon (lonsdaleite)
    (c) Buckminsterfullerene / buckyball / fullerene

18 Glee (Old Norse: *gly*)
    (a) (Proof by mathematical) induction (i.e. a domino effect of proofs)
    (b) (Proof by) contraposition / contrapositive
    (c) (Proof by) exhaustion (accept 'complete induction')

19 Induction
    (a) Pauline Kael
    (b) Julie Burchill
    (c) Clive James

20 Augmented Reality
    (a) Calcite / calcium carbonate
    (b) (James) Smithson
    (c) Iron (Greek: *sidēros*, 'iron')

21 Frost
    (a) Lascaux (Cave) / Grotte de Lascaux
    (b) Borneo
    (c) Wookey Hole

22 Pascal-second (pa-s / *pas*)
    (a) Northumberland (Coast)
    (b) Solway (Coast)
    (c) Norfolk (Coast)

23 Asgard
    (a) Shrewsbury
    (b) (First Battle of) St Albans
    (c) Towton

24 Zone of proximal development
    (a) Fennel
    (b) Celery
    (c) Parsnip

25 Garda (*Gárda Síochána*, of course)
    (a) 'The dogs of war'
    (b) 'Serpent's egg'
    (c) *The Fault in Our Stars*

The Hosts

Part 1
1962–1987

Arthur Bamber Gascoigne
(24 January 1935–8 February 2022)

'No quiz host has ever seemed more like they could answer all the questions themselves,' writes Victoria Coren Mitchell of Bamber Gascoigne. Coren Mitchell hosts the BBC quiz show *Only Connect*, and it's the show many a competitor on *University Challenge* says they would like to tackle.

Bamber Gascoigne was regarded by seemingly everyone who worked with him as a delightful, uber-intelligent, genial host, whose 'I'll have to hurry you' contrasts with his successor Jeremy Paxman's slightly more abrupt 'Come on!' He coined those famous phrases, 'Your starter for 10, no conferring' and 'Fingers on buzzers'.

Dubbed the friendly face of academia, Gascoigne died from heart failure in February 2022 at the age of 87 at his home in Richmond, London, where he had lived for 55 years. He could trace his family back to the 1400s, when the Anglo-Norman Gascoignes settled in Yorkshire 500 years after the Conquest. Born in London, he was educated at Sunningdale prep school in Berkshire before winning scholarships to both Eton and Magdalene College, Cambridge, where he read English Literature. After continuing his studies at Yale in the USA, he married ceramicist and photographer Christina Ditchburn, whom he had met at Cambridge in 1965.

Gascoigne's lineage included military men, a mayor of London and a prime minister of Northern Ireland. In 2014 he unexpectedly inherited, from his great-aunt Mary Innes-Ker, the Duchess of Roxburghe, a stately home, the 50-room West Horsley Place in Surrey. Once owned by Henry VIII, the house was dilapidated but, instead of selling, Gascoigne and his wife had the vast property renovated and turned into a community arts centre. In its 350-acre grounds now sits a 700-seat opera house.

After university, where he began reviewing plays, and following his national service in the Grenadier Guards, Gascoigne became a theatre critic for *The Spectator* and *The Observer*. In 1962, he was invited by Granada Television to help create a new quiz show for students based on the American programme *College Bowl*, which began in 1959. Expected to run for three months or so, *University Challenge* quickly found a loyal following and, despite audience figures fluctuating as it was shifted around the schedules of ITV's regional companies, it ran for 25 years in its first incarnation. Its success was undoubtedly down in large part to Gascoigne's patrician manner, likeability and tremendous intelligence, which he wore 'lightly and smilingly', as journalist Mark Lawson wrote in *The Guardian* after his death. With the appearance and air of a friendly don, Gascoigne – 27 years of age when the programme began – was only a few years older than his student contestants.

Gascoigne went on to present 913 episodes over the initial 25 years, turning down the opportunity to return to the quizmaster's chair when the BBC decided to resurrect the format in 1994 because he was too busy with his many arts-based interests. As well as presenting *University Challenge*, Gascoigne was an author, historian, publisher, documentary-maker and playwright. Alongside created documentaries, he devised and presented a BBC Two arts quiz, *Connoisseur*, which ran for two series from May 1988.

Known for his genial manner, Gascoigne never seemed to mind being parodied or represented on screen, notably by Griff Rhys Jones in the anarchic 1980s comedy *The Young Ones* and by Mark Gatiss in the 2006 film based on David Nicholls's book *Starter for Ten* (2003), starring James McAvoy as a student eager to appear on *University Challenge*.

His interests were wide and varied. As well as being immersed in the arts he was a keen river swimmer – his house in Richmond overlooked the Thames. Awarded a CBE in 2018 for services to the arts, he was a trustee of the National Gallery and the Tate, was on the board of directors of the Royal Opera House and was a member of the council of the National Trust.

After his death in 2022, many tributes were made to the urbane, ever-polite cultural polymath. Stephen Fry described him as 'such an elegant, intelligent man, completely charming', while 2017 contestant Bobby Seagull added: 'scholarly, gentle and yet commanding, he joins the pantheon of great gameshow hosts'. David Aaronovitch, who appeared as part of the controversial 1975 University of Manchester team and again on a 2018 Christmas special says: 'Bamber Gascoigne looked like he was a boffin, he looked like his brain was enormous. You felt he knew all the answers.'

Try Your Luck

Match

Your starter for ten:

1 Leaders of which political party have shared their names with the following? A victory of Alfred the Great over the Danes; the US ambassador to the United Kingdom at the start of the Second World War; the pilot of *Bluebird*, who died on Coniston Water; and a common alloy of iron, carbon and other metals.

Three bonus questions on physics:
(a) If a nucleus of the isotope lead-214 undergoes two beta-minus decays followed by alpha decay, what isotope is the result?
(b) What six-letter term denotes nuclei that are identical in proton and neutron number, but have different excitation energies?
(c) When one isomer decays to another, what form of radiation is emitted?

Your starter for ten:

2 Pedro Pony, Rebecca Rabbit and Suzy Sheep are friends of the title character of which preschool children's animated series?

Three questions on mythical creatures in Jorge Luis Borges' *Book of Imaginary Beings*. Name each one from the description; they all begin with the same letter:
(a) 'Nobody seems to have laid eyes on this "woman of the fairies". She is less a shape than a mournful screaming that haunts the Irish night and the Scottish Highlands.'
(b) 'Through the ages [it] grows increasingly ugly and horrendous. Its name comes from the Greek and means "little king". What remains constant is the deadly effect of its stare and its venom.'
(c) 'Before the Christian era, [it] was a magnification of the elephant or of the hippopotamus. It is now – precisely – the ten famous verses describing it in Job, and the huge being which these lines evoke.'

Your starter for ten:

3   Taking its name from the Painted Porch in Athens where members congregated, which Hellenistic school of philosophy emphasized moral worth, duty and justice, together with sternness of mind? Its prominent practitioners include the author Seneca and the emperor Marcus Aurelius.

Your bonuses are on names. For each question, I need three answers beginning with the letters 'A', 'B' and 'C' respectively:
(a) The surnames of the novelists who won the Booker Prize for *The Blind Assassin*, *Milkman* and *The Luminaries*.
(b) The clubs that first won the FA Cup in 1930, 1914 and 1927, respectively; all three played in the English Premier League in the 2018–2019 season.
(c) The surnames of the British prime ministers who were in office in the years 1909, 1928 and 1978.

Your starter for ten:

4   'I wish [Martin] was my surname, for my own is not a very pretty one, and it takes a long time to sign.' These are the words of the title character of which novel by Charles Dickens?

Your bonuses are on Italians with shared initials. In each case, give the forename and surname of both individuals:
(a) A 16th-century artist noted for the work known as *Lives of the Artists*; and a fashion designer who died in 1997.
(b) A Venetian architect who was influenced by Vitruvius; and a footballer who was man of the match in the 2006 FIFA World Cup final.
(c) A baroque composer noted for his *Adagio in G Minor*; and the 13th-century author of *Summa Theologicae*.

Your starter for ten:

5   Established to mark the Millennium, a repository at the Wakehurst site of the Kew Royal Botanical Gardens contains a comprehensive collection of what specimens, representing almost all native British and many non-native plant species?

Three questions on astronomical catalogues:
(a) In 1786, which astronomer royal, with his sister, published the *Catalogue of One Thousand New Nebulae and Clusters of Stars*?
(b) 3C 273, the 273rd member of the Third Cambridge Catalogue of Radio Sources, is among the closest to Earth of what class of highly luminous objects?
(c) Born in 1730, which French astronomer compiled a catalogue of objects

that might be mistaken for comets, including what are now known to be galaxies, star clusters and various nebulae?

Your starter for ten:

6 'In my family ... we liked to while away the evenings by making ourselves miserable, based solely on our ability to speak the language viciously.' These are the words of which American playwright? Born in 1947, he is the author of *American Buffalo* and *Oleanna*.

Your bonuses are on former 'princely states' of British India that shared their names with major cities. In each case, identify the state from the description:
(a) Ruled by Muslim Nizams but with a predominantly Hindu population, a state centring on the South Indian city that is the location of Charminar and Telugu film production.
(b) A principality centred around the city that is now the capital of Madhya Pradesh; in 1984, it experienced the worst industrial accident in history following the release of gas from an insecticide plant.
(c) Situated in the Marwar region of Rajasthan, the largest princely state in the Rajputana Agency; the city gives its name to a specialized item of clothing.

Your starter for ten:

7 I need a precise two-word answer here. Which title character of a nursery rhyme 'met a pieman / Going to the fair'?

Your bonus questions are on Dante:
(a) Meaning 'sweet new style' in English, what is the Italian name of the literary movement with which Dante is most associated?
(b) In Dante's *Inferno*, the Second Circle of Hell is populated by those who have succumbed to which of the Seven Deadly Sins? The narrator of the work meets both Cleopatra and Helen of Troy there.
(c) Which Italian poet and scholar wrote the biography *Life of Dante* and delivered the first public lectures on *The Divine Comedy* in the 1370s?

Your starter for ten:

8 What two-word term describes the aim of machines such as Robert Fludd's 1618 'closed-cycle water mill' and John Gamgee's ammonia-filled 'zeromotor' of 1880? The action in question violates the first and second laws of thermodynamics.

Your bonuses are on trees. Give the common name from the description. All three answers begin with the same two letters:
(a) Sometimes known as 'the upside-down tree' and 'Africa's tree of life', which

tree is now said to be the world's biggest and longest-lived flowering plant?
(b) Also known as the Indian fig tree, which unusually shaped tree has aerial roots that descend from its branches and take root in the soil below?
(c) Found from Southern Mexico to Bolivia, which fast-growing tree has a name meaning 'raft' or 'float' in Spanish?

Your starter for ten:

9 The first British parliamentary election to use the secret ballot was held at a by-election in 1872 in which West Yorkshire town? The wax seal on the ballot box was made with a stamp from a local factory where it was used to mark the liquorice sweets formerly known as Pomfret cakes.

Your bonuses are on monochrome art:
(a) *White Flag* is a 1955 work by which US Abstract Expressionist? It comprises a US flag painted over entirely with white encaustic.
(b) Born in Canada in 1912, which Abstract Expressionist produced multiple works consisting of barely perceptible ruled lines on off-white backgrounds? She is associated with the Taos art colony in New Mexico.
(c) Depicting a tilted, off-centre white square on a slightly warmer white square ground, *Suprematist Composition: White on White* is a work of 1918 by which Russian artist?

Your starter for ten:

10 Who is being quoted here, in translation: 'For who, in our most beautiful temple, could set this light in another or better place, than that from which it can at once illuminate the whole?' The statement appears in the 1543 work *On the Revolutions of the Heavenly Spheres'*.

Three questions on social welfare:
(a) Also known as the Berkshire Bread Act, what local method of supplementing the wages of poor families was named after the village where it was devised in 1795?
(b) The Poor Law Amendment Act was passed by the government of which prime minister, in the same decade as the first Reform Act?
(c) 'Ninepence for fourpence' was a slogan that accompanied the launch of the National Insurance scheme introduced by which chancellor in 1911?

Your starter for ten:

11 *Memoirs from Beyond the Grave* and *The Genius of Christianity* are among the works of which French statesman and intellectual? Minister of foreign affairs under the restored Bourbon monarchy, he is noted in culinary history as the eponym of a thick fillet of beef steak.

Three questions on ducks:
(a) Also called sawbill, the name of which diving duck derives in part from the Latin meaning 'goose'?
(b) In contrast to diving ducks, what word ending in '-ing' is applied to surface-feeding ducks such as the mallard?
(c) The binomial *Anas acuta* refers to the tapering feature that gives which dabbling duck species its common name?

Your starter for ten:
12 I need the names of the two countries whose border is the location of Margherita Peak, the third-highest point in Africa.

Three questions on medieval history:
(a) A son of John of Gaunt, Cardinal Henry Beaufort was a leading figure in the regency government during the minority of which king?
(b) Henry Beaufort's niece, Joan, married which king of Scotland at Southwark Cathedral in 1424?
(c) A descendant of Henry's brother John, Margaret Beaufort was the mother of which king?

Your starter for ten:
13 What four words follow 'I summon up...' in the second line of Shakespeare's sonnet no. 30? In the 1920s, C.K. Scott Moncrieff used the phrase for the title of his translation of Proust's *À la recherche du temps perdu*.

Your bonuses are on the coast of Great Britain. In each case, name the most populous town that lies on the coast between the two named locations:
(a) Paignton and Teignmouth; Agatha Christie was born here in 1890.
(b) Aberdeen and Fraserburgh; the town's football club was promoted to Scottish League One in 2019.
(c) Finally, Whitby and Bridlington; the town is associated with the playwright Alan Ayckbourn.

Your starter for ten:
14 The fifth-largest moon of Saturn and a sea that separated Laurasia and Gondwana in the Mesozoic era are both named after which mythological goddess, the consort of Oceanus?

Your bonuses are on Latin American dictators. In each case, name the country ruled by the following:
(a) Manuel Noriega, convicted of numerous crimes after his overthrow by US forces in 1989.

(b) Rafael Trujillo; trained by the US military during their occupation of his country, he was ruler from 1930 until his assassination in 1961.
(c) Members of the Somoza family ruled which country from 1937 to 1979?

Your starter for ten:

15 What first name is shared by the following: the British artist who painted *Sunflower and Dog Worship*; the US psychologist who wrote *Obedience to Authority*; and the director of *Eyes Wide Shut* and *Dr Strangelove*?

Three questions on physical research facilities:
(a) Which research facility at Batavia, Illinois includes the MiniBooNE and MINERvA experiments, as well as the Tevatron collider?
(b) Located near Didcot and named after two physicists, which complex includes the Diamond Light Source, the ISIS Neutron Source and the Central Laser Facility?
(c) The transuranic element dubnium is named after a research facility in which country?

Your starter for ten:

16 Give two surnames promptly if you buzz for this. In 2018, the UK became the first country to win the three 'Grand Tours' – of Italy, Spain and France – in the same year with three different riders. Name two of them.

Three questions on cricketers in detective fiction:
(a) First appearing in 'The Ides of March' in 1898, which antihero is an Old Etonian who plays cricket for the Gentlemen of England?
(b) First appearing in 1923, which fictional detective's cricketing prowess during his schooldays at Eton earned him the nickname the Great Flim?
(c) In the short story 'The Field Bazaar', published in 1896, which character is revealed to have played for the Edinburgh University cricket team?

Your starter for ten:

17 In the second line of one of his odes, what does John Keats describe as the 'close bosom-friend of the maturing sun'?

Three questions on a German thinker:
(a) The ideas of differential and integral calculus were founded independently in the 17th century by Isaac Newton and which German polymath, born in Leipzig in 1646?
(b) The foundation of virtually all modern computing, what form of number representation did Leibniz describe in the 1701 *Essay on a New Science of Numbers*?

(c) Based on Leibniz, the unfailingly optimistic Dr Pangloss is a character in which satire of 1759 by Voltaire?

Your starter for ten:

18 Which French town is the main setting for Ken Russell's 1971 film *The Devils*, about a group of 17th-century French nuns who were allegedly the victims of demonic possession?

Three questions on fictional islands:
(a) The Antarctic island of Caprona, or Caprak, features prominently in a trilogy of early 20th-century adventure novels by which US author?
(b) Which fictional island nation was the subject of an elaborate hoax perpetrated by *The Guardian* on April Fool's Day 1977? Its name derived from that of a type of letterform.
(c) The North Pacific island of Gondal featured in the games and early writings of which literary siblings?

Your starter for ten:

19 Who is the only Nobel laureate to date to have played first-class cricket? Born in 1906, he received the Croix de Guerre for his work with the French Resistance, and his literary works include *More Pricks Than Kicks* and *Murphy*.

Three questions on a historical figure:
(a) In a play by Shakespeare, Charmian and Iras are named among the attendants of which historical figure, who lived in the 1st century BC?
(b) According to a legend depicted in a painting by Tiepolo, what naturally occurring object, used in jewellery, did Cleopatra dissolve in a drink during a banquet arranged in honour of Mark Antony?
(c) Areas of ancient Egypt known as Cleopatra's Mines were a major source of which coloured cyclosilicate mineral, a variety of beryl?

Your starter for ten:

20 Defeat by Genoa at the Battle of Meloria in 1284 marked the beginning of the decline of which maritime republic, situated at the mouth of the River Arno? In 1564, it was the birthplace of Galileo.

Three questions on tapestries:
(a) In 1515, the Medici Pope Leo X commissioned which artist to design a series of full-scale tapestries for the Sistine Chapel, depicting the lives of St Peter and St Paul?
(b) Which pioneer of the arts and crafts movement designed the series of six

wall hangings based on Malory's *Morte d'Arthur* and known as the Holy Grail tapestries?

(c) In the 1970s, which British artist collaborated with the West Dean Tapestry Studio to produce a series of large-scale tapestries based on his drawings of mothers and children?

Your starter for ten:

21 *The Dry Garden* and *The Damp Garden* are books by which pioneering garden designer and writer? The winner of ten successive gold medals at the Chelsea Flower Show from the 1970s, she died in 2018, aged 94.

Three questions on novels about queens:

(a) Philippa Gregory's 2011 novel *Red Queen* concerns Margaret Beaufort, the mother of which English king?

(b) *The Captive Queen*, a novel by Alison Weir, concerns which queen? She left her first husband, Louis VII, to marry a future king of England in 1152.

(c) In the 2006 novel *Queen Camilla*, the royal family are in internal exile and Prince Charles agrees to a Restoration on the condition that his wife can be queen. Who is the author?

Your starter for ten:

22 The work of the Scottish engineer William Roy played a prominent part in the founding of which government agency in 1791? Its two-word name includes a term for military stores or artillery.

Your bonuses are on popes. In each case, identify the regnal name shared by the following:

(a) The second, who authorized the Norman conquest of England; and the sixth, the father of Lucrezia Borgia?

(b) The third, who decreed the second and final excommunication of Henry VIII; and the sixth, who concluded the Second Vatican Council in 1965?

(c) The eighth, who put Galileo on trial; and the second, who launched the First Crusade?

Your starter for ten:

23 In mathematics, what class of number is defined as any number that can be expressed as a fraction 'p over q', where p and q are integers, and q is not equal to zero?

Your bonuses are on compound words. In each case, give the word from the description:

(a) Conflating two familiar terms, a generic eight-letter word that refers to online resources; the OED says it is often 'a conscious use of incorrect terminology to emphasize a person's lack of knowledge about, or objection to, new technology'.

(b) A verb defined in the OED as: 'to explain needlessly, overbearingly, or condescendingly, in a manner thought to reveal a patronizing or chauvinistic attitude'.

(c) A disdainful blanket term for activities such as football, cricket or rugby; if you search for this on the OED website, it asks: 'Did you mean "shortfall", "shortwall" or "spitball"?'

Your starter for ten:

24 I need the name of an author here. A British soldier in the American War of Independence, the wife of the poet John Milton, a Byzantine general under Justinian the Great, and the fourth emperor of Rome are among the title characters of novels by which author and classical scholar, born in Wimbledon in 1895?

Your bonuses are on the first Cabinet of Donald Trump. In each case, name the Cabinet member from the description:

(a) First, the former CEO of Exxon Mobil, appointed secretary of state.

(b) The retired four-star general known as Mad Dog who was appointed secretary of defense.

(c) Finally, the senator for Alabama who was appointed attorney general.

Your starter for ten:

25 Written in doublestruck or blackboard bold form, what letter of the alphabet is used in mathematics to represent the set of all integers?

Your bonuses are on videogames included in the V&A exhibition entitled *Design/Play/Disrupt*. Give the title of each game from the description:

(a) An adventure game first released in 2012. The player guides a red-robed figure through a desert towards a distant mountain. Containing no speech or text, it is often cited as an example of an 'art game'.

(b) A point-and-click game developed by cardboard computer. It centres on the delivery driver Conway and his encounters while navigating the fictional road of the game's title.

(c) An action-adventure game first released in 2016. Here, the player is free to explore potentially millions of planets, each with a unique procedurally generated ecosystem.

The Answers

1   Liberal Democrats (Battle of Ashdown; Joseph P. Kennedy; Donald Campbell; steel)
    (a) Lead-210
    (b) Isomer
    (c) Gamma

2   *Peppa Pig*
    (a) Banshee
    (b) Basilisk / basilicok (also called a 'cockatrice' but this does not fit the question)
    (c) Behemoth (not Leviathan, a sea monster, also referenced in Job)

3   Stoicism / Stoics (*Stoa Poikilē*, the Painted Porch)
    (a) (Margaret) Atwood, (Anna) Burns and (Eleanor) Catton
    (b) Arsenal, Burnley and Cardiff (City)
    (c) Asquith, Baldwin and Callaghan

4   *Martin Chuzzlewit*
    (a) Giorgio Vasari and Gianni Versace
    (b) Andrea Palladio and Andrea Pirlo
    (c) Tomaso Albinoni and Thomas Aquinas

5   Seeds (Millennium Seed Bank)
    (a) (William) Herschel (whose sister was Caroline, of course)
    (b) Quasars
    (c) (Charles) Messier

6   David Mamet
    (a) Hyderabad
    (b) Bhopal
    (c) Jodhpur

7   Simple Simon
    (a) *Dolce stil nuovo*
    (b) Lust
    (c) (Giovanni) Boccaccio

8   Perpetual motion
    (a) Baobab (the genus *Adansonia*)
    (b) Banyan (*Ficus benghalensis*, or the subgenus *Urostigma*)
    (c) Balsa (*Ochroma pyramidale*)

9   Pontefract (There had been a secret ballot in 1870 for the london school board)
    (a) (Jasper) Johns
    (b) (Agnes) Martin
    (c) (Kazimir) Malevich

10   (Nikolaus) Copernicus
     (a) Speenhamland (system)
     (b) (Earl) Grey (Charles Grey, 2nd Earl Grey)
     (c) (David) Lloyd George

11   (François-René de) Chateaubriand
     (a) Merganser (Latin: *merge*, 'dive'; *anser*, 'goose')
     (b) Dabbling / dipping
     (c) Pintail

12   Uganda and DRC / Democratic Republic of the Congo (i.e. the highest point on Mount
     Stanley or Mount Ngaliéma; third after Mounts Kilimanjaro and Kenya)
     (a) Henry VI
     (b) James I
     (c) Henry VII

13   'Remembrance of things past' (not 'In search of lost time', of course)
     (a) Torquay (not Torbay, a larger area that includes Paignton)
     (b) Peterhead
     (c) Scarborough

14   Tethys
     (a) Panama
     (b) Dominican Republic (not Dominica, of course)
     (c) Nicaragua

15   Stanley (Spencer, Milgram, Kubrick)
     (a) Fermilab / Fermi National Accelerator Laboratory
     (b) Rutherford Appleton Laboratory / RAL
     (c) Russia (Joint Institute for Nuclear Research in Dubna)

16   (Chris) Froome / (Geraint) Thomas / Simon Yates (not Adam Yates, Simon's twin, but
     we've only asked for surnames)
     (a) (A.J.) Raffles (by E.W. Hornung)
     (b) (Lord Peter) Wimsey (by Dorothy L. Sayers; 'Flimsy' had previously been his
     disparaging nickname)
     (c) (Dr John) Watson (by Arthur Conan Doyle)

17   Autumn ('To Autumn')
     (a) (Gottfried Wilhelm von) Leibniz
     (b) Binary (notation)
     (c) *Candide*

18   Loudun
     (a) Edgar Rice Burroughs (*The Land That Time Forgot*, *The People That Time Forgot*, *Out of Time's Abyss*)

(b) San Serriffe

(c) The Brontës / Brontë sisters

19 Samuel Beckett
    (a) Cleopatra
    (b) Pearl
    (c) Emerald

20 Pisa
    (a) Raphael
    (b) (Edward) Burne-Jones
    (c) Henry Moore

21 Beth Chatto
    (a) Henry Tudor / Henry VII
    (b) Eleanor of Aquitaine
    (c) Sue Townsend

22 Ordnance Survey
    (a) Alexander
    (b) Paul
    (c) Urban

23 Rational number
    (a) Interweb
    (b) Mansplain / mansplaining
    (c) Sport(s)ball

24 (Robert) Graves (Roger Lamb, Marie Powell, Belisarius and Claudius, respectively)
    (a) (Rex) Tillerson
    (b) (Jim) Mattis
    (c) (Jeff) Sessions

25 Z
    (a) *Journey*
    (b) *Kentucky Route Zero*
    (c) *No Man's Sky*

Famous
Contestants

Part 1

University Challenge has attracted numerous celebrities willing to compete on its alumni editions, Christmas specials and professionals rounds. Some appeared as students for their universities and, having made a name for themselves, were happy to return for their alma mater. Others have been keen to represent their chosen profession.

The programme is so respected it has no problem attracting well-known people to appear on its celebrity specials, even though by doing so they are exposing their knowledge to the ultimate scrutiny. What if they don't answer a single question? Or proffer ridiculous answers under the disdainful gaze of Jeremy Paxman?

The 'celebrity' programmes actually began in Bamber Gascoigne's day, although these originally consisted of winning student teams competing against university dons. In 2003, the programme invited teams of professionals from the British Geological Society or the Royal Naval College to lawyers, poets and journalists (for whom future Conservative minister, then a leader writer for *The Times*, Michael Gove appeared and whose team ironically beat a foursome representing the House of Commons by 215–25) or the TUC. This meant that, for the first time, non-university (under)graduates could appear. The first series was won by a team from the Inland Revenue.

The programme has attracted a huge number of journalists, actors, writers, comedians and politicians who have relished the chance to show another side of themselves by appearing on the programme. In fact, you'd be hard-pressed to find a celebrity who hasn't appeared on one of the many special editions. Throughout this book, some of the most famous celebrities to appear on the programme, whether as students or later in life, remember their experiences...

*

Among the well-known names to have taken part as a student is the eminent journalist and the BBC's World Affairs editor, **John Simpson**, who represented Magdalene College, Cambridge in 1965. 'Magdalene was a very laid-back, rather disorganized place in those days, and I remember seeing a solitary handwritten notice on a board that said something like, "Granada TV has asked us to provide a team to represent the college on *University Challenge*. Please write your name below if you are interested." There were only three names there, so I thought I'd add mine, just for a laugh. I don't think it occurred to me I'd be chosen, but no one else put their name down…

'I was amazingly nervous when we reached the studios. The lights, the sets, the business of make-up, the glamorous people hanging round so nonchalantly, all persuaded me I'd made a huge mistake in coming. But Bamber Gascoigne was a close friend of my director of studies at Magdalene and he came over and talked to me in such a friendly, encouraging way, joking and telling anecdotes about his time at the college, that I felt much better.

'When the first round started, I felt somehow galvanized. I pressed the buzzer on the very first question – I've no idea now what it was – and saw the cameras swing round in my direction, and amazingly got it right. And the next one, and the next one. After that I was on a roll. Afterwards, counting it up, we realized I'd answered 70 per cent of all the questions asked and got them all right – and so when a really tricky one came up I just trusted my luck. "According to a recent musical on the London stage," Bamber said, "what would an 18th-century lady have said to her friends when Casanova came to town?" I had no idea, but I pressed the buzzer and blurted out, "Lock Up Your Daughters!" God knows why I should have thought of that, because I certainly hadn't seen it, but there are times when your mind just seems to expand and open itself to ideas you never knew you had.

'Anyway, we smashed our first opponents. In the second round, I answered about 50 per cent of the questions and got most of them right, but I didn't have that same sensation of floating above the studio. We still won at a trot. And eventually (the semi-final, I think) we came up against a very charming small Welsh theological college called St David's, Lampeter, and we crashed out. Very few of the questions were on the areas I knew anything about, and somehow we simply faded away.

'I thought everyone would make fun of us when we got back to Cambridge, but scarcely anyone seemed to have noticed, which was naturally a big relief. Still, the whole experience was hugely enjoyable – a taste of the big, real world for me, a quiet only child brought up by my father on the Suffolk coast – and Bamber was very encouraging. "You might do quite well on television," he said. "Give it a try when you graduate." I joined the BBC a year later.'

*

Renowned contestants in the *University Challenge* celebrity specials include award-winning actress **Miriam Margolyes OBE,** who was a student reading English Literature at Newnham College, Cambridge when she appeared on *University Challenge* in the very first series in 1962–1963. Having been a member of Cambridge Footlights, the hotbed of young satirical comedy which grew in prominence in the 1960s, Miriam left Cambridge wanting to be an actress. A planned tour of Europe fell through and she sold encyclopaedias door to door before successfully auditioning for the BBC Drama Repertory Company in radio.

Her participation in *University Challenge*, as well as being her first TV appearance in a long and successful career on stage and screen, is notable for Miriam being the first woman to swear on British television. The muttered 'F*** it' on a wrong answer was bleeped out. Miriam says: 'I met Bamber Gascoigne again quite recently, and he said he had remembered me, which was very gratifying but it was probably because I swore.'

Miriam's Newnham team won their first match but lost their second. 'I remember we were told that Newnham had been invited to take part, and we had to find a team to go forward. I've always loved general knowledge quizzes. We had heats, and our team was arrived at. It was just great fun, and we really liked Bamber Gascoigne, I'm so sorry he has just died; he meant something to me. He was absolutely lovely – very friendly and chatty. He was slightly a dandy in his clothes, very warm and amused by us, very mild and benevolent.

'Bamber was sort of avuncular and laid back whereas Jeremy, who I have met when I was a guest at Sandringham once and who was charming, very sweet, I think is more wolfish.'

Miriam, who divides her time between England and Australia, watches *University Challenge* when she can. 'It's a very good format for a quiz. It's very entertaining to see young people becoming themselves, to see their emerging personalities. I'm impressed with how clever the students are. They're much cleverer than we were, no doubt about that. I enjoy watching it, I like seeing the interplay between the teams and also seeing many more women taking part.' (Newnham is a women's college.)

Miriam says she is very proud to have been on *University Challenge*. 'I think it's one of the loveliest things that happened to me at Cambridge and in my life. I went on national television and I made a bit of an arse of myself because I swore, but it was a very happy experience and all the people who were in my team remained my friends.'

Would Miriam like to have appeared on the programme today, in an age of instant comment on Twitter? 'No,' she says firmly. 'Social media is a foul, putrid thing.'

Match

Your starter for ten:

1   Who is this? Born in Indiana in 1891, he was president of the Yale University Glee Club and is reputed to have served with the French Foreign Legion during the First World War, entertaining troops with a portable piano. As a composer and lyricist, his works include the songs 'Begin the Beguine', 'Love for Sale' and 'Night and Day'.

Three questions on prominent members of the Royal Statistical Society:

(a) Born in 1791, which founding member of the then Statistical Society of London is credited with inventing the first automatic digital computer?

(b) Which economist gives his name to the 1942 report that helped shape Britain's post-war welfare state policies?

(c) Noted for reducing the death rate of soldiers in military hospitals from 40 per cent to 2 per cent, who was elected the first female member of the Statistical Society in 1858?

Your starter for ten:

2   Athlone and Mullingar are towns in which inland county of Ireland? It is the only Irish county whose English name begins with a compass direction.

Three questions on writer-actors in British television:

(a) Which actor created, wrote and starred in the comedy-dramas *Crashing* and *Fleabag*? Her other credits as showrunner include the 2018 series of *Killing Eve*.

(b) Which writer and actor won two BAFTAs in 2016 for her sitcom *Chewing Gum*, in which she starred as Tracey, a sheltered Christian? In 2018, she became the youngest person to give the McTaggart lecture at the Edinburgh Television Festival.

(c) *Detectorists* was a comedy series written and directed by which actor, who also starred opposite Toby Jones?

Your starter for ten:

3 Who was the UK prime minister in the year that saw the release of Led Zeppelin's debut album; the death of Brian Jones of The Rolling Stones; and the recording of John Lennon's 'Give Peace a Chance'?

Your bonuses are on species of fish whose common names contain the name of a mammal. Identify each species from the description:
(a) A name given to several small shark species of the family *Squalidae*. A common species in British waters is the 'spiny' variety, also called the 'mud shark'.
(b) A freshwater fish of the minnow family with the binomial *Danio rerio*, it is a common model organism for the study of vertebrate development and embryology.
(c) In terms of its evolution, an isolated genus that, together with the pipefish and sea dragons, comprise the family *Syngnathidae*.

Your starter for ten:

4 Which scientist's surname is represented in a challenge-response test designed to distinguish human input from machine input, and known by the acronym CAPTCHA?

Your bonuses are on pairs of foodstuffs whose common names begin with the same four letters. In each case, give both names from the descriptions:
(a) A large tropical fruit of the *Bromeliad* family; and the edible seeds of various species of conifer, used to make pesto.
(b) Two fruits: *Citrus maxima*, similar in appearance to a large grapefruit; and a member of the genus *Punica*, whose common name comes from the Latin for 'seeded apple'.
(c) The national fruit of India; and a variety of *Beta vulgaris* also known as the 'field beet' or 'fodder beet'.

Your starter for ten:

5 The British painter John Callcott Horsley is generally noted for two things: his refusal to work from the nude model, which earned him the nickname 'Clothes-Horsley'; and his design in 1843 of the first example of what now ubiquitous seasonal item?

Three questions on the novels of Robert Harris:
(a) *Imperium*, *Lustrum* and *Dictator* form a trilogy that focuses on the life and career of which Roman statesman?
(b) Harris's 2013 novel *An Officer and a Spy* concerns the persecution and wrongful conviction of which historical figure?

(c) Adam Lang, who features prominently in Harris's 2007 novel *The Ghost*, is a thinly disguised characterization of which public figure?

Your starter for ten:

6   Which novel of 1932 by James Normal Hall and Charles Nordhoff was the basis of several films and a stage musical? It concerns a rebellion in the South Pacific in 1789.

Three questions on astrophysics:
(a) In the process of Big Bang nucleosynthesis, fusion reactions during the first few minutes of the universe built up certain light nuclei, including what stable isotope with atomic mass number three?
(b) What specific isotope is the heaviest to be produced in detectable quantities during Big Bang nucleosynthesis, accounting for about one in ten billion primordial nuclei?
(c) What isotope is the lightest to be generated in Big Bang nucleosynthesis? Because it is rapidly burned in stars, the cosmic abundance of this isotope has decreased since the Big Bang.

Your starter for ten:

7   What multiple of eleven is the sum of the number of states in the Federal Republic of Germany and the number of Spanish autonomous communities?

Three questions on the US politician Nellie Tayloe Ross:
(a) In which US state was Ross elected to serve as governor in 1924? Its constitution was the first in the world to grant full voting rights to women.
(b) After her term as governor, Ross led the campaign for the women's vote for which presidential candidate in 1932?
(c) As the first female director of the US Mint, Ross oversaw the introduction in 1938 of a new nickel depicting which early US president? He still appears on the coin.

Your starter for ten:

8   Born in about 1882, Abd el-Krim led a national liberation movement in which present-day country? He established the Republic of the Rif in 1923, and was defeated only after a long campaign by French and Spanish forces.

Three questions on solid geometry:
(a) Which of the five platonic solids has faces that are all pentagonal in shape?

(b) If a platonic solid has 'e' edges, 'f' faces, and 'v' vertices, what is the numerical value of 'f' plus 'v' minus 'e'?

(c) For solids such as the cylinder, Klein bottle and torus, what is the numerical value of 'f' plus 'v' minus 'e'?

Your starter for ten:

9 Executed in 1540, which political figure is the subject of Hilary Mantel's 2020 novel *The Mirror and the Light*?

Three questions on blood:

(a) In blood classification, the designation Rh is derived from the use of the blood of which monkeys in a basic test?

(b) Gilbert's syndrome is caused by raised levels of what yellow substance, formed in the body as a by-product of the breakdown of old red blood cells?

(c) Which specific blood type is considered 'universal' because it can be given to anyone?

Your starter for ten:

10 The difference in the acceleration of gravity between Earth's equator and poles is equal to approximately five, as measured in what derived SI unit?

Your bonuses are on reptiles that are native to the UK:

(a) The common lizard has what alternative name, indicating that it incubates its eggs inside its body and so gives birth to 'live young'?

(b) *Coronella austriaca* has what two-word common name? A rare constrictor, it is similar in appearance to the adder, although the pattern on its back is less well-formed.

(c) *Anguis fragilis* has what two-word common name? A smooth, golden-grey legless lizard, it is often found in garden compost heaps.

Your starter for ten:

11 An archaic term for a cleric or theologian, what six-letter word is often used informally to mean 'highly pleasing' or 'delightful'? It was also the name adopted by the US performer Glenn Milstead for his on-stage alter ego.

Your bonuses are on jargon used in the TV police drama *Line of Duty*. In each case, give the term from the abbreviation:

(a) For what single word does the letter 'U' stand in the abbreviation UCO?

(b) Second, what three-word term is denoted by the abbreviation OCG?

(c) Finally, for what do the letters 'AC' stand in the name of the police unit AC-12?

Your starter for ten:

12 What single-word common name links *Dendrocopos major*, *Dendrocopos minor* and *Picus viridis*? They are birds known respectively as 'greater spotted', 'lesser spotted' and 'green'.

Three questions on the Prix Goncourt:

(a) Simone de Beauvoir won the Prix Goncourt in 1954 for which roman à clef?

(b) In 2014, the former psychiatrist Lydie Salvayre won the prize for her novel *Pas pleurer*, which focuses on which 20th-century conflict?

(c) Who was the first Moroccan woman to win the prize, doing so in 2016 for her novel *Lullaby*?

Your starter for ten:

13 In which constituency did Lisa Forbes win a by-election held on 6 June 2019 only to lose the seat in the general election six months later? The tomb of Catherine of Aaragon is located in the city in question, which lies just southwest of the Fens.

Three questions on minerals:

(a) The halide minerals are compounds that consist of metals and a halogen element. They include fluorite, a compound of which metal and which halogen?

(b) From the Greek for 'frost', what name is given to the halide mineral sodium aluminum fluoride, used as a solvent in the electrolytic production of aluminium?

(c) The halide mineral sylvite is a chloride of what metal?

Your starter for ten:

14 One of the earlier collectors of the work of Paul Cézanne, which doctor was the subject of portraits by his patient Vincent van Gogh, painted towards the end of the artist's life?

Three questions on the Second World War:

(a) The secret service known as the SOE was formed in 1940 to carry out subversive activity in enemy-held territory. For what do the letters SOE stand?

(b) Born in New Zealand, who operated under the codename 'Hélène' when assigned as a member of the SOE to support the French Resistance, a period recalled in her 1985 memoir, *The White Mouse*?

(c) Killed in a concentration camp after also working for the SOE in France, who was the subject of the 1958 film *Carve Her Name with Pride*?

Your starter for ten:

15 Answer as soon as your name is called. The number 'a-a' in hexadecimal corresponds to what decimal number?

Your bonuses are on pre-Columbian Mesoamerica. In each case, name the civilization from the description. All three names comes from the Nahuatl language:
(a) Its name meaning 'inhabitants of the rubber country', a civilization of the Mexican Gulf coast from about 1200 to 400 BCE, it is distinguished by a number of large-scale sculptures of human heads.
(b) Their name meaning 'people from a cloudy place', a people of Southern Mexico noted for their skill in metallurgy and ceramics.
(c) From a toponym meaning 'place of the reeds', a people that dominated Central Mexico until supplanted by the Aztecs.

Your starter for ten:

16 Based on a poem by Longfellow, the late-19th-century musical adaptation *Song of Hiawatha* is among the works of which English composer? His name recalls that of a romantic poet born in 1772.

Three questions on astrophysics:
(a) In 2015, the LIGO observatory in the USA detected a 'chirp' of gravitational waves for the first time, coming from what kind of event?
(b) This gravitational wave signal provided evidence that, as predicted by the general theory of relativity, a black hole has no more than three observable properties. One of these properties is spin. Name the other two.
(c) This lack of complex observable features was expressed by the physicist John Wheeler in the phrase 'black holes have no...' what?

Your starter for ten:

17 'Am I my brother's keeper' and 'the land of the living' are among expressions coined by which English scholar, executed in Brabant in 1536? He published the first vernacular English translation of the New Testament from Greek and Hebrew texts.

Your bonuses are on British birds of prey. Give the common name in each case:
(a) *Buteo buteo*, a common bird of prey whose call can be mistaken for a cat; it has dark wing-edges and a finely barred tail.
(b) *Milvus milvus*, a bird with a reddish-brown body, angled wings and deeply forked tail; it was saved from national extinction by a long-running protection programme. I need the two-word common name.
(c) Found in Scotland, *Haliaeetus albicilla*, the largest UK bird of prey; adults have brown body plumage, a paler head and neck, and distinctive tail feathers.

Your starter for ten:

18 In Shakespeare's *Twelfth Night*, which shipwrecked character adopts the name Cesario, having disguised herself as a boy?

Three questions on differential equations:
(a) The Lotka-Volterra equations are a pair of first-order, non-linear differential equations used to model what interaction or 'theory' in animal activity?
(b) The Lane-Emden equation is a second-order, ordinary differential equation and is a dimensionless form of Poisson's equation, developed in what branch of physics?
(c) The Navier-Stokes equations are a system of partial differential equations governing the motion of what?

Your starter for ten:

19 Give both the title and the author of the poem of 1818 that finishes: 'Round the decay / Of that colossal wreck, boundless and bare / The lone and level sands stretch far away'?

Three questions on winners of the Wolfson History Prize:
(a) The 2008 winner of the Wolfson Prize, *God's Architect*, concerns which 19th-century figure?
(b) Jonathan Sumption, a future justice of the Supreme Court, won the 2010 prize for *Divided Houses*, the third volume of his history of which conflict?
(c) *Conversions and Confessions* is the subtitle of Robin Lane Fox's 2016 prize-winner, a biography of which religious figure?

Your starter for ten:

20 Its name meaning 'useless' in Greek, what genus of mosquito is a vector of the malaria parasite?

Your bonuses are on Roman emperors. In each case, identify the emperor from the words of the historian Mary Beard:
(a) First: 'Some of the modern admirers of the gentle philosopher-emperor would be less admiring if they reflected on the brutality of his suppression of the Germans, proudly illustrated [on] his commemorative column.'
(b) Born in the year 12 CE, he 'may have been assassinated because he was a monster, but it is equally possible that he was made into a monster because he was assassinated'.
(c) Born in 9 CE, 'he was reputed to be a shrewd manager of the imperial finances, right down to putting a tax on human urine, a key ingredient in the laundry and cloth-processing industry.'

Your starter for ten:

21 Work this out before you buzz. Edward III and David II were on the English and Scottish thrones in the year 1331, or 'eleven cubed'. Who was on the throne of Great Britain in 'twelve-cubed'?

Three questions on a shared name:

(a) What is the English name of the waterfall known to the Pemon people of Venezuela by a name meaning 'waterfall to the deepest place'?

(b) Angel Clare, the son of a clergyman, marries which ill-fated heroine of a novel of 1891?

(c) Doctor Angelicus is a byname of which 13th-century scholastic philosopher, the author of the *Summa Theologiae*?

Your starter for ten:

22 What three letters all begin the names of the following: polyphosphate granules within bacterial cytoplasm; a constructed language devised by Johann Schleyer; an Italian tribe in Shakespeare's *Coriolanus*; an SI unit equivalent to the joule per coulomb; and a major river that flows into the Caspian Sea?

Three questions on beaches:

(a) Regularly voted one of Britain's best beaches, Barafundle Bay lies a few miles southwest of Tenby in which national park?

(b) Sometimes likened to locations in the tropics, Luskentyre Sands is on the west coast of which large Hebridean island?

(c) An annual skinny dip to raise money for mental health charities takes place at Druridge Bay, a seven-mile-long beach in which English county?

Your starter for ten:

23 What country's flag bears five stars whose colour appears in the name of its second-longest river, more than 5,000 kilometres in length? Its background colour is the name of another river that rises in the southwest of the country in question and meets the sea in neighbouring Vietnam.

Three questions on events that marked their 75th anniversary in 2021:

(a) In February 1946, which Norwegian was elected as the first UN Secretary-General? He resigned in 1952.

(b) In March 1946 in Fulton, Missouri, who said: 'Behind that line lie all the capitals of the ancient states of Central and Eastern Europe'?

(c) In a 1946 referendum, which European country voted to become a republic, having been ruled by the House of Savoy?

Your starter for ten:

24 What multiple of ten results when one multiplies the number of piano concertos by Beethoven and Rachmaninov?

Three questions on Italian intellectuals in the 18th century:
(a) *Elements of Public Economy* and *Crimes and Punishment* are among the works of which Milanese economist and criminologist, born in 1738?
(b) Works on *The Discipline of Metaphysics* and *Universal Christian Theology* are among the publications of which philosopher and economist, born in 1713?
(c) *The New Science* in 1725 was the magnum opus of which Neapolitan philosopher?

Your starter for ten:

25 What word can mean both to depose or bring down a government and, in cricket, a run scored as a result of inaccurate fielding, by a ball that goes too far?

Your bonuses are on winners of the Nobel Peace Prize. In each case, name the laureate from the description:
(a) The Iranian recipient of the 2003 prize; she was cited for 'her efforts for democracy and human rights … especially … the rights of women and children'.
(b) The Yemeni recipient of the 2011 prize, cited for her 'non-violent struggle for the safety of women and for women's rights'.
(c) The recipient of the 2014 prize; she was cited for her struggle 'for the right of all children to education'.

The Answers

1   Cole Porter
     (a) (Charles) Babbage
     (b) (Lord William) Beveridge
     (c) Florence Nightingale

2   (County) Westmeath (Contae na hIarmhí)
     (a) (Phoebe) Waller-Bridge
     (b) Michaela Coel (Michaela Ewuraba Boakye-Collinson)
     (c) Mackenzie Crook

3   (Harold) Wilson (all 1969)
     (a) Dogfish
     (b) Zebrafish
     (c) Seahorse

4   (Alan) Turing
     (a) Pineapple / pine nuts
     (b) Pomelo and pomegranate (Latin: *pome*, 'apple'; *granum*, 'seed')
     (c) Mango and mangold (accept mangel or mangelwurzel)

5   Christmas card
     (a) Cicero
     (b) (Alfred) Dreyfus
     (c) Tony Blair

6   *Mutiny on the Bounty*
     (a) Helium-3 (not tritium, which is not stable)
     (b) Lithium-7 (prompt for a more specific answer on 'lithium'; not beryllium)
     (c) Deuterium (accept hydrogen-2 but not hydrogen)

7   Thirty-three (sixteen plus seventeen)
     (a) Wyoming
     (b) Franklin D. Roosevelt (1882–1945)
     (c) (Thomas) Jefferson (1743–1826)

8   Morocco
     (a) Dodecahedron
     (b) 2 (this is a consequence of Euler's theorem)
     (c) 0

9   Thomas Cromwell (prompt on 'Cromwell', of course)
     (a) Rhesus (rhesus macaque, *Macaca mulatta*)
     (b) Bilirubin
     (c) O Negative (prompt on 'O' – must hear 'Negative')

10   Centimetres per second squared
    (a) Viviparous (lizard) / *Zootoca vivipara*
    (b) Smooth snake
    (c) Slow worm

11   Divine
    (a) Undercover (i.e. Undercover Operative / Officer / Operation)
    (b) Organized Crime Group
    (c) Anti-Corruption

12   Woodpecker
    (a) *The Mandarins* / *Les mandarins*
    (b) Spanish Civil War
    (c) Leïla Slimani

13   Peterborough (Brecon and Radnorshire was on 1 August)
    (a) Calcium and fluorine
    (b) Cryolite (also known as Greenland spar; Greek: *cryo*)
    (c) Potassium

14   (Dr Paul-Ferdinand) Gachet (1828–1909)
    (a) Special Operations Executive
    (b) (Nancy) Wake
    (c) (Violette) Szabo

15   170 (a = 10, so (10 x 16) + 10)
    (a) Olmec
    (b) Mixtec
    (c) Toltec

16   Samuel Coleridge-Taylor (the poet being Samuel Taylor Coleridge, obviously)
    (a) Collision (or merging) of two black holes
    (b) Mass and electric charge
    (c) 'Hair'

17   (William) Tyndale
    (a) (Common) buzzard
    (b) Red kite
    (c) White-tailed eagle (accept sea eagle or erne)

18   Viola
    (a) Predator-prey (theory or equations) / parasite-host (theory)
    (b) Astrophysics / astronomy
    (c) (Incompressible) fluids (accept but qualify liquids, gases, viscous fluids)

19 'Ozymandias' by Shelley
    (a) (Augustus / A.W.N.) Pugin
    (b) The Hundred Years' War
    (c) (St) Augustine (of Hippo)

20 Anopheles
    (a) Marcus Aurelius
    (b) Caligula (formally known as Gaius)
    (c) Vespasian

21 George II (i.e. 1728)
    (a) Angel Falls
    (b) Tess (of the d'Urbevilles / Tess Durbeyfield)
    (c) (St Thomas) Aquinas

22 V-o-l (volutin; Volapük; Volsci / Volscians; volt; Volga)
    (a) Pembrokeshire Coast
    (b) Harris (accept Lewis and Harris)
    (c) Northumberland

23 China (yellow and red, of course)
    (a) (Trygve) Lie
    (b) (Winston) Churchill (the Iron Curtain speech, of course)
    (c) Italy

24 Twenty (five by four)
    (a) (Cesare) Beccaria
    (b) (Antonio) Genovesi
    (c) (Giambattista) Vico

25 Overthrow
    (a) (Shirin) Ebadi
    (b) (Tawakkol) Karman
    (c) Malala (Yousafzai)

Girls vs Boys
St Hilda's College, Oxford

Oriel College, Oxford
(1966)

It was a Christmas tradition that the reigning champions (the winners from the previous series) should face another team in a festive special show.

The all-male team of Oriel College, Oxford were the winners in the summer, and challenging them were the all-female team of St Hilda's, who had narrowly missed (by 10 points) a place in the final.

St Hilda's
Heather Spooner from Devon, reading Politics, Philosophy and Economics
Gilly Evans from London, then working in an advertising agency
Susan Fairhead (captain) from Solihull, who had become a teacher
Julia Gold from Oxford, researching ghost stories

Oriel
Neil Murray from Newfoundland, researching in English
Jonathan Reeve from Wimbledon, reading Medicine
Peter Fulford-Jones (captain) from Essex, now a lecturer in Classics
Roger Tomlin from Monmouthshire,
studying the late Roman emperor Valentinian

Your starter for ten:

1 Who used to read out the following extract from a letter advertising a hotel: 'There is a French widow in every bedroom affording delightful aspects'?
[The question was successfully interrupted ahead of the quote]

Bonus questions:
(a) What is the working name of Mrs Bill Travers?
(b) What is the working name of Lord Glenavy?
(c) What is the working name of Walker Smith?

Your starter for ten:

2 What is the name of the statue which I am describing? It was carved by Michelangelo from a huge block of marble—
[The question was successfully interrupted]

Bonus questions:
The following quotations come from epilogues spoken in Shakespeare's plays. Which are the plays?
(a) 'It is not the fashion to see the lady in the epilogue'
(b) 'As you from crimes would pardoned be, / Let your indulgence set me free'
(c) 'Gentles, do not reprehend: / If you pardon, we will mend'

Your starter for ten:

3 The clue to a particular problem, posed originally in the reign of William III, was to turn left on entering, thereafter to turn right—?
[The question was successfully interrupted]

Bonus questions:
I'm going to give you some words which we have coined from familiar Greek roots, and I want you to tell me what they would mean if they were real words.
(a) A 'gynaeclast'
(b) An 'echidnaphile'
(c) A 'hyppophagite'
(d) A 'telebromite' or 'telebromist'

Your starter for ten:

4 Who appeared briefly in a hotel foyer dangling a baby in a torn curtain?

Bonus questions:
How did these heroes die?
(a) Siegfried

(b) King Saul
(c) Saint Sebastian

Your starter for ten:

5 [This was a music round. St Hilda's won the starter by correctly identifying 'God Save the Queen' from a fugue-like passage from Beethoven; they went on to answer a set of bonus music questions on operatic heroines, but could only manage five points]

Your starter for ten:

6 What is wrong with this statement? The Trojan horse was a device which the Greeks adopted after the death of Odysseus—
[The question was successfully interrupted]

Bonus questions:
I'm going to read you some definitions from the Shorter Oxford English Dictionary, and I want to give me the word being defined.
(a) 'Of women having or affecting literary tastes, from the assemblies which met at Montague House in London in about 1750 in order to substitute for card playing literary conversation.'
(b) 'A situation or, in logic, a syllogism of the nature of a dilemma but involving three alternatives instead of two.'
(c) 'The lowest class of the community in ancient Rome, regarded as contributing nothing to the state but offspring.'
(d) 'A vision of a distant moving object or scene electrically transmitted and produced. Also the process by which this is effected.'

Your starter for ten:

7 Where precisely was the red dragon of Wales superseded by the white unicorn of Scotland in 1603?

Bonus questions:
In what do these characters appear?
(a) Caswell Bligh
(b) Jack Point
(c) Leopold Bloom

Your starter for ten:

8 What is the seventeenth letter in the English alphabet?

Bonus questions:
I'm going to give you the titles under which three English plays are now being

performed in Paris or have very recently been performed. I want you to give me the original title, and it has to be absolutely exact.

(a) *Vivre [et penser] comme des porcs*

(b) *La prochaine fois je vous le chanterai*

(c) *Témoignage irrecevable*

Your starter for ten:

9 The name that was given by Paracelsus to his famous medical preparation, which he described as including gold and pearls, but with opium as its main ingredient, is now used to mean the simple alcoholic tincture of opium. What is it?

[Neither team got the right answer]

Your starter for ten:

10 Of what Renaissance pope did the Venetian ambassador say, 'The advancement of his children is the only thing that he seems to care about'?

[Again, neither team got the right answer]

Your starter for ten:

11 The pseudonym which was used by L.L. Zamenhof in his brochure of 1887 explaining his new international language later became used for the language for—?

[The question was successfully interrupted]

Bonus questions:

(a) Which famous English poet entered in *Who's Who* as her recreations 'music and silence'?

(b) Whose entry has recreations 'listening to the sound of his own voice, preferably on gramophone records, and not answering letters'?

(c) The author of a famous escape story about the Second World War lists 'fighting officiousness in all its forms'. Who is he?

Your starter for ten:

12 [The teams were shown a set of eyes from a television adaptation and asked to name the characters; Oriel correctly identified Ian Carmichael and Denis Price as Bertie Wooster and Jeeves and then went on to identify Dudley Cook and Peter Cook's eyes, but not those of Patrick Macnee and Diana Rigg or Mike and Bernie Winters]

Your starter for ten:

13 What unexpected people have had the privilege of assisting with performances of *Aida* at Covent Garden ever since an unsuccessful

performance, which Queen Victoria attended, and which led her to command that proper soldiers be provided?

Bonus questions:
In each part of this question, I am going to give you the name of one woman and the names of three people, two of whom she could possibly have married and the third of whom she absolutely could not have married. I am assuming that divorce is always a possibility and that people can't marry until they are 16, but can marry at any age after that. Each time, I need the one she couldn't have married.
(a) Mrs Siddons, and the three men are David Garrick, John Philip Kemble and William Charles Macready.
(b) Lady Anne, daughter-in-law of Henry VI, and the men are Edward IV, Edward V and Richard III.
(c) Charlotte Brontë, and the three men are William Cobbett, Master William Betty and Currer Bell?
(d) Major Barbara, and the three men are Charles Lomax, John Tanner and Adolphus Cusins?

Your starter for ten:
14 Who in particular asks people to 'get up out of their seats'—?
[The question was successfully interrupted]

Bonus questions:
(a) Which saints with similar legends are both patrons of hunting?
(b) Which huntsman was the grandson of Ham?
(c) Which riding man lost his moustache to play a hunting part in *Mr John Jorrocks*?

Your starter for ten:
15 What book is made up of five elegies which bemoan the destruction of Jerusalem—?
[The question was successfully interrupted]

Bonus questions:
(a) To what were 'kissing strings' attached?
(b) Who was a *Kissin' Cousin* in 1964?
(c) What, in bakers' terms, is a kissing crust?

Your starter for ten:
16 Name the national shrine overlooking the Potomac River in Virginia, which was the home of George Washington until his death?

Bonus questions:
Of what countries were these people kings?
(a) Sennacherib
(b) Ahab
(c) Artaxerxes

Your starter for ten:
17 What man has been shared by all these women? Fernande Olivier, Olga Khokhlova, Marie-Thérèse Walter, Dora Maar, Françoise Gilot—?
[The question was successfully interrupted]

Bonus question:
What kings were on the throne of England when these plays were first performed?
(a) Shakespeare's *Coriolanus*
(b) *Pygmalion*

The gong sounds

St Hilda's amassed 150 points against Oriel's 115.

The Answers

1   Gerard Hoffnung
    (a) Virginia McKenna
    (b) Patrick Campbell
    (c) Sugar Ray Robinson

2   David
    (a) *As You Like It*
    (b) *The Tempest*
    (c) *A Midsummer Night's Dream*

3   The maze at Hampton Court
    (a) One who is highly critical of women (accept similar)
    (b) A lover of snakes (vipers to be precise)
    (c) Someone who eats horses
    (d) One who stinks from afar

4   Alfred Hitchcock
    (a) Stabbed in the back
    (b) Killed in battle
    (c) Beaten to death with rods or cudgels (he recovered from being shot with arrows)

5   [Music round]

6   Odysseus was not dead – he was still alive.
    (a) Bluestocking
    (b) Trilemma
    (c) Proletaria
    (d) Television

7   On the Royal Coat of Arms
    (a) *The Power Game*
    (b) *The Yeomen of the Guard*
    (c) *Ulysses*

8   Q
    (a) *Live Like Pigs*
    (b) *Next Time I Will Sing to You*
    (c) *Inadmissible Evidence*

9   Laudanum

10 Alexander VI (the great Borgia Pope)

11 Esperanto
    (a) Edith Sitwell

(b) Osbert Sitwell

(c) Eric Williams

12 [Picture round]

13 Any of the five regiments of Foot Guards (Coldstream, Welsh, Grenadier, Scots and Irish Guards)

(a) John Philip Kemble was her brother

(b) Edward V was only 13 (and was one of the Princes in the Tower)

(c) Currer Bell was her pseudonym

(d) John Tanner was in *Man and Superman* not *Major Barbara*

14 Billy Graham

(a) St Eustace and St Hubert

(b) Nimrod

(c) Jimmy Edwards

15 (The Lamentations of) Jeremiah

(a) Bonnets – ties under the chin

(b) Elvis Presley

(c) Two loaves where the crusts touch in the oven, but when broken apart there is bread between them

16 Mount Vernon

(a) Assyria

(b) Israel

(c) Persia

17 (Pablo) Picasso

(a) James I

(b) George V

Try Your Luck
Match

Your starter for ten:

1 'I think women are foolish to pretend they are equal to men. They are far superior, and always have been.' Which British author and Nobel laureate said those words in an explanation of why his best-known novel was exclusively about boys, rather than girls?

Three questions on warriors:
(a) Boudicca was queen of which ancient Celtic tribe, who lived in and around present-day East Anglia?
(b) In Greek mythology, what was the name of the Amazon queen said to have been killed by Achilles?
(c) Born in 1157, Tomoe Gozen was a warrior in which country? She distinguished herself at the battle of Awazu in 1185.

Your starter for ten:

2 The Visayas are the central archipelago of which island nation? Including Panay, Samar and Cebu, they lie about 1,000 kilometres east of Southern Vietnam.

Your bonuses are on Christmas scenes in children's stories:
(a) In which novel is a young boy so moved by the thin face and poor clothes of the young orphan Sara Crewe that he insists on giving her his sixpence at Christmas? The author is Frances Hodgson Burnett.
(b) On waking up on Christmas Day, which title character runs downstairs singing: 'Merry Christmas, Marilla! Merry Christmas, Matthew! Isn't it a lovely Christmas?'
(c) In which 19th-century novel does a mother persuade her daughters to donate their Christmas breakfast to a poor and starving family who live nearby?

Your starter for ten:

3　In which play by Shakespeare does a nobleman say: 'At Christmas I no more desire a rose / Than wish a snow in May's new-fangled mirth'? The words are spoken by Berowne, in the presence of Longaville, Dumain and King Ferdinand of Navarre.

Three questions on an epic poem:
(a) In 2017, the British classicist Emily Wilson became the first woman to publish an English translation of which epic poem?
(b) Madeline Miller's 2018 rewrite of *The Odyssey* takes as its title and subject which island-dwelling sorceress?
(c) Based on the name of Odysseus's wife, what is the title of Margaret Atwood's 2006 reinterpretation of *The Odyssey*?

Your starter for ten:

4　Traditionally used in relation to competitions or the awarding of prizes, the Latin term *proxime accessit* has what meaning, when describing the final placings of the candidates, players or teams?

Three questions on a family of proteins:
(a) The SMC protein family consists of a number of ATPases involved in DNA packaging and repair. For what genetic entity does the letter 'C' stand in SMC?
(b) What name is given to the complexes that include the SMC2 and SMC4 proteins, along with varying kleisin and heat proteins? They play an integral role in the compaction of chromosomes in mitosis.
(c) The SMC complex cohesin ensures the pairing of sister chromatids in mitosis. It is degraded by the APC, at the onset of what phase of mitosis, during which chromatids segregate into daughter cells?

Your starter for ten:

5　Which Swedish scientist won the Nobel Prize in Chemistry in 1903 for his work on the electrolytic theory of dissociation? An equation describing the effect of temperature on the velocity of a chemical reaction is named after him.

Three questions on a royal figure:
(a) 30 January 2019 marked the 370th anniversary of what event that took place outside the Banqueting House in Whitehall?
(b) In the death sentence, the High Court of Justice described Charles as a 'tyrant'. Give any one of the three descriptive words or expressions that immediately followed the word 'tyrant'.

(c) In 1650, which poet wrote of Charles's execution, 'He nothing common did or mean / Upon that memorable scene'?

Your starter for ten:

6 Born in Glasgow in 1920 and dying there in 2010, which Scottish poet and academic was, in 2004, named Scotland's first official national poet, with the Scots title 'Makar'.

Three questions on the world in the first year of the Common Era, or AD 1:
(a) In the year AD 1, which empire ruled much of present-day Iran and Iraq and parts of contiguous countries including Syria and Armenia?
(b) Founded in 206 BCE, which imperial dynasty ruled China in AD 1? A single-word answer is sufficient.
(c) The year AD 1 falls in the pre-classical period of which civilization of Central America that centred on Northern Petén in Guatemala?

Your starter for ten:

7 Give two forenames and the shared surname promptly. Both political activists, who were the older sisters of Adela, born in Manchester in 1885. 2018 saw the unveiling in Manchester of a statue of their mother, Emmeline.

Three questions on astronomy:
(a) With a mean diameter of about 530 kilometres, what is the brightest asteroid as seen from Earth, occasionally reaching a magnitude of about 5.5, which makes it visible to the naked eye? It was orbited by NASA's *Dawn* spacecraft in 2011 and 2012.
(b) *Dawn* confirmed that Vesta is the parent body of about 6 per cent of meteorites found on Earth, a meteorite clan known by the acronym HED; give me any of the three meteorite groups that give rise to that acronym.
(c) Larger than Vesta, which asteroid did *Dawn* orbit from March 2015?

Your starter for ten:

8 What event inspired the early 19th-century poem that ends: 'Ye are many – they are few'? Present-day protesters marked the bicentenary of the event on a rainy day in August 2019.

Three questions on plants:
(a) Conifers are a division of what broad category of plants, with a name denoting that they reproduce by an exposed seed, or ovule?

(b) What palm-like woody gymnosperms are known to have existed in the Mesozoic era? Often used as ornamental plants, they include the modern sago palm.

(c) Also known as the maidenhair and widespread during the Jurassic period, which fruit-bearing deciduous tree is valued as a fungus- and insect-resistant ornamental tree?

Your starter for ten:

9   In which country is the ancient city of Hippo Regius, associated with the early Christian saint Augustine, and now known as Annaba? It lies on the Mediterranean coast, close to the border with Tunisia.

Three questions on constellations:

(a) The classical 48 constellations were originally listed by which Greek mathematician and astronomer of the 2nd century AD in his *Almagest*?

(b) Which 18th-century French astronomer classified some fourteen constellations in the southern hemisphere, many named after instruments including the compass and the telescope?

(c) In total, how many constellations are recognized by the International Astronomical Union? You can have three either way.

Your starter for ten:

10 Phacops and Paradoxides are examples of which extinct group of arthropods, characterized by an exoskeleton and a triply segmented body that superficially resembles a woodlouse?

Three questions on the Wodehouse Prize for Comic Fiction:

(a) What language completes the title of Marina Lewycka's 2005 winning novel: *A Short History of Tractors in* …?

(b) The name of which Indian city on the River Ganges completes the title of Geoff Dyer's 2011 winning work: *Jeff in Venice, Death in* …?

(c) Which country completes the title of Paul Torday's 2007 winning novel: *Salmon Fishing in the* …?

Your starter for ten:

11 Born in Chicago in 1925 and known for his dark humour and gothic sensibility, which prolific writer, illustrator and designer won a Tony Award in 1978 for the costume design for the revival of the play *Dracula*?

Three questions on fruit:

(a) Named after a Californian judge who first grew them in his garden, loganberries are commonly believed to be a hybrid of what two fruits?

(b) Which small purple fruit, often called a berry, grows on a palm tree and is sold dried or powdered as a dietary supplement for its high antioxidant content?

(c) 'The wind in the willow played / Love's sweet melody, / But all of those vows you made / Were never to be.' Which fruit appears in the title of the song containing this complaint?

Your starter for ten:

12 What initial letter is that of only a small number of countries, including those whose UNESCO World Heritage sites include the Coro and its Port, Chief Roi Mata's Domain and Ha Long Bay?

Three questions on a chemical compound:

(a) The crystalline mineral chalcanthite is the pentahydrate form of what compound? Other names for it include blue vitriol.

(b) In 2008, which Birmingham-born artist used concentrated copper sulphate solution to fill a London bedsit with crystals, in his work entitled *Seizure*?

(c) Named after a 19th-century German chemist, which test for aldehydes or reducing sugars uses two reagents: copper sulphate, and a solution of Rochelle salt in alkali?

Your starter for ten:

13 Sometimes called a 'water bear' or 'moss piglet', which animal has a name meaning 'slow-paced'? Less than a millimetre in length, it is able to withstand sub-zero temperatures and long-term desiccation, and in 2007 became the first animal known to survive exposure in space.

Three questions on an 18th-century conflict:

(a) The conflict known in North America as the French and Indian War was mostly coincident with which European conflict, ongoing when George III acceded to the throne?

(b) The Seven Years' War arose when the Habsburgs attempted to regain Silesia, seized from them by which ruler during the War of the Austrian Succession?

(c) In late 1759, British naval superiority was established for the remainder of the war when Edward Hawke defeated the French at which bay in Brittany?

Your starter for ten:

14 Dominant in the Mesozoic era and now found more frequently in colder and drier regions, what group of plants have exposed ovules or seeds, usually in the form of cones? The term means 'naked seeds' in Greek.

Three questions on the Zoological Society of London's surveys of wildlife living in the River Thames, which was declared 'biologically dead' in the 1950s:
(a) In 2020, the ZSL reported sightings in tidal waters of the 'short-snouted' species of what fish of the genus *hippocampus*?
(b) Since the first ZSL survey in 2013, numbers of what marine mammal in the river have risen, with a recent count of several thousand of the 'grey' and 'harbour' species?
(c) 'Tope' and 'starry smooth-hound' are small species of what fish? They give birth to live young and are thought to use the Thames Estuary as a nursery.

Your starter for ten:
15 In entries in the Welsh Academy's *Encyclopedia of Wales*, what common adjective appears before 'Book of Carmarthen', 'Mountain', 'Mountains' and 'Death'? It is one of two colours on the flag of St David.

Three questions on the Greek alphabet:
(a) Used in physics to represent the quantum wave function, what is the penultimate letter of the Greek alphabet? I need you to spell your answer.
(b) Give two of the three Greek letters whose names are seven letters long. All three names contain elements meaning 'bare', 'smooth' or 'little'.
(c) Used in an English expression meaning 'not the slightest amount', what is the ninth letter of the Greek alphabet?

Your starter for ten:
16 What is the full four-word name of the piece of European legislation regarding information privacy that came into force in May 2018 and is generally known by its initials, GDPR?

Three questions on Latin abbreviations:
(a) Meaning 'other things being equal', for what Latin expression do the letters 'cp' stand?
(b) Found on British coins, and meaning 'By the grace of God', for what do the letters 'D.G.' stand?
(c) Used in cross-referencing and meaning 'which see', for what do the letters 'qv' stand?

Your starter for ten:
17 'I saw, to my great astonishment, that scientific time does not endure.' Those are the words of which philosopher? Born in Paris in 1859, he wrote *Time and Free Will* and was awarded the 1927 Nobel Prize in Literature.

Three questions on physics:
(a) In the standard model of particle physics, which two elementary particles have the same mass, charge and spin?
(b) Among standard-model fermions, how many have masses greater than that of a proton?
(c) What letter denotes each of the two electrically charged bosons, which mediate neutrino emission and absorption?

Your starter for ten:
18 In 2019, during the second Ashes Test at Lord's, Marnus Labuschagne became the first 'concussion substitute' when which player was forced to retire from the match?

Three questions on the mechanisms of markets:
(a) What two-word metaphor did Adam Smith use to indicate the mechanisms through which beneficial social and economic outcomes may arise from the self-interested actions of individuals?
(b) A cause of market failure, what is the term for consequences arising from an economic activity that affect someone other than those engaged in the activity, and are not reflected fully in prices?
(c) The economist Arthur Pigou argued that market failures caused by positive externalities or benefits can be offset by what type of economic mechanism?

Your starter for ten:
19 *The Triumph of the Innocents*, *The Scapegoat* and *The Light of the World* are among works by which English painter, a founder of the Pre-Raphaelite Brotherhood, along with Millais and Rossetti?

Three questions on battles:
(a) The ridge known as Senlac Hill is generally accepted as the location of what decisive battle?
(b) Early in his reign, which king of Scotland defeated an English army at Loudoun Hill in Ayrshire?
(c) The Battle of Vinegar Hill was followed by an act that abolished the parliament of what country?

Your starter for ten:
20 With reference to the titles of two works of fiction, what number results from dividing Jules Verne's *Leagues Under the Sea* by Patrick Hamilton's *Streets Under the Sky*?

Three questions on the Bavarian University of Ingolstadt:
(a) Which enduring fictional character conducted experiments in chemistry, physiology and galvanism at Ingolstadt? He first appeared in a novel of 1818.
(b) Which Ingolstadt theologian was a principal Catholic antagonist of Martin Luther and the joint author of a papal bull that condemned 41 of Luther's 95 theses?
(c) In 1776, Ingolstadt's professor of canon law, Adam Weishaupt, formed which secret society at the university?

Your starter for ten:

21 Name any one of the three men who served as US president in 1841.

Your bonuses are on 20th-century UK prime ministers. In each case, identify the person whose surname matches the etymology described:
(a) Thought to be derived from Germanic words meaning 'bold' and 'friend', a surname that was also the name of the Count of Flanders, one of the leaders of the Fourth Crusade.
(b) A surname formed from a Scottish prefix meaning 'son of', combined with a Gaelic word meaning 'bald' or 'tonsured'.
(c) In office after Macmillan, a prime minister's surname that derives ultimately from a Gaelic word meaning 'contention' or 'strife'.

Your starter for ten:

22 Imagine taking the remaining chocolates from an opened advent calendar that had originally held one per window: grouping them in threes leaves one left over; in fours leaves three left over; and in fives leaves four left over. How many chocolates are there?

Three questions linked by a word:
(a) Thomas Hardy turned away from the writing of fiction after which novel of 1895 met with severe disfavour? Its characters include Arabella Donn and Sue Bridehead.
(b) The *Daily Obscurer* and the *Weekly Chloroform* are publications owned by the characters Sweater and Grinder in which novel of 1914 by Robert Tressell?
(c) 'My English text is chaste, and all licentious passages are left in the obscurity of a learned language.' These are the words of which historian, born in 1737?

Your starter for ten:

23 After beryllium, which of the alkaline earth metals of the periodic table has the lowest atomic number?

Your bonuses are on Welsh locations named after biblical places. Identify the place names from the description:
(a) Its name meaning 'house of bread' in Hebrew, a village in Carmarthenshire that shares its name with a town in the Judean Hills, a little to the south of Jerusalem.
(b) A village south of Caernarfon; it is named after a historic city of Lower Galilee believed to be the boyhood home of Jesus.
(c) A former slate-quarrying village on the edge of Snowdonia; it takes its name from a pool in Jerusalem where, according to John's Gospel, Jesus healed a paralysed man.

Your starter for ten:
24 What two letters begin French words meaning 'oven', 'fern', 'lightning', 'crowd' and 'ant'?

Your bonuses are on the first monarchs of European royal houses. From each description, give the regnal name, the regnal number and the royal house:
(a) First, a French monarch born in Navarre in 1553; he reputedly declared that 'Paris is well worth a mass.'
(b) An Italian monarch born in Turin in 1820; he was the first sovereign of unified Italy.
(c) Finally, a British monarch born in Germany in 1660; he was married to Sophia Dorothea of Celle.

Your starter for ten:
25 'Drina', 'Sighs', 'San Luis Rey' and 'Terabithia' are words that appear along with what general type of structure in the titles of fictional works by the Nobel laureate Ivo Andrić and the US authors Richard Russo, Thornton Wilder and Katherine Paterson?

Three questions on the electoral college of the USA. In each case, name the state from the description:
(a) Carrying 29 votes, a southeastern state that voted in 2012 for Barack Obama and in 2016 for Donald Trump.
(b) Carrying 5 votes, a midwestern state that splits its votes by congressional district; since 1968, it has voted almost entirely for Republican candidates?
(c) Finally, carrying 55 votes, a western state that has voted for every Democratic candidate since 1992?

The Answers

1   (Sir William) Golding (referring to *Lord of the Flies*, of course)
    (a) Iceni
    (b) Penthesilia
    (c) Japan

2   Philippines
    (a) *A Little Princess*
    (b) *Anne of Green Gables* (L.M. Montgomery)
    (c) *Little Women* (Louisa M. Alcott)

3   *Love's Labour's Lost*
    (a) (Homer's) *Odyssey*
    (b) Circe
    (c) *The Penelopiad*

4   Runner-up / second place
    (a) Chromosome(s) (structural maintenance of chromosomes)
    (b) Condensin (complexes)
    (c) Anaphase

5   (Svante) Arrhenius
    (a) The execution of Charles I
    (b) Traitor / murderer / public enemy
    (c) (Andrew) Marvell ('An Horatian Ode upon Cromwell's Return from Ireland')

6   Edwin (George) Morgan
    (a) Parthian (accept Arsacid)
    (b) (Western) Han
    (c) Mayan

7   (Estelle) Sylvia and Christabel (Harriette) Pankhurst
    (a) Vesta
    (b) Howardite; Eucrite; Diogenite
    (c) Ceres

8   Peterloo (Massacre) / St Peter's Field Massacre (from Shelley's *The Masque of Anarchy*)
    (a) Gymnosperms (distinguished from the flowering plants, or angiosperms)
    (b) Cycads
    (c) Ginkgo (biloba)

9   Algeria
    (a) (Claudius) Ptolemy
    (b) (Nicolas-Louis de) Lacaille
    (c) 88 (so accept 85–91)

10 Trilobites
(a) Ukrainian
(b) Varanasi
(c) Yemen

11 Edward Gorey
(a) Raspberry and blackberry
(b) Acai / açaí (berry)
(c) Blueberry ('Blueberry Hill' of course, performed by Fats Domino)

12 V (the sites are in Venezuela, Vanuatu and Vietnam)
(a) Copper sulphate / cupric sulphate
(b) (Roger) Hiorns
(c) Fehling's (test / solution / reagent; Hermann von Fehling, 1812–1885)

13 Tardigrade
(a) Seven Years' War
(b) Frederick the Great / II
(c) Quiberon (Bay)

14 Gymnosperms
(a) Seahorse
(b) Seal
(c) Shark

15 Black
(a) Psi
(b) Epsilon, upsilon, omicron
(c) Iota (as in 'not one iota', of course)

16 General Data Protection Regulation
(a) *Ceteris paribus*
(b) *Dei Gratia / Deo Gratias*
(c) *Quod vide / quae vide*

17 (Henri) Bergson
(a) Photon and gluon
(b) Four
(c) W

18 Steve Smith
(a) Invisible hand
(b) Externalities
(c) Subsidy

19 (William) Holman Hunt
(a) Hastings

(b) Robert I / Robert the Bruce
(c) Ireland

20 One (*Twenty Thousand Leagues Under the Sea*, *Twenty Thousand Streets Under the Sky*)
(a) (Victor) Frankenstein
(b) (Johann) Eck
(c) (The) Illuminati

21 (Martin) van Buren / William Henry Harrison / (John) Tyler (1 January–4 March; 4 March–4 April; 4 April–31 December; not Benjamin Harrison, who was in office in 1889–1893)
(a) (Stanley) Baldwin
(b) (Harold) Macmillan
(c) (James) Callaghan (Gaelic: O Ceallachain)

22 Nineteen (modular arithmetic: 19 = 1 mod 3; 19 = 3 mod 4; 19 = 4 mod 5. The reference to an advent calendar implies the number is less than or equal to 24 – as the grouping condition can be satisfied for 79, 139, etc.)
(a) *Jude the Obscure*
(b) *The Ragged-Trousered Philanthropists*
(c) (Edward) Gibbon

23 Magnesium (atomic number 12; beryllium is 4, calcium 20, strontium 38, barium 56, radium 88)
(a) Bethlehem
(b) Nazareth / Nasareth
(c) Bethesda

24 Fo- (four, fougère, foudre, foule, fourmi)
(a) Henri IV / Bourbon
(b) Victor Emmanuel II / Savoy
(c) George I / Hanover

25 Bridge (*The Bridge on the Drina*, *Bridge of Sighs*, *Bridge of San Luis Rey*, *Bridge to Terabithia*)
(a) Florida (New York is the only other state to carry 29 votes)
(b) Nebraska (the only midwestern state to carry 5 votes)
(c) California (the only state to carry 55 votes, of course)

Challenging Tales
Manchester Mayhem

In 1975, the University of Manchester, then called the Victoria University of Manchester, came up against Downing College, Cambridge in a first-round match. In order to make a political statement – reported as an objection to the perceived elitism of Oxford and Cambridge, though in reality the students' actions had a wider aim – the team answered starter questions with either the names of revolutionaries or generally silly answers. Nearly 25 years on, the stunt is still referenced, although no copy of that particular programme is known to exist.

'It's entered into a form of mythology, really,' says team member David Aaronovitch, who went on to become an award-winning journalist. 'The mythology is such that it partly informed, I am told, the depiction of *University Challenge* in *The Young Ones* because at least two of them were Manchester students, although of course they hadn't been there at the time. The folklore of our episode went on for some time.'

At that time, says David, the Students' Union decided that the *University Challenge* team should be elected at a union general meeting. 'There were no "your starter for 10" selection interviews; you stood up at the general meeting and said why you thought you should go on the team. I don't know if that's ever been done before or since. Then you were voted in, and that was the group of people they put forward.' David stood on a platform of drawing attention to the elitism of University Challenge 'because they didn't let polytechnics in and the Oxbridge colleges had about 18 teams each, and it is still pretty much true, although the polytechnics subsequently became universities. We thought it was a whole lot of stuck-up people with gonks.' He had been at Oxford for two terms before Manchester: 'They kicked me out, but it wasn't because I had an animus towards it; I would still have thought it was unfair when I was at Oxford.'

As the occasion approached, the team was sent guest tickets but David remembers the university anarchists forged a run of 200 tickets to infiltrate the audience. 'When we were asked to give our names, we gave ridiculous subjects we were supposed to be studying. I think I said I was studying Marxist Theory; I wasn't. If it sounds lame now, I think it probably sounded pretty lame at the time. Then we were giving some ridiculous answers that have gone down in history as answering everything with the name of a revolutionary, but I don't really remember that. I just remembered a whole set of slightly absurd answers, and we must have got a couple of starters right or this couldn't have happened. We were asked what the road was that led from Kyoto to something or other in Japan, and one of us answered the Yellow Brick Road. It was that kind of thing.

'But at a certain point they stopped the whole thing. There was chanting in the audience, and they said they couldn't carry on and were going to cancel the whole thing. So we carried on being partly silly and partly not, and we got about 40 points. So protest made, and they got something of a programme out of it. But what then happened was as soon as it had been broadcast there was a big letters page in the *Manchester Evening News* which was headlined "Manchester team a disgrace". All these people were expressing a sense of disappointment that their city had been let down by us, and I remember thinking, "Oh, bollocks." It never occurred to me that anyone would be upset by this other than the producers. The reaction to what we'd done was pretty rapid.'

David says he remembers Bamber Gascoigne being irritated by the team's antics. 'Why would he not be? But I met him subsequently, and I don't believe he was ever particularly unpleasant about it, despite what we'd done. I remember thinking that he was a good guy really. We didn't not want it to be broadcast – don't imagine for five seconds we'd actually thought it through. We wanted it to be broadcast, otherwise what was the point?'

David's teammate and co-conspirator, Quentin Smith, who became a solicitor and the chairman of the children's charity Wooden Spoon, remembers: 'I was probably the architect of this. There was a febrile atmosphere at Manchester University in the early to mid-1970s. There was a very active Students' Union, and one of the big campaigns that we ran at the time was to get the university to disinvest in South Africa. So what you want as an activist is an opportunity for a big public platform, and I discovered that Manchester University was to be invited to participate in *University Challenge*. There was an Anarchist Society, but it was actually called the Libertarian Society. We did various things, public campaigns and stuff like that, but anti-Apartheid disinvestment was a big one.

'We were having fun at the recording, but it wasn't offensive. There was nothing rude or anything to give them grounds for pulling the show. Bamber Gascoigne was really sympathetic. He came over to us afterwards, and said, "What was all that about?" We told him, and he was really interested. He liked us. He didn't say, "You've ruined the show" or "That was an opportunity lost" or anything like that.'

The broadcast went into University of Manchester folklore. 'We were surprised about its longevity, but it's probably a recognition of the programme's position in entertainment, both then and now, that it should be sustained.

There was a lot of support for it. And things changed; sometimes you have to take a slightly longer view. I can't for a moment take credit for the investment policy of the university, but I feel confident in saying that it wouldn't have been harmful to pressure that would have been applied to people on the University Council. Those people who were making those decisions would have been aware of a strong movement, particularly among students and how the university wanted to be presented.'

David adds: 'Then, of course, *University Challenge* died its first death in a kind of way, because of the sorts of things that we were thinking at the time, that it was sort of obsolete and a bit elitist, a bit dated. Miraculously, the BBC rediscovered it, recommissioned it, and it came back stronger in many ways, than it had been in the first place.'

Sidney Sussex, Cambridge

Sidney Sussex, Cambridge
(1979)

Early in the New Year of 1979, a seasonal special featured the students of Sidney Sussex challenging their dons.

This was the tenth time students had faced their dons on *University Challenge*. Sidney were the 1978 champions and their captain was David Lidington, who went on to become Leader of the House of Commons, Lord Chancellor and Secretary of State for Justice.

The Students
John Gilmore from Barbados, researching History
John Adams from Gatley, Manchester, reading Clinical Medicine at Oxford
David Lidington (captain) from Northwood Middlesex, reading History
Nick Graham from Maryport, Cumberland, reading English

The Dons
Michael Wadsworth, Chaplain
Paul Dawson, Senior Research Fellow in English Literature
Derek Beales, teaching History
Christopher Parish, postgraduate Dean, Faculty of Clinical Medicine

Your starter for ten:

1 What was the name of the hero of a very popular book called *The Life and Adventures of a Cat*, published in 1760, who became such a well-known character his name came to be used as a general term for all male cats?

Bonus questions:
(a) What Paleozoic fish was found alive and well and living off the South African coast in 1938?
(b) What type of fish are officially described as bilaterally asymmetrical?
(c) What is the peculiarity of the types of fish known as the star gazers?

Your starter for ten:

2 Under what name is Wood Sorrel shipped in large quantities from Ireland—?
[The question was successfully interrupted]

Bonus questions:
(a) The title *Gone with the Wind* comes from the line, 'I have forgotten much, Cynara!' Who wrote that line?
(b) The tile *From Here to Eternity* comes from the couplet, 'Gentlemen-rankers out on a spree, / Damn from here to eternity' Who wrote that?
(c) Give me the title and the author of the works from which *Eyeless in Gaza* was taken?

Your starter for ten:

3 Which novel published in 1958 was originally subtitled *The Confessions of a White Widowed Male*, the title itself being the nickname the narrator gives to the female protagonist?

Bonus questions:
(a) In which country is the state religion Shia Islam?
(b) The Gabars of Iran are the few remaining followers of which religion or religious leader?
(c) There are a certain number of Nestorians in Iran – of which religion are they a part?

Your starter for ten:

4 What is the name of the main square in Peking [now Beijing]?

Bonus questions:
(a) Who said, 'Lord Salisbury and I have brought you back peace, but a peace I hope with honour'?

(b) Which war had ended when he said that?

(c) It was a round number of years after Disraeli made this statement that Chamberlain made his ill-fated echo of it. How many years?

Your starter for ten:

5   What was the name of the society founded by Frederick James Furnivall for the publishing of literary source material, which can often be found in footnotes under the initials EETS?

Bonus questions:

(a) What is the French title of the novel in letter form which was written in 1782 by an artillery officer Pierre Choderlos de Laclos?

(b) What is the French title of the short book published secretly in France during the last war by an author using the pseudonym Vercors?

(c) Who is the famous soldier who is created in the novel of the 1920s by Jaroslav Hašek?

Your starter for ten:

6   [The next round was a music round, and the Students stole the starter after an incorrect interruption from the Dons; they went on to get four more pieces of music and managed to answer two of the questions]

Your starter for ten:

7   Which politician, originally a miner, become Member of Parliament for Llanelli in 1936, Deputy Leader of the Labour Party in 1956 and Secretary of State for Wales from 1964 to 1966?
[Neither team got the correct answer, so another starter was asked]

Your starter for ten:

8   In what field was the family of Isaac Kaufmann Funk distinguished, the firm of IK Funk becoming in 1877 Funk and Wagnalls?

Bonus questions:

(a) Who delivered four lectures in 1866, which he grouped together under the title *The Crown of Wild Olives*?

(b) The song 'Windmills of Your Mind' was played during a gliding sequence in which film?

(c) What 'rounds the mortal temple of a King' according to Richard II?

Your starter for ten:

9   Which playwright is married to Margaretta D'Arcy—?
[The question was correctly interrupted]

Bonus questions:

(a) What is the legal name for a document given by a ship's captain to the custom office, giving full details of his cargo?

(b) The title of a novel by Dos Passos and the name of a pop group are taken from which railway station where people change trains to get to and from the centre of New York.

(c) By what name has the mystery man been generally known who was buried in 1703 under the name of 'Marchioly' after years in prison, but is now widely accepted to be Count Matthioli a minister to the Duke of Mantua?

Your starter for ten:

10 What two Latin words were found together with a picture of a dog on a mosaic flooring—?
[The question was successfully interrupted]

Bonus questions:

(a) Which private detective made his first appearance in the novel *The Maltese Falcon*?

(b) Which private detective appeared in *Farewell My Lovely*—?
[The question was successfully interrupted]

(c) Which character, described as a one-man police force, was created by Mickey Spillane?

Your starter for ten:

11 The pleasure of what particular discipline is Wordsworth celebrating in his poem 'Nuns Fret Not at Their Convent's Narrow Room'?
[Neither team got the starter correct]

Your starter for ten:

12 Whose sieve is used to sort out prime numbers, the owner of the sieve being a scientist of Alexandria of the third century BC?
[Again, neither team got the starter correct]

Your starter for ten:

13 Who is the founder of Toc H or Talbot House—?
[The question was successfully interrupted]

Bonus questions:

(a) In what play do George and Martha cherish a fantasy son who is symbolically murdered during a drunken party?

(b) Whose pet plays are published as *Pièces Noires*, *Pièces Roses*, *Pièces Brillantes* and *Pièces Grinçantes*?

(c) What is the title of James Joyce's only play?

Your starter for ten:

14 I'm going to read you a passage from the *Oxford Companion to Music* and I want to know what word is being described, albeit, some would say, somewhat inaccurately. 'This is quick waltz tune for the piano, four hands, performed by school girls as an amusement in a traditional manner, the flat hand being held perpendiculary and the notes struck with its side—'
[The question was successfully interrupted]

Bonus questions:
(a) What was the actual profession of the man who, in 1818, published his heavily censored edition of Shakespeare?
(b) What was Bowdler's yardstick of what was acceptable, a yardstick reflected in the title that he gave to his work?

Your starter for ten:

15 What is the ancient name of the modern town of Iznic in Turkey, which under its ancient name is famous in Christian Byzantine history as the seat of two ecumenical councils in 325 and 787 and is the named origin of a famous creed?

Bonus questions:
(a) During a game of Eton Fives, how many people are in the court – counting both sides?
(b) What is the accidental origin of the very irregular shape of an Eton Five score?
(c) Which public school has given its name to another variety of fellows played in a court with no irregularities?

Your starter for ten:

16 [The next round was a picture round. The students correctly identified the top of the Grand Central Station and went on to identify the cities of Venice, Persepolis and London from close-ups of building features, but didn't identify Bombay (modern-day Mumbai)]

Your starter for ten:

17 Who was the child, later himself a playwright and poet laureate, who was christened in Oxford in 1606, and who apparently had William Shakespeare as his godfather—?
[The question was successfully interrupted]

Bonus questions – some American McCarthys:

(a) Which McCarthy lost the Democratic nomination in 1968 to Hubert Humphry?

(b) Mary McCarthy's second husband was a famous author and critic. Who?

(c) Of which state was Joseph McCarthy a senator?

Your starter for ten:

18 Which English critic, much influenced by French literary theories, dismissed *Othello* as a bloody farce?

Bonus questions:

(a) What is the alternative name for the Qing Dynasty in China?

(b) What is the alternative name for the grammatical figure known as Syllepsis?

(c) What is the alternative name for the 1st Viscount Sidmouth, who was Prime Minister from 1801 to 1804?

Your starter for ten:

19 What famous and vivid phrase was Carlisle inspired to write, probably by a passage in Madame De Stael—?

[The question was successfully interrupted]

Bonus questions – some historical novels of the 19th century:

(a) Which was Flaubert's novel about ancient Carthage?

(b) Which is George Eliot's novel set in 15th-century Florence?

(c) Which of Dickens' novels is about London in 1780?

Your starter for ten:

20 Which great physician and classical scholar was the first president of the College of Physicians, had been tutor to Henry VII's son Prince Arthur and became physician to Henry VIII?

Your starter for ten:

21 Some mental arithmetic – pencils allowed. I want to know how much money the youngest of Mr Smith's three children received when Mr Smith shared a thousand pounds between them in the exact ratio of their ages? The ages being 9, 6 and 5.

Bonus questions:

(a) In which year did Franco leave his post as Commander of the Canary Islands and seize control of Spanish Morocco?

(b) Franco declared himself neutral in 1939 and was neutral again by 1943. What was the official description of his position between those two dates?

(c) In 1941, Franco sent so-called volunteers to fight beside the Germans on which front?

Your starter for ten:

22 Under what title was a young Scottish girl, Catherine Glover made the subject of a novel by Walter Scott—?
[The question was successfully interrupted]

Bonus questions:
(a) Which document begins with the words, 'In the first book, Theophilus, I wrote about all that Jesus did and taught from the beginning until the day when he was taken up to heaven...'
(b) Which novel begins with the words, 'Whether I shall turn out to be the hero of my own life, or whether that station will be held by anybody else, these pages must show'?
(c) Which book begins with the words, 'I wish either my father or my mother, or indeed both of them, as they were in duty both equally bound to it, had minded what they were about when they begot me'?

Your starter for ten:

23 What phrase, sounding more like an anarchist than an atom, was used in 19th-century chemistry to describe a molecule in which one of the atoms has one of its valences unoccupied?
[No team answered]

Your starter for ten:

24 What was the name of the commission which was set up in India to report on the injustices committed during Mrs Ghandi's State of Emergency?

Bonus questions:
(a) What is unusual about Coco, who, at the age of six, is being taught at Stanford University to use sign language with a vocabulary of 40 words?
(b) In the *Ramayana*, what is the name of the monkey god who helps Rama rescue his wife Sita?
(c) Which supposedly sour Shakespearian heroine says to her father, 'She is your treasure, she must have a husband. I must dance barefoot on her wedding day and, for your love to her, lead apes in hell'?

Your starter for ten:

25 It is perfectly possible that some world-famous sculptures might be known today as the Kincardine Relief if we—?
[The question was successfully interrupted]

Bonus questions:
(a) Where did the great tradition of the music hall have its roots in the 19th century and earlier?
(b) Musical entertainments accompanied by the organ had been a feature of taverns in the mid-17th century. Why were there so many organs in the pubs at that time?
(c) What was the name of the theatre under the arches of Charing Cross station where traditional music hall was kept alive after the Second World War?

Your starter for ten:
26 Who or what was born during an eclipse in 1764—?
[The question was successfully interrupted]

Bonus questions:
(a) What is Ernest John Moncrieff's other name?
(b) What in a ship is the function of the jack staff?
(c) For what constituency was Jack Ashley first elected Member of Parliament in 1966?

Your starter for ten:
27 What was widely and familiarly known as John Company—

The gong sounds

At the gong, the Students had 295 points and the Dons 180.
This meant that the score on the programme between
Students and Dons stood at five matches apiece.

The Answers

1   Tom
     (a) Coelacanth
     (b) Flatfish (i.e. flounder)
     (c) They have eyes on the top of their head

2   Shamrock
     (a) Ernest Dowson
     (b) Kipling
     (c) *Samson Agonistes* by (John) Milton

3   *Lolita*
     (a) Iran
     (b) Zoroaster (Zoroastrian)
     (c) Christianity

4   Tiananmen Square
     (a) Disraeli
     (b) Turko-Russian War
     (c) 60 years

5   Early English Text Society
     (a) *Les Liaisons Dangereuses*
     (b) *La Silence de la Mer*
     (c) (*The Good Soldier*) Švejk

6   [Music round]

7   James Griffiths

8   Publishing (dictionaries and encyclopaedias in particular)
     (a) John Ruskin
     (b) *The Thomas Crown Affair*
     (c) *The Hollow Crown*

9   John Arden
     (a) Manifest
     (b) Manhattan Transfer
     (c) *The Man in the Iron Mask*

10   *Cave Canem* ('Beware of the dog')
     (a) Sam Spade
     (b) Philip Marlowe
     (c) Mike Hammer

11   The sonnet form (it's a sonnet about sonnets)

12   Sieve of Eratosthenes

13   Tubby Clayton
     (a) *Who's Afraid of Virginia Woolf*
     (b) Jean Anouilh
     (c) *Exiles*

14   'Chopsticks'
     (a) Physician – (Thomas Bowdler)
     (b) 'With propriety to be read aloud to the family' (*The Family Shakespeare*)

15   Nisaea
     (a) Four – two aside
     (b) Buttresses of the chapel between which it is played
     (c) Rugby (Fives)

16   [Picture round]

17   William Davenant
     (a) Eugene
     (b) Edmond Wilson
     (c) Wisconsin

18   Thomas Rymer
     (a) Manchu Dynasty
     (b) Zeugma
     (c) Henry Addington

19   Sea-green incorruptible
     (a) *Salammbô*
     (b) *Romola*
     (c) *Barnaby Rudge*

20   Thomas Linacre

21   £250
     (a) 1936
     (b) 'Non-belligerent'
     (c) Russian

22   The fair maid of Perth
     (a) The Acts of the Apostles
     (b) *David Copperfield*
     (c) *The Life and Opinions of Tristram Shandy*

23   Free radical

24   The Shah Commission
    (a) Gorilla
    (b) Hanuman
    (c) Katherine (from *The Taming of the Shrew*)

25   Elgin Marbles (Thomas Bruce was the Earl of Elgin and Kincardine)
    (a) In pubs and taverns
    (b) Puritans had taken them out of the churches
    (c) The Players' Theatre

26   A race horse
    (a) Jack Worthing in *The Importance of Being Ernest*
    (b) Where the Union Jack flag is flown in the bow
    (c) Stoke-on-Trent South

27   The Honourable East India Company

Try Your Luck
Match

Your starter for ten:

1   In the film *Breakfast at Tiffany's*, Audrey Hepburn's so-called 'little black dress' was the work of which French fashion designer, who died in March 2018?

Three questions on the magazine editor Tina Brown:
(a) Having edited *Tatler* in the UK, Brown moved to New York in 1983 at the age of 29 to relaunch which magazine? It shares its name with a novel that first appeared in 1847.
(b) In 1992, Brown took over the editorship of what publication? During her tenure its contributors included John Updike and Harold Brodkey.
(c) In 2008, Brown launched which US digital news site? It takes its name from a fictional newspaper in Evelyn Waugh's novel *Scoop*.

Your starter for ten:

2   Founded in the 8th century, the Shailendra dynasty saw the construction of which large Buddhist monument about 40 kilometres from Yogyakarta on the island of Java?

Three questions on 20th-century Latin American authors:
(a) The 1968 semi-autobiographical work *Betrayed by Rita Hayworth*, in which a boy fantasizes about the lives of Hollywood film stars, is the debut novel of which Argentinian author?
(b) What is the surname of the family whose lives over seven generations are detailed in Gabriel Garcia Marquez's 1967 work *One Hundred Years of Solitude*?
(c) Which Peruvian author was the 2010 recipient of the Nobel Prize in Literature? His works include *The Time of the Hero*, first published in 1963.

Your starter for ten:

3   Give the single word that completes this short verse concerning number

theory: 'Sift the twos and sift the threes, / The sieve of eratosthenes. / When the multiples sublime, / The numbers that remain are –' what?

Your bonuses are on National Trust properties famed for their snowdrops:
(a) Which ruined Cistercian abbey in North Yorkshire is noted for snowdrops planted along the banks of the River Skell, which joins the Ure near Ripon?
(b) According to the National Trust website, 'Swathes of snowdrops carpet the pleasure grounds' at Petworth House, a 17th-century mansion in which ceremonial county?
(c) Set high above the River Thames, which former home of the Astor family has a webpage dedicated to 'Snowdrop Watch'?

Your starter for ten:
4 'The Great Charlemagne' is the national anthem of which small European country? It commemorates its liberation from the Moors in the 9th century.

Your bonuses are on biological terms that end with the same four letters. Identify each term from the description:
(a) The most common metabolic bone disease, characterized by the thinning of bones, increasing the tendency to sustain fractures from minor stresses.
(b) Any association between members of two different species that live together, even if those species benefit, harm or have no effect on each other.
(c) The cause of death of the authors Katherine Mansfield, Anton Chekhov and Franz Kafka.

Your starter for ten:
5 What three letters end words meaning: the Earth Mother in Inca mythology; 'mountain' in Japanese; 'play' or 'stage work' in Greek; the name of the explorer who reached Calicut in India in 1498; and the capital of Bahrain?

Your bonuses are on pairs of words that differ only in that one of them ends with an additional letter 't'. Give both words from the definition:
(a) A tiny piece or speck of a substance, such as dust; and a polyphonic vocal composition particularly popular during the Renaissance period?
(b) A city northeast of Milan, home to the football club Atalanta; and a plant in the citrus family commonly used in perfumes and infusions?
(c) The layer of the Earth that stretches from the Moho to the Gutenberg discontinuity; and a large portable shield used by attacking forces in medieval siege warfare?

Your starter for ten:

6   What six-letter name is given to an organic chemical compound, also
     known as a diol, that contains two hydroxyl groups? The most common
     example is used in antifreeze.

Your bonuses are on scientific terms. In each case, give the term from the definition.
All three answers have the same middle letter:
(a) A seven-letter Greek-derived term meaning an involuntary or unconscious
grinding or clenching of the teeth?
(b) Any one of a class of plant hormones involved in regulating growth and
root initiation; its name comes from the Greek for 'to increase'?
(c) Finally, an SI prefix denoting a multiple of 10 to the 18?

Your starter for ten:

7   Who was nominated for the Nobel Peace Prize in 1937, 1938, 1939, 1947
     and, finally, shortly before being assassinated in January 1948?

Three questions on New Year's Day in the early 19th century:
(a) On New Year's Day 1801, the first public reception was held at the
president's house, later known as the White House, in Washington, DC; who
was president?
(b) New Year's Day 1804 saw the proclamation of which Caribbean republic?
(c) On New Year's Day 1812, Shute Barrington sent troops to break a miners'
strike in Chester-le-Street. What ecclesiastical office did he hold at the time?

Your starter for ten:

8   After the name of a county in North Carolina, what word originated in
     a 19th-century congressional debate when the member for the county
     insisted on speaking because, he said, the people of his district expected it?
     The word is now used generally for political claptrap or nonsense, spoken
     solely to gain the favour of electors.

Three questions on astrobiology:
(a) In 2020, the possible astronomical detection of phosphine gas led to the
suggestion that this substance might be a by-product of microbial life in the
atmosphere of which planet?
(b) In 2019, in the Gale Crater on Mars, NASA's *Curiosity* rover detected
unusually high concentrations, above twenty parts per billion, of what gas, also
considered a possible by-product of life?
(c) To prepare for bio-sign searches in exoplanet atmospheres, the Hubble
space telescope used a total lunar eclipse in 2020 to detect the ultraviolet
absorption signature of what trace gas in Earth's atmosphere?

Your starter for ten:

9 In classical architecture, what part of a building was typically created using tegulae and imbrices, semi-cylindrical fittings overlapped to form a continuous surface?

Three questions on bowlers who have taken 500 or more wickets in Test cricket:
(a) In August 2020, which England bowler became the first seamer, and fourth bowler overall, to take 600 wickets? He made his Test debut in 2003, and achieved this feat after 156 matches.
(b) Which West Indies fast bowler became the first to take 500 wickets, achieving this feat against South Africa in 2001?
(c) Which Sri Lankan spinner has taken the most Test wickets, with 800 in 133 matches? He retired from Test cricket in 2010.

Your starter for ten:

10 In the 1870s, who composed the pieces known as 'Anitra's Dance' and 'In the Hall of the Mountain King', part of his incidental music for Ibsen's *Peer Gynt*?

Your bonuses are on pairs of words that differ only in the presence of the two letters 'd' and 'i' at the beginning of one, for example 'visor' and 'divisor' or 'shy' and 'dishy'. In each case, give both words from the definitions:
(a) A diagram depicting the relationship between two or more variables; and the combination of two letters to represent a single sound, for example 'th' or 'sh'?
(b) A poem intended to be sung; and a semiconductor device that allows current to flow in one direction only?
(c) A plucked string instrument played, for example, in a painting by Caravaggio; and to diminish the concentration of a liquid?

Your starter for ten:

11 In early December, which French city holds the annual event known as the *Fête des Lumières*, or Festival of Lights? This features the illumination of the Fourvière basilica, a few kilometres north of the confluence of the Rhone and the Saône.

Three questions on climate classification:
(a) Born in 1846, which German climatologist gives his name to a biome-based climate classification system first published in 1900? He later collaborated with Rudolf Geiger.
(b) Köppen identified five major climate types; tropical, dry, temperate, polar and which other?

(c) H climate is a sixth category sometimes added to modified maps to account for the uniqueness of certain regions. What does 'H' represent?

Your starter for ten:

12 'Three, four, five' and 'five, twelve, thirteen' are examples of groups of integers known by what two-word term, after an ancient mathematician? They refer to the lengths of the sides of a triangle.

Three questions on people who were the second to hold a position:
(a) Linus, who may have been born in Tuscany and died in about AD 79, is believed to have been the second holder of what enduring office?
(b) Louis I, King of the Franks, succeeded his father in 814 to become the second holder of an imperial position now known by what three-word title?
(c) In 1953, the Swedish statesman Dag Hammarskjöld became the second person to head which international organization?

Your starter for ten:

13 What geographical term appears along with 'Dolls', 'Horses' and 'Fear' in the titles of novels by Jacqueline Susann, Jean Auel and Arthur Conan Doyle?

Three questions on a platonic solid:
(a) Plato's dialogue *Timaeus* assigns elements to four of the five regular platonic solids, except which one, with the Schläfli symbol {5, 3}?
(b) In his *Mysterium Cosmographicum*, Kepler fitted platonic solids between the orbits of the known planets. Which two were separated by the dodecahedron?
(c) How many direct symmetries does a regular dodecahedron have?

Your starter for ten:

14 The Bristol resident Robin Gunningham, the designer Jamie Hewlett and the musician Robert Del Naja are among those speculated to have adopted what prominent artistic pseudonym?

Three questions on card games in literature:
(a) A shared love of gambling, leading to a tense one-on-one poker game, brings together the eponymous protagonists of which novel by Peter Carey?
(b) A favourite of European high-born gamblers well into the 19th century, which card game was the one at which Nikolai Rostov lost a fortune in Tolstoy's *War and Peace*?
(c) Played by Toby Crackit in *Oliver Twist*, in which game is the winner the first player to reach 61 or 121 points?

Your starter for ten:

15 At a similar latitude to St Petersburg and the Shetland Islands, Cape Farewell is the southernmost point of which island, more than three times the size of Texas?

Three questions on women in the Bible:
(a) Which book of the Old Testament is named after a Moabite woman who adopts the religion of her Israelite mother-in-law, saying, 'Your people will be my people, and your God, my God'?
(b) In Genesis, Jacob is tricked into marrying Leah, the sister of which woman, whom he eventually also marries after seven more years of labour for her father, Laban?
(c) The name of which female prophet appears in the title of a song in Chapter 5 of the Book of Judges? It is considered one of the oldest pieces of Hebrew poetry.

Your starter for ten:

16 A shortened form of a title meaning 'barbarian-subduing general', what six-letter term is often used to indicate the de facto leaders of Japan from the late 12th century to 1867?

Three questions on mathematics:
(a) Given a real-valued function 'f', what name is given to a point where the derivative of f at that point is 0 and its second derivative is strictly less than 0?
(b) Coinciding with the maximum under certain conditions, the least upper-bound of a set of real numbers is known by what single-word name?
(c) What is the supremum of the set of real values of the hyperbolic tan function?

Your starter for ten:

17 Which layer of the Earth's atmosphere includes the orbits of the lowest-altitude satellites? Beginning at the mesopause, it extends to about 500 kilometres and is characterized by temperatures that rise with altitude.

Your bonuses are on technical terms. In each case, give the word from the description. All three answers begin with the same three letters:
(a) In medicine, inflammation of the brain; an epidemic form of this condition, known as 'Japanese', is caused by a mosquito-borne virus?
(b) In art, a form of painting using pigments in hot wax used, for example, by the ancient Greek artist Pausias?
(c) In geography, part of a country or territory that is entirely surrounded by another?

Your starter for ten:

18 What five-letter word links: an ironic synonym for 'force' in Evelyn Waugh's *Scoop*; and the second word of the name of the alternative rock group often known by the initials T.M.B.G.?

Three questions on astronomy:
(a) What ten-letter contraction is a term describing a type of telescopic mount that pivots both vertically and horizontally?
(b) What seven-letter syllabic abbreviation denotes a disk of dust and gas orbiting a young star that may show a stage before planet formation?
(c) Denoting powerful active galactic nuclei, 'quasar' is a term contracted from which two adjectives?

Your starter for ten:

19 What five-letter word links all of the following: in musical theatre, an understudy who takes multiple roles; anti-mechanization riots by agricultural workers in the 19th century; a French rococo painting in the Wallace Collection; a voting trend; and part of a nickname for the musician Benny Goodman?

Three questions on Saraswati, the Hindu goddess of knowledge and the arts:
(a) According to Hindu mythology, which god is Saraswati's consort? Usually depicted with four heads and four arms, he is the Hindu god of creation.
(b) In which ancient Hindu texts was Saraswati personified as a sacred river?
(c) Saraswati is often depicted riding a white variety of which water bird, the largest member of the family *Anatidae*?

Your starter for ten:

20 What single Latin word is abbreviated to 'cf' when used as a suggestion to compare a text with other specified material?

Three questions on poisons in the novels of Agatha Christie:
(a) Which poison was used in *The Mysterious Affair at Styles*? It is an alkaloid, derived from the seeds of the tree *Nux vomica* and easily absorbed into the bloodstream.
(b) Which nitrogen-group element is used as a curry ingredient in the 1957 novel *4.50 from Paddington*?
(c) Which poison is used in *And Then There Were None* and *A Pocket Full of Rye*? In the title of a novel of 1945, it is described as 'sparkling'.

Your starter for ten:

21 'My music is not designed to grab instantly. It's designed to wear for a

lifetime, to hold up like a fine cloth.' Which singer-songwriter said that? Her studio albums include *Night Ride Home*, *Taming the Tiger* and *Hejira*.

Your bonuses are on prominent British politicians who were involved in the defence of colonial slavery. In each case, name the person from the description:
(a) The foreign secretary from 1807 to 1809, and again from 1822; he was the MP for Seaford at the time of his death in 1827.
(b) The son of a Liverpool merchant who owned several thousand slaves in Jamaica and Demerara; his first parliamentary constituency was Newark and his last was Midlothian.
(c) The home secretary for much of the 1820s; he was MP for Tamworth from 1830 to 1850.

Your starter for ten:
22 What initial letter begins the names of the following new world animals: water-loving snakes of the genus *Eunectes*; insectivorous mammals of the suborder Vermilingua; and wool-bearing mammals of the camel family?

Three questions on a name:
(a) Born in Wessex in about 680 and also known as Winfrith, which saint is sometimes called the apostle of Germany after his missionary work in continental Europe?
(b) Opposing the influence of both Pope Boniface VIII and Clement V, who wrote the polemical works *Convivio* and *De Monarchia* in the 14th century?
(c) Less than ten miles wide at its narrowest point, the Strait of Bonifacio separates which two Mediterranean islands?

Your starter for ten:
23 Which two social psychologists give their names to the effect described in their 1999 paper 'Unskilled and Unaware of It'? The effect is summed up by Charles Darwin's observation: 'Ignorance more frequently begets confidence than does knowledge.'

Your bonuses are on people who participated in the Fulbright Scholar Program, founded in 1946. Name each person from the description:
(a) The winner of the Outstanding Contribution to Music Award at the 2004 Classical Brits; a US soprano who performed at the Beijing Olympics and Barack Obama's inauguration.
(b) The US literary figure who wrote a novel under the pseudonym Victoria Lucas; her poetry collections include *Ariel* and *The Colossus and Other Poems*.
(c) Born in Inverness, the leader of the Liberal Democrats from 1999 to 2006.

Your starter for ten:

24 The birthplace of Joseph-Louis Lagrange and Primo Levi, which city on the River Po was the first capital of unified Italy and the venue of the Winter Olympics in 2006?

Three questions on historical films:

(a) In 1968, Katharine Hepburn won an Academy Award for her role as Eleanor of Aquitaine in which film?

(b) In 1969, Genevieve Bujold was nominated for the Best Actress Academy Award for her role as a 16th-century queen consort of England in which film?

(c) In 1998, Judi Dench won the Best Supporting Actress award for her portrayal of a Tudor monarch in which film?

Your starter for ten:

25 Concatenating the standard two-letter abbreviations for the US states of Georgia, New York, Maine and Delaware gives the name of which moon of Jupiter?

Three questions on mythological deities:

(a) In Egyptian mythology, who was the son of Neith and is sometimes cited as the husband of Hathor and the father of Ma'at?

(b) In Norse mythology, who was the son of Buri, the husband of Bestla, and the father of Odin?

(c) In Greek mythology, who was the son of Uranus, the husband of Rhea and the father of Zeus?

The Answers

1 (Hubert de) Givenchy
   (a) *Vanity Fair*
   (b) *The New Yorker*
   (c) *The Daily Beast*

2 Borobudur (the world's largest Buddhist temple)
   (a) Manuel Puig
   (b) Buendía
   (c) Mario Vargas Llosa

3 Prime
   (a) Fountains (Abbey)
   (b) West Sussex (not East Sussex)
   (c) Cliveden

4 Andorra ('El gran Carlemany')
   (a) Osteoporosis
   (b) Symbiosis
   (c) Tuberculosis

5 -ama (Pachamama, yama, drama, Da Gama, Manama)
   (a) Mote and motet
   (b) Bergamo and bergamot
   (c) Mantle and mantlet

6 Glycol (ethylene glycol is used in antifreeze)
   (a) Bruxism (Greek: *brukhein*, 'to gnash the teeth')
   (b) Auxin (Greek: *auxein*, 'to increase')
   (c) Exa-

7 (Mohandas / Mahatma) Gandhi
   (a) John Adams
   (b) Haiti
   (c) Bishop of Durham

8 Bunkum / bunk (Buncombe County)
   (a) Venus
   (b) Methane
   (c) Ozone

9 Roof (*tegulae* – flat roof tiles; *imbrices* – the joins of the former)
   (a) (James) Anderson
   (b) (Courtney) Walsh
   (c) Muttiah Muralitharan

10 (Edvard) Grieg
    (a) Graph and digraph
    (b) Ode and diode
    (c) Lute and dilute

11 Lyon
    (a) (Wladimir) Köppen
    (b) Continental
    (c) Highland

12 Pythagorean triples
    (a) Pope / papacy / Bishop of Rome
    (b) Holy Roman Emperor
    (c) United Nations / UN

13 Valley (*Valley of the Dolls*, *The Valley of Horses*, *The Valley of Fear*)
    (a) Dodecahedron
    (b) Earth and Mars
    (c) 60

14 Banksy
    (a) *Oscar and Lucinda*
    (b) Faro
    (c) Cribbage / crib

15 Greenland
    (a) Ruth (whose mother-in-law was Naomi)
    (b) Rachel
    (c) Deborah ('Song of Deborah')

16 *Shogun* (*Seii Taishogun*)
    (a) (Local / relative) maximum (not turning point / stationary point)
    (b) Supremum
    (c) 1

17 Thermosphere
    (a) Encephalitis
    (b) Encaustic
    (c) Enclave

18 Might ('Other nations use force; we Britons alone use might'; They Might Be Giants)
    (a) Altazimuth (from altitude and azimuth)
    (b) Proplyd (from proto-planetary disk)
    (c) Quasi and stellar

19 Swing (swing; the Swing Riots of 1830; *The Swing* or *Les hasards heureux de l'escarpolette*,
    Fragonard, 1767; swing of votes between elections; the King of Swing)

(a) Brahma
(b) The Vedas
(c) Swan

20   *Confer* (accept *conferatur*, both mean 'compare')
(a) Strychnine
(b) Arsenic
(c) Cyanide

21   Joni Mitchell
(a) (George) Canning
(b) (William) Gladstone
(c) (Robert) Peel

22   A (anacondas, anteaters and alpacas)
(a) (St) Boniface
(b) Dante (Alighieri)
(c) Corsica and Sardinia

23   (David) Dunning and (Justin) Kruger (Dunning-Kruger effect)
(a) (Renée) Fleming
(b) Sylvia Plath
(c) Charles Kennedy

24   Turin / Torino (capital from 1861 to 1865)
(a) *The Lion in Winter*
(b) *Anne of the Thousand Days*
(c) *Shakespeare in Love* (as Elizabeth I, of course)

25   Ganymede (GA + NY + ME + DE)
(a) Ra / Re
(b) Borr or Burr
(c) Cronus / Kronos

Where Are They Now?

Part 1

Over 60 years *University Challenge* audiences have been awed by the knowledge and talent of the people who have appeared to represent their universities. In more than half a century *University Challenge* has entertained and educated us. It's a largely unchanging yet challenging format and, although its two hosts have been highly instrumental in keeping it front and centre of the viewing nation's consciousness, it would be nothing without the student participants.

These clever, inspirational young people, with the world at their feet, were at the start of adulthood, many going on to become central figures in their chosen fields, leading in the worlds of academia, education, the arts, the media, politics and charity.

Throughout this book, some of the many noteworthy contestants from over the years recall their experiences on one of the world's longest-running television quizzes...

*

Among recent memorable contestants is **Bobby Seagull**, who struck a real chord when he appeared for in the 2016–2017 series as captain of Emmanuel College, Cambridge. He was a mature student, having returned to university at the age of 30 to do his PGCE. His enthusiasm while answering questions saw his name begin to trend on Twitter, especially after going head to head with Canadian Eric Monkman, the endearingly earnest captain of Wolfson College, Cambridge. The pair became friends, writing a quiz book and creating and presenting a TV show, *Monkman and Seagull's Genius Guide to Britain*. During Monkman's appearances on *University Challenge* – his team lost out in the final to Balliol College, Oxford, though in one round Monkman was responsible for securing 120 of his team's 170 points – the hashtag 'monkmania' dominated the Twittersphere.

Bobby recalls: 'The Monkman–Seagull semi-final I think was the closest semi-final for about 13 years. We lost it on the penultimate question when Eric answered a question on Russia correctly. He was the best quizzer on my series. A lot of people commented on that match – Louis Theroux, Stephen Fry, even Hacker the Dog from CBBC. It became like a zeitgeist moment and made it into the *Radio Times'* top five TV moments of the year. I had a lot of joy being on the show.'

Before retraining as a teacher, Bobby was a trader for, among others, Lehman Brothers – 'Yes, that one,' Bobby says, referring to the bank's collapse which happened after he left. He is still teaching maths part time at a secondary school in London. He is passionate about the power of maths in people's lives, but he combines this with a great deal of media work. 'I write for the *Financial Times*. I've published a couple of books. I present, I pitch new idea for television shows, and there's a lot of charity ambassador work too. A lot of it is because of *University Challenge*.'

Incredibly, Bobby reveals he never watched the show before he went on: 'I obviously knew the importance of the show. I've always had a good general knowledge. My knowledge came from reading rather than quizzing, though. I'd never been a quizzer.' One of four brothers, Bobby's parents immigrated to Britain from southern India in the 1970s and Bobby grew up on a council estate in East London, in one of the most deprived boroughs in the UK. Every Saturday, his accountant father would take the boys to East Ham library. 'As a family we valued education, but it was an all-round education. We played sport, we watched *Top of the Pops*, *Blue Peter* and *Byker Grove*, so on *University Challenge* I didn't just have the classical knowledge; I knew quirky stuff like pop culture.' Bobby secured a scholarship to Eton to do his A levels. Indeed, all four brothers ended up at Oxbridge. 'I think that's quite rare, coming from a council estate,' Bobby notes. 'The scholarship to Eton was an amazing opportunity, but I always had this zest for knowledge.'

That was evident during Bobby's appearances on *University Challenge*. He remembers production companies started to message him when it was transmitted, asking him if he had ever screen-tested for television? 'I'd never considered, even for a second, a career in media but people were saying things like, "You should be the new Johnny Ball"! Every year there's a couple of people who go viral – that's the nature of the show – but when I was interviewed a lot in the newspapers and on television, rather than just talking about the experience of being on the show, I think I very quickly steered it towards, "That's great, but I really want to use it to talk about education, reading, maths." I think that's given me longevity.'

But it's not all maths and inspirational talks – Bobby has appeared on *The Real Dirty Dancing* on E4, *The Jeremy Vine Show* and Richard Osman's *House of Games*. 'I've got such a varied career where I am now. I'm a charity ambassador, a teacher, an educator, television presenter, and I am honest enough to admit, without *University Challenge* I wouldn't have had these opportunities. Now I think I can be a part-time teacher, and positively influence the shape of education in the UK, especially maths and reading. They're the two things that brought me a lot of joy. I think I just love learning and knowledge, and I think that came across on *University Challenge*. I'm just someone that's always loved it, but now have a bigger platform to share that.'

Bobby says he thoroughly enjoyed his time on the show and credits the production team, the question writers and the researchers with being the 'unsung heroes'. 'They are the ones who put so much work in to make the show and I think they should be given a massive round of applause because, although the occasional contestant and the host get the glamour, without the people behind the scenes there wouldn't be a show.'

And Bobby's advice for any students considering applying to join a team for the programme? 'I would say if you're a fan of the show, definitely give it a shot. The reality is, most people probably won't get on because you might not get into your institution's team. And secondly, there's a process of selecting by the programme.

'Social media can magnify people in a positive or negative way. So you have to be careful if you're very sensitive about Twitter. I do tell people if you are very sensitive or very concerned, it is something that you should bear in mind. I think the benefits outweigh the risks, but it's something to bear in mind that there are trolls on Twitter that are looking to pull down anyone whether they look slightly strange, or whether they've got a different surname.

'But it's a once-in-a-lifetime opportunity. With other games, like *Mastermind*, you can keep applying every year for the rest of your life, but with *University Challenge* you have a limited timeframe while you're at university. So I'd say definitely apply.'

*

Jenny Ryan is now best known by her alter ego – she is the Vixen on ITV quiz shows *The Chase* and *Beat the Chasers*. As a student at Leeds University she was part of its *University Challenge* team, reaching the semi-finals in 2003. It was her first televised quiz show, and she went on to appear on programmes including *Mastermind* (specialist subject *Buffy the Vampire Slayer*), *Only Connect* and *The Weakest Link* as well as being a QI Elf.

It was 'sheer chance' that she joined her university team as she happened to be in the Students' Union building when the posters were going up. 'It was a parody of *The Shining*, but with Jeremy Paxman's face looming through the hole in the door instead of Jack Nicholson's. I immediately thought of my grandad, who loved quizzes so much that when he died the obituary in the local paper described him as "Quiz King Kevin", and I decided to go for it as a tribute to him. I was a bit surprised to be selected for the team but absolutely delighted. All those years Grandad spent teaching me the basics of general knowledge were not in vain!'

As a team they had had long discussions about the division of subjects and who had the strongest knowledge in which area. 'We decided that, if musicals came up, then I would be the one going for it, so when a question about *The Rocky Horror Show* came up I was furious to be beaten to the buzzer – even though it was by a member of my own team! And I will never forget astonishing Jeremy, who was not expecting a 19-year-old woman to know anything about Steely Dan!' She found she enjoyed the filming experience: 'Somehow I felt at home in the studio, which thinking back was a sign of what the future held for me. It was exciting for me, as a local [Jenny is from Bolton] and as a TV fan, to be in the iconic Granada Studios, especially when we managed to get in Tony Wilson's way not once but twice within the first hour. The production team were so lovely and very keen to put us all at our ease – no mean feat when they had a couple of dozen giddy students to keep calm. The incentive of a couple of beers after recording didn't do any harm, and we were delighted when Jeremy himself joined us, and even had a drink and a photo with our teddy bear mascot!'

Jenny says *University Challenge* infected her with the quiz-show bug. 'I also met quite a number of *University Challenge* alumni at post-recording drinks, several of whom remain good friends to this day including the captain of my quiz league team. Through them I found out about the "quiz circuit", and quizzing quickly became my number one hobby – ultimately, this led to getting an email one day from the producers of a quiz show called *The Chase*, asking if I would be interested in auditioning to become a Chaser. I never could have imagined all those years ago that I'd be able to make a career out of my love for quizzes and television, but here we are!'

*

In 2015 one Greek phrase was all it took to lodge a young **Ted Loveday** into viewers' collective consciousness and that phrase was *hapax legomenon* ('a term said only once'). Ted, in his cream chunky cable-knit sweater, became an instant online hit, his interruption of Paxman's question with the correct answer spawning a Twitter meltdown and many a good-natured GIF and meme. Ted was in his second year reading History and Law at Gonville and Caius College, Cambridge when he took part in the programme – he had been chosen as the reserve the previous year but his team were not selected to go on the programme. The following year, his team were the series champions, beating Magdalen College, Oxford in the final (205–105) and making it the second time Cambridge had had back-to-back winners in 41 years.

Now a barrister, Ted remembers the occasion well. 'I knew when I was answering the question that it was an unusual and impressive answer. But I had no idea where it would go or how people would react! It was slightly weird, it really surprised me –especially as it appealed to a lot of teenagers and students who I wouldn't have expected to be the obvious audience. It took a couple of years for the interest to fade away. We ended up doing the rounds on the radio, interviews and all kinds of shows – ranging from Alan Carr's *Chatty Man* to *Educating Joey Essex*. All great fun. By the way, Joey Essex was really a naturally smart guy. You've got to be smart to be that successful in his world.

'I guess I remembered *hapax legomenon* because I'm just the sort of person who reads really widely. If I see a quirky literary term like that, I will remember it. Everyone's brain is different and it just happens that the things that my brain focuses on are ones that work well for University Challenge, like little nuggets of academic knowledge. I don't have a great memory for lots of other things – what holiday I went on in what year, or events in my own life. And ironically I'm not great at pub quizzes.'

The media interest was surprising to Ted because it went on for some time. 'That might have been because we made it to the final, it might have been *hapax legomenon*. But I was really impressed by the amount that the media and the British public are interested in *University Challenge*. Its cultural impact is phenomenal because, deep down, people have so much appetite and admiration for learning and knowledge. I respect that.

'When we were up against Magdalen College, Oxford in the quarter-finals they gave us a real run for our money. It was tight and we narrowly pipped them towards the end of the episode – but we sort of built up a friendly rivalry with them. That match made a big impression on us, and we thought, 'If we're up against them again, we're going to really struggle.' In the green room you watch other episodes, you talk to the producers and the other contestants, you get an impression of who are the ones to watch. Everyone was saying you did not want to be against Magdalen College. We were terrified because we were told they were really fierce. And after the quarter-final, because of the way the groups were arranged, we met them again in the final. But it was a friendly rivalry.'

What are Ted's tips for preparing for such intense rounds? 'We prepared a lot in terms of watching old episodes and mugging up. We built a great team dynamic over time. And luckily our captain, Anthony Martinelli, was a medical student and he got us all on a regime. You know, no alcohol the night before, healthy diet, and he had us drinking espresso half an hour before the episode so that we would have our reactions superfast at just the right moment.'

*

When **Frederick Leo**, reading History, led his St Edmund Hall, Oxford team to the final in 2019 (beaten by Edinburgh 155–140) he impressed viewers with his quickfire buzzer action and his ability to get the majority of his team's starter questions correct. But Freddy had a legacy to live up to – his father had appeared on *University Challenge* more than 30 years before. 'I'm from Berlin originally, where I grew up. I went to a German American school. I have a German mother and an American father who did one of his degrees in England, and while he was doing that degree, actually went on *University Challenge*. So I'm second generation. He sometimes tells the story around the dinner table, and I think when we were younger we would be kind of bored by it. As I grew older, and more able to appreciate it, I found in our attic one of his old *University Challenge* books, which had these questions. I remember being able to answer almost nothing and I was floored by it. I think quiz shows in German were just easier but, you know, humiliation turned into inspiration and I started to watch the show. And that's what made me eager to apply to the team once I got to the UK.

'When I got to Oxford, I joined the quiz society, which was useful because you got some experience buzzing.' (Freddy was noted for his swift and energetic application of the *University Challenge* buzzers.) 'If you're in the quiz society, they do try to seed in those more difficult or more obscure knowledge areas, like very advanced philosophy or that sort of thing.'

Freddy's team were beaten in the final by the University of Edinburgh, but Freddie remembers they were the friendliest of rivals: 'We really liked the University of Edinburgh team. We liked all the teams but, with them, we'd always been in the same filming block so we'd watch each other's progress and sort of stoically congratulate each other on our progress throughout the series. And then when we met in the final, it was almost like a match among friends. That kind of overshadows the slight annoyance, I guess, of being beaten in the final.

'Something that I think the public sometimes doesn't know about enough is that it can seem like this big adversarial thing is building up over a whole year. But, in reality, it's happened over maybe three weekends. It's a very intense experience; a lot of stuff condensed into a couple of days. But part of that intensity is bonding with everybody who's there and under the same pressure, even if they might be temporary rivals.'

Freddy appeared on the programme after it had been shown on British TV for more than half a century. 'It's part of British university culture,' he says. Being bilingual, he amused the audience with some of his answers – 'white carrot' for parsnip for example. 'In some ways it's an advantage because for the parsnip question the clue they gave was that it was called *Pastinaca* in scientific Latin, and *Pastinake* is the German word. That's just part of being multilingual or bilingual or whatever, and it does make for comic relief sometimes, which is fine.'

Freddy says *University Challenge* provided 'a sort of intensity of experience which can be quite hard to reproduce in everyday life, in a positive way. It's made me fill my life with more practical, active things and involvements. Now I feel that I'm doing something that's equally significant or exciting. I think it was an energy boost, too.' Freddy now works in the charity sector, for the International Youth Federation, focusing on child poverty.

*

Ralph Morley, the captain of the Trinity College, Cambridge team which won the 2014 series, has gone down in *University Challenge* history for two reasons. The first is his super-fast interruption of a question on Margaret Thatcher. 'Well, what else could it be?' he answered when Jeremy Paxman looked up from his question card and asked how he knew the answer so quickly. The second is Paxman humorously calling his team 'smartarses'.

'I remember that question because I was utterly convinced that the question was something like, "In the 20th century, who was prime minister for the longest?" I was convinced that Jeremy Paxman said the word "longest", something which made it very obvious to me that the answer had to be Margaret Thatcher. I buzzed and said very confidently, "Margaret Thatcher." Paxman said something like, "How on earth did you know that?" Because I thought that he had said the word "longest", I came back with an unusually confident retort and said, "Well, who else could it be?" Of course, it was only when I watched the broadcast that I realized that, of course, the reason that this was so surprising was because he had not actually got as far as saying the word "longest". So I don't know to this day whether it was simply because my brain had made two and two make five, but it happens to be the case that five was enough to get by. It was not actually an exercise of skill. It was sheer good luck. It had a long afterlife, to the delight of my friends. It's been remixed into a clip on YouTube and even TikTok. Various of my friends have said, "You know, when I'm feeling down, one of the things I do is go and look up your clip on YouTube." So if that's a service I provide to my friends in this life, I'm very grateful.'

Ralph read Classics at Cambridge and is now a barrister specializing in commercial law. He had grown up in a household where his parents used to love watching *University Challenge*. 'I remember that, even at quite a young age, maybe when I was nine or ten, that the treat on a Monday would be being allowed to stay up until eight o'clock to watch *University Challenge*. Of course, at nine or ten I had no idea what was going on. And I think my abiding memory was being confused about why the 'Caius' in 'Gonville and Caius College' was pronounced "keys".

'I've always been quite good at pointless trivia, not useful things, but pointless trivia. It was always in my mind that it might be quite a fun thing to do. In my first year I filled in the application form to be on the Trinity team. I was selected for the team but we didn't get through. Then the captain from that year was going on to other things and asked me if I wanted to organize it. So I said, "Oh well, why not?"'

The producers sent out a questions pack, and Trinity had a try-out where they were asked questions. 'You do your best to answer them. What I did the following year in organizing the trials was two things. I got a friend of mine to ask me all the questions. I think there's something like 150 or 200. So we had a long evening with pizza and wine, where he asked me all the questions. We marked them and we knew which ones I'd got right or wrong.

'And then we organized a try-out in which I asked the first 40 questions. I said to myself, well if four people get better than I did, then they could be on the team and if three people got the same or better than I did, then I would scrape in on the team. And from that we got the best four people, fortunately including me or else that would be the end of my story. About 40 people applied to be on the Trinity team that year.

'I remember very vividly our first match of filming was on Valentine's Day in 2013.' It was the last day of filming that took place in the old Granada studios and their subsequent rounds took place at MediaCity. 'During the sample questions in the first round against Christchurch, Oxford, who were a very competent team, when they were testing the buzzers, we didn't get anything right; it was a bit of a bloodbath but the first question proper was one on Catullus, the Roman poet, and I had just done an essay on Catullus so that helped us get off to a flying start. My abiding memory of that round and then subsequently the final was you go back home and then work starts again the following day. I was back in lectures and, of course, you can't tell anyone at all what's happened because that would be bad form so you just have to nod and say, "Oh, how's your day?" You can't tell people anything at all.'

Despite Jeremy Paxman humorously calling Ralph's team 'smartarses', Ralph remembers him as being 'very nice to us'. 'I didn't get the sense that he was out to trip us up; he was much less grumpy [than his reputation].' Ralph emphasizes that it was very much a team performance. 'I wouldn't say that any of us was a superstar player in the way that someone like Gail Trimble or Eric Monkman was, but I think that we had a very strong ensemble. We all contributed to our victories as a team, and that was really lovely in the final where everybody got questions at critical moments.'

Try Your Luck
Match

Your starter for ten:

1 Generally attributed to the same author as the Gospel according to Luke, what is the fifth book of the New Testament?

Three questions on English cricket in 2021:
(a) Joe Root became England's leading run-getter across all formats when he overtook which left-handed batter who served as captain in 2009–2017?
(b) Which English bowler overtook the record of 619 Test wickets achieved by India's Anil Kumble to become the third-leading wicket-taker and most successful pace bowler in Tests?
(c) A new domestic competition inaugurated in 2021, the Women's Regional T20 has been named after which former England women's captain?

Your starter for ten:

2 On a chronological list of US presidents, who occupies the same position as Henry Pelham on a list of British prime ministers, or U Thant on a list of secretaries-general of the United Nations?

Your bonuses are on the Chatham House Prize, awarded for significant contributions to international relations. Name each winner from the description:
(a) The 2014 winner; the eradication of polio is one of the priorities of the foundation she and her husband established in 2000.
(b) The 2005 winner, partly in recognition of the 'courage and skill he demonstrated in steering a peaceful process of political change in Ukraine'.
(c) The international organization awarded the prize in 2015, 'in recognition of their work in combating the 2014 Ebola outbreak in West Africa'.

Your starter for ten:

3 The Brazilian composer and singer Caetano Veloso made a noted appearance as himself in which 2002 film by Pedro Almodóvar? The film concerns two men both caring for women in comas.

Three questions on the writer Neil Gaiman:
(a) Born in Hampshire in 1960, Gaiman's first credit as author was for a 1984 paperback biography of which British pop band?
(b) What is the title of Gaiman's dark fantasy series of comics, running from 1989 to 1996? Its protagonist is Morpheus, a manifestation of the ability of sentient beings to dream.
(c) For which novel did Gaiman receive the 2009 Newbery Medal? It concerns an orphan raised by ghosts in a cemetery.

Your starter for ten:

4   A word meaning 'park' or 'enclosure' in the ancient Avestan language is cited as the origin of what eight-letter word that links: a large-scale painting by Tintoretto; a bird on the flag of Papua New Guinea; and two long poems of the later 17th century?

Your bonuses are on book titles. In each case, you will hear descriptions of two novels; the last three letters of the first title begin the title of the second, for example, *Song of Achilles* and *Les Misérables*. Name both novels for the points.
(a) A 1911 novel by Max Beerbohm, subtitled *An Oxford Love Story*, and a novel of 1913 by D.H. Lawrence, concerning the family of Paul Morel.
(b) Set in 1950s Indochina, Graham Greene's political thriller about the CIA agent Alden Pyle and Anthony Trollope's novel about the spirited Alice Vavasour.
(c) The first of Hilary Mantel's Booker Prize-winning accounts of the life of Thomas Cromwell and Erich Maria Remarque's fictionalized account of his First World War experiences.

Your starter for ten:

5   By chance rather than etymology, what four-letter affirmation appears at the end of words meaning: a round structure at the base of the forebrain; an opening or orifice in a human bone; a male organ in flowering plants; and, in Japan, Chinese-style wheat noodles?

Your bonuses are on pairs of names or titles in which the last word of the first answer gives the first word of the second, for example, 'Hey Jude' and *Jude the Obscure*. In each case, give both answers from the descriptions:
(a) A female character in Mozart's *The Magic Flute* and the two-word popular name of a 1642 painting by Rembrandt.
(b) The Liberal Party's last UK prime minister and a Hungarian-American businessman born in 1930.
(c) A 14th-century Middle English frame story and an 1881 opera by Offenbach.

Your starter for ten:

6   'Tenthly, one should pour tea into the cup first. This is one of the most
    controversial points of all; indeed in every family in Britain there are
    probably two schools of thought on the subject.' Who wrote those words
    in his 1946 article 'A Nice Cup of Tea'?

Your bonuses are on pairs of words that differ only by the addition of a second
letter 'r', for instance 'bass' and 'brass'. Give both words from the definitions:
(a) In music, a set of two notes or pitches played together; and, in Greek
mythology, a type of tree nymph?
(b) The ancient city in Tunisia at which the Roman politician Cato the
younger died; and a genus of plants that includes stinging nettles?
(c) A ceremonial mallet; and a small stone defined on the international
particle scale as having a diameter of between 2 and 63 millimetres?

Your starter for ten:

7   What name is generally given to the French protestant supporters of John
    Calvin who were granted religious toleration in 1598 under the Edict of
    Nantes?

Three questions on Ireland:
(a) Clew, Blacksod and Killala are bays in which Irish county, situated
immediately north of County Galway?
(b) Sharing its name with a county of Ulster, which bay has shorelines in
Counties Sligo and Leitrim?
(c) Dingle Bay and Tralee Bay form part of the coastline of which Irish
county?

Your starter for ten:

8   Born in Sweden in 1929, which artist is noted for his large-scale, soft
    sculptures of everyday objects such as ice-cream cones and hamburgers?

Three questions on footnotes in academic writing:
(a) What four-letter term is used to indicate a word or author that has just
been mentioned? In Latin, it means 'the same'.
(b) What two-letter abbreviation refers readers to another source for the
purpose of comparison?
(c) Often written as a four-letter abbreviation, what term refers to the source
cited in the previous reference? In Latin, it means 'in the same place'.

Your starter for ten:

9   Established by the Treaty of London in 1949 and distinct from the

European Union, which association of states seeks to develop common principles based primarily on the European Convention on Human Rights?

Three questions on the US astronomer Andrea Ghez:
(a) In 2020, Ghez was awarded a share in the Nobel Prize in Physics for providing evidence that what type of object is at the core of our galaxy?
(b) Ghez proved the existence of the black hole at the centre of the Milky Way using the Keck Observatory in which US state?
(c) Ghez shared the Nobel Prize with the German astrophysicist Reinhard Genzel and which British mathematical physicist? The latter was cited for 'the discovery that black hole formation is a robust prediction of the general theory of relativity'.

Your starter for ten:
10 Originally meaning a godparent or sponsor, what word came to mean a woman's female friend invited to be present at a birth, but is now used negatively for a person who passes on trifling or prurient rumours, especially concerning the private affairs of others?

Three questions on Franz Liszt:
(a) Liszt studied music theory under which Italian composer, who also taught Beethoven and Schubert? He appears as a character in Peter Shaffer's play *Amadeus*.
(b) Liszt championed the works of many of his contemporaries, including which composer, whose early operas include *Rienzi* and *The Flying Dutchman*?
(c) Later in his life, Liszt became a member of the 'third' order of which mendicant Christian religious order, founded in the early 13th century?

Your starter for ten:
11 Which two contiguous coastal US states have capitals named after explorers born roughly 100 years apart in Devon and Genoa, respectively?

Three questions on words that contain all five vowels once and once only. Give each word from the definition:
(a) A unit of energy equivalent to one billion, or ten to the power of nine, newton-metres; the five vowels occur in the order 'i-a-o-u-e'.
(b) A lanthanide element first discovered in 1885; its name comes from the Greek for 'green twin'? The five vowels occur in the order 'a-e-o-i-u'.
(c) An adjective meaning 'restraint in relation to food or drink'? The five vowels occur in alphabetical order.

Your starter for ten:

12 First published in 1811, which novel was developed from an earlier draft entitled 'Elinor and Marianne'?

Three questions on contrafacta, a contrafactum being the recurrence of a melody with entirely new lyrics:
(a) The 1960s French song 'Comme d'habitude' was given new lyrics by Paul Anka, and became a standard under what title?
(b) What is the present-day title of the national anthem which is a contrafactum of 'To Anacreon in Heaven', a song associated with a London gentlemen's club founded in the 18th century?
(c) Which 1978 hit for David Essex, from the musical *Evita*, is a contrafactum of 'Don't Cry for Me Argentina'?

Your starter for ten:

13 *The Sea of Fertility* is the English title of a tetralogy by which author? He died by ritual suicide in 1970, following an unsuccessful attempt to incite a military coup in his home city of Tokyo. His other novels include *Confessions of a Mask* and *The Temple of the Golden Pavilion*.

Three questions on United Nations goodwill ambassadors:
(a) The winner of the Best Actress Oscar for *The Hours*, who became a goodwill ambassador in 2006?
(b) Six-time FIFA Player of the Year and a goodwill ambassador for women and girls in sport, Marta Vieira da Silva captained which team at the 2019 Women's World Cup?
(c) The winner of an Oscar for her role as Fantine in *Les Misérables*, who became an ambassador in 2016? She also narrated the film *Girl Rising* about female education.

Your starter for ten:

14 *The History of Economic Analysis* and *Business Cycles* are among the works of which economist, born in the Austro-Hungarian Empire? He is noted for popularising the concept of 'creative destruction'.

Three questions on a shared name:
(a) 'There was a boy called Eustace Clarence Scrubb, and he almost deserved it.' This is the opening sentence of which book of 1952?
(b) Eustace Chapuys was appointed imperial ambassador to the court of Henry VIII in 1529, serving which Holy Roman Emperor?
(c) Founded in 1925, which periodical is associated with the character Eustace Tilley? His image appeared on the front cover of the first issue.

Your starter for ten:

15 I need a three-letter word here. Meaning 'sea', what place-name element appears in all the following names: the gulf into which the Yellow River discharges; the smallest and southernmost province of China; and a major city near the mouth of the Yangtze?

Three questions on a pan-continental organization:
(a) With its headquarters at Addis Ababa, which organization succeeded the OAU in 2002? I need a two-word name.
(b) Which country was suspended from the African Union in 2009 after Andry Rajoelina seized power? The suspension was lifted five years later following elections.
(c) In 2017 which country joined the African Union, having left its predecessor the OAU in 1984 after a dispute over the status of Western Sahara?

Your starter for ten:

16 Which novel by Virginia Woolf was inspired in part by Knole House in Kent, and by members of the Sackville family that owned it? The novel is subtitled *A Biography*.

Three questions on states of India:
(a) A little larger than Cornwall, which state became part of India in 1962, having once been the capital of the Portuguese Asian empire?
(b) Known as the Pink City after its distinctive buildings, what city is the capital of the state of Rajasthan?
(c) I need a two-word term here. Kolkata is the capital of which state that is bordered by Bhutan and Nepal to the north and northwest?

Your starter for ten:

17 Set in the Carney farmhouse in Northern Ireland in 1981, which play by Jez Butterworth has a title that alludes to the mythical figure Charon, who took souls from this world to the next?

Three questions on ancestors of the present Duke of Cambridge:
(a) Through the direct male line, the Duke of Cambridge's paternal great-great-grandfather is George I, the king of what country until his death in 1913?
(b) The father of George I of Greece, Christian IX, was the king of what other European country between 1863 and 1906?
(c) Who was both the Duke of Cambridge's father's father's mother's mother's mother's mother, and his father's mother's father's father's father's mother?

Your starter for ten:

18 In geometry, which conic section is described by the equation: $x^2/a^2 + y^2/b^2 = 1$?

Three questions on a plant:

(a) Distinguished by lilac or pink flowers, what deciduous climbing shrub of the pea family is named after a US anatomist born in 1761?

(b) 'Wisteria Maiden', a tale of unrequited love, is a noted dance in what traditional Japanese dramatic form?

(c) In a work of 1919, which French novelist recalls: 'talking thus with Madame Swann beneath her parasol … as though in the coloured shade of a wisteria bower'?

Your starter for ten:

19 The largest species in the world by mass of spider, frog and beetle are all named after which biblical figure, mentioned in the First Book of Samuel?

Three questions on the solar system:

(a) What gas makes up 96.5 per cent of the atmosphere of Venus?

(b) Comprising most of the remaining 3.5 per cent on Venus, what gas makes up about 94 per cent of the atmosphere of Titan?

(c) What gas makes up about 6 per cent of the atmosphere of Titan? On Earth, it is a greenhouse gas, with proportionately a much higher warming effect than carbon dioxide.

Your starter for ten:

20 Meaning 'high plateau', what Spanish term indicates the flat intermontane area of Bolivia and Southern Peru, lying at an elevation of more than 3,000 metres?

Three questions on theories of evolution:

(a) Named after a French biologist, which theory is based on the principle that physical changes developed by organisms in their lifetime are transmitted to their offspring? It is also known as the inheritance of acquired characteristics.

(b) Advanced in the early 1900s by the Dutch scientist Hugo de Vries, which theory suggests that new species are formed from sudden and unexpected alterations in their defining traits?

(c) The watchmaker analogy, arguing that a design implies a designer, was employed by which English clergyman and utilitarian in his 1802 work *Natural Theology*?

Your starter for ten:

21 What common colloquial word may be spelt by concatenating the initial letters of the capitals of Kenya, Canada, Cape Verde and Scotland?

Three questions on Benjamin Britten's librettists:
(a) Which Yorkshire-born poet wrote the words for the Britten operetta *Paul Bunyan*, first performed in 1941? The two worked together on the 1936 documentary *Night Mail*.
(b) Which prominent novelist collaborated with Eric Crozier on the libretto for Britten's *Billy Budd*?
(c) Myfanwy Piper provided the English libretto for which of Britten's operas, based on a novella by Thomas Mann?

Your starter for ten:

22 With a name meaning 'along the sea', which province historically occupied the region of the German and Polish Baltic coast that includes the cities of Stettin and Gdansk? It gives its name to a breed of toy dog.

Your bonuses are words that appear in titles of the Japanese videogame franchise *Tales of*. In each case, give the single word from the description:
(a) What word appears in both the title of a release originally scheduled for 2020 and in the first line of W.B. Yeats's poem 'The Lake Isle of Innisfree'?
(b) I need a precise answer here. A Greek word meaning 'harmony', the English form of this word designates a prominent type of orchestral composition.
(c) Meaning 'great deep', the final word of the title of Jack London's 1902 account of poverty in the East End: *The People of the...* what?

Your starter for ten:

23 Answer as soon as your name is called. How many degrees is twenty pi over six radians?

Three questions on a shared word:
(a) Named after a Scottish scientist, what three-letter term denotes a logarithmic unit used to compare the intensity of power levels such as sound? It is often subdivided into tenths.
(b) The US designer Norman Bel Geddes is closely associated with what stylistic feature, associated with the Art Deco and Modernist movements? Its name is often used as a descriptor of efficient aerodynamic design.
(c) The title character of a book of the Old Testament, which major prophet is a central figure in the book of the Apocrypha known as 'Bel and the Dragon'?

Your starter for ten:

24 Native to southeast Europe and Asia, the roots of the plant *Glycyrrhiza glabra* are used commercially to make what item of confectionery, associated with the Yorkshire town of Pontefract?

Your bonuses are on words that begin with the same unusual combination of consonants:
(a) In Greek myth, what monster terrorized the city of Thebes until Oedipus answered its riddle correctly?
(b) Its name meaning 'wedge-shaped', what compound bone forms the base of the cranium behind the eyes?
(c) Widely used by florists and gardeners, plants of what genus are also known as bog moss or peat moss?

Your starter for ten:

25 In what major mountain range is the point on Earth that is farthest from the planet's centre, this being the summit of Chimborazo, which rises to 6,263 metres?

Your bonuses are on surnames that relate to mills or milling. In each case, give the surname from the description:
(a) The French politician and journalist who in July 1789 publicly implored his fellow citizens to take up arms; he later published *The Streetlamp's Address to the Parisians*.
(b) The Italian golfer who, alongside his brother Edoardo, represented Europe at the 2010 Ryder Cup.
(c) The US law enforcement official who was director of the FBI from 2001 to 2013.

The Answers

1   Acts (of the Apostles)
      (a) (Alistair) Cook
      (b) (James) Anderson
      (c) (Charlotte) Edwards

2   (Thomas) Jefferson (i.e. the third on the list)
      (a) Melinda Gates
      (b) (Viktor) Yushchenko
      (c) Médecins sans frontières / MSF / Doctors Without Borders

3   *Hable con ella / Talk to Her*
      (a) Duran Duran
      (b) *Sandman*
      (c) *The Graveyard Book*

4   Paradise (*Il Paradiso*, one of the world's largest paintings, in the Doge's Palace in Venice; bird-of-paradise; *Paradise Lost / Regained*. Avestan: *pairidaeze*)
      (a) *Zuleika Dobson / Sons and Lovers*
      (b) *The Quiet American / Can You Forgive Her?*
      (c) *Wolf Hall / All Quiet on the Western Front*

5   Amen (putamen, foramen, stamen, ramen)
      (a) Queen of the Night and *Night Watch*
      (b) David Lloyd George and George Soros
      (c) *The Canterbury Tales* and *Tales of Hoffmann*

6   (George) Orwell
      (a) Dyad and dryad
      (b) Utica and urtica
      (c) Gavel and gravel

7   Huguenots
      (a) (County) Mayo
      (b) Donegal (Bay)
      (c) (County) Kerry

8   (Claes) Oldenburg
      (a) Idem
      (b) C.f.
      (c) Ibid (accept 'ib' or 'ibidem')

9   The Council of Europe
      (a) (Supermassive) black hole
      (b) Hawaii (on Mauna Kea)
      (c) (Sir Roger) Penrose

10　Gossip (from the Old English words *god* and *sib*)
　　(a) (Antonio) Salieri (1750–1825)
　　(b) (Richard) Wagner (1813–1883; he became Liszt's son-in-law, of course)
　　(c) Franciscan

11　North and South Carolina (their capitals being Raleigh and Columbia)
　　(a) Gigajoule
　　(b) Praseodymium (Greek: *prasios*, 'leek-green'; *didym*, 'twin')
　　(c) Abstemious

12　*Sense and Sensibility* (by Jane Austen, of course)
　　(a) 'My Way'
　　(b) 'The Star-Spangled Banner'
　　(c) 'Oh What a Circus'

13　Yukio Mishima
　　(a) Nicole Kidman
　　(b) Brazil
　　(c) Anne Hathaway

14　(Joseph) Schumpeter (1883–1950)
　　(a) *The Voyage of the Dawn Treader* (C.S. Lewis)
　　(b) Charles V
　　(c) *New Yorker*

15　Hai (Bohai, Hainan, Shanghai)
　　(a) African Union (formerly Organisation of African Unity, of course)
　　(b) Madagascar
　　(c) Morocco

16　*Orlando*
　　(a) Goa
　　(b) Jaipur
　　(c) West Bengal

17　*The Ferryman*
　　(a) Greece
　　(b) Denmark
　　(c) (Queen) Victoria

18　Ellipse
　　(a) Wisteria (Caspar Wistar)
　　(b) Kabuki
　　(c) (Marcel) Proust

19 Goliath
    (a) Carbon dioxide
    (b) Nitrogen
    (c) Methane (CH_4)

20 *Altiplano*
    (a) Lamarckism (Jean-Baptiste Lamarck, 1744–1829)
    (b) Mutation (theory)
    (c) (William) Paley

21 Nope (Nairobi, Ottawa, Praia, Edinburgh, of course)
    (a) W.H. Auden
    (b) E.M. Forster
    (c) *Death in Venice*

22 Pomerania (Slavic: *po morze*, 'by / on the sea')
    (a) Arise ('I will arise and go now, and go to Innisfree'; *Tales of Arise*, eventually released in September 2021)
    (b) Symphonia (*Tales of Symphonia*, 2003)
    (c) *Abyss* (*Tales of the Abyss*, 2005)

23 600
    (a) Bel (after Alexander Graham Bell, of course)
    (b) Streamlining (accept streamline, streamlined)
    (c) Daniel

24 Liquorice
    (a) Sphinx
    (b) Sphenoid
    (c) *Sphagnum*

25 The Andes (specifically, the Cordillera Occidental on the equatorial bulge)
    (a) (Camille) Desmoulins
    (b) (Francesco) Molinari
    (c) (Robert S.) Mueller (III)

Drafts and Checkers

As well as the question-setters who work full-time on the programme, *University Challenge* has around a dozen freelance question-setters who are commissioned to write 35 starter questions and 25 bonus sets each per series. They will probably do one batch of those each, but some might do two batches.

Questions editor Tom Benson is a prolific question-setter, sometimes writing nearly half a series' posers. He also handles the incoming batches of questions from the freelancers. He will edit those and then send them to Peter Gwyn, the executive producer, for a further edit.

Questions producer and former contestant Richard Gilbert explains: 'A couple of the freelance question-setters have been with us for years. However, we do try to rotate it, and if there's somebody who has performed well on the show, or at least demonstrates the kind of knowledge that we think we lack or we don't represent, then they might be asked if they want to submit a trial batch. We'll have a look at those and see whether we think they are what we need, and then we'll hire them to write a set. In recent years we've had a few contestants go through that process.'

How do the question-setters come up with hundreds of questions, year after year? Richard explains his process: 'At any point I will have dozens of tabs open for academic articles, or even Wikipedia, of just things that I'm trying to familiarize myself with. And because I write and edit the picture and music questions, that's my remit, anything that strikes me as remotely visual or musical, I will keep a track of as well. I think, "Would that work as a question? Can I get a set of four out of that?" Because the picture and music rounds work so that you have a starter question, and three questions that follow from the starter, which doesn't happen with the regular questions.

'So I'll be trying to find themes between certain parts of history or certain characters in history – that tends to be my specialism, language and things like that. And, occasionally, you'll just be walking around your everyday life and you'll hear something interesting, then make a little mental note of it. And you get back into the office on Monday morning, pursue it – most of the time they're dead ends, but you just have to be generally interested in as many things as possible, I guess. Having said that, you're getting no science questions from me!'

After the question-setters' batches come in and are edited, they go to the programme's verifiers, whose job is to catch any mistakes.

*

Sara Low has been verifying questions for 40 years. She has a background in teaching and began checking the questions for *The Krypton Factor* (the ITV gameshow that ran from 1977 to 1995). Sara was then asked to set up a team of freelance verifiers to work across a range of TV shows.

'My husband is a priest, and we had a congregation full of clever women, a lot of whom had young children and a lot of whom were retired, but were the kind of people who did the *Times* crossword before breakfast, so putting together a team was actually very easy and several of those people are still working with me now. They're a great team.'

Sara has worked on *University Challenge* for more than 30 years, and currently her team, which now also includes some very clever men, is verifying questions for *Mastermind, University Challenge, The Chase, Eggheads* and *Only Connect*.

Sara says: 'People always think you'd be really good on a pub quiz. But actually I'm not at all because I see so many questions. It just goes in one ear and out the other. I don't retain it at all. Some of my team do. You would want some of my team on your pub quiz team but you wouldn't want me. You'd want me if you wanted something found out. That's what I'm good at.'

When the questions are sent to Sara and the team, they check every word of the question and they are looking for two things. 'We're obviously looking to make sure the answer is correct,' says Sara, 'but just as important, we're looking to make sure that there is no other possible answer. We've looked at thousands of questions. Most of the time what we're doing is saying, "If you ask it like this, then this is the only answer." We're rewording to make sure that any possible alternative is excluded.'

When Sara began verifying, she and her team would use books. 'We would still actually prefer to use books, but very often we're looking at them online. We would still, for example, use the *Oxford Companion to English Literature*, but we might actually be looking at it online rather than physically. If you're used to handling books and reading hard copy, you are much more likely to spot mistakes.'

For verifying *University Challenge* questions the team works on hard copy. When the questions arrive, they are printed out. 'On screen, I find your brain tells you what should be there, rather than what is there,' says Sara. 'On hard copy you tend to see mistakes straight away.'

Sara says she hopes to carry on verifying *University Challenge*'s questions for as long as she can. 'We all enjoy it; it's interesting. There are some subjects that are being introduced which are new university subjects, about which there haven't been an awful lot of questions before. That will be an increasing challenge to make sure that we understand enough about the questions, in some areas of social science for example.'

Richard Gilbert adds: 'Based on the handful of questions that I've seen from back in the day, I would say the questions are generally harder these days because of the broadening of the canon – there's more science and when we ask about literature, what we mean by literature ranges from contemporary to classical. When we ask about history, we ask more about world history than just British political history. So there will be necessarily fewer questions about Latin literature. There'll be fewer questions about British political history of the 18th century.

'It doesn't mean those things are gone from the canon, it's just they're not the be-all and end-all.'

Try Your Luck

Match

7

Your starter for ten:

1 What is the pH of a solution formed by mixing 10 millilitres of one molar hydrochloric acid with 10 millilitres of one molar sodium solution?

Your bonuses are on saints' days during Advent. Identify each saint from the description:
(a) A 4th-century bishop of Myra and patron saint of children and sailors, celebrated on 6 December.
(b) A patron saint of tailors and blacksmiths; this saint's day is celebrated on 13 December and opens the Christmas season in Sweden. A Caribbean island is named after her.
(c) Celebrated on 30 November, one of Jesus's apostles who is believed to have been crucified on an X-shaped cross.

Your starter for ten:

2 Announced in 2017, the Tapanuli is a third species, after the Bornean and the Sumatran, of which ape, of the genus *Pongo*?

Your bonuses are on the Vatican's list of 'important films' about religion. In each case, name the film from the description:
(a) First, a Russian film of 1969 by Andrei Tarkovsky about a 15th-century monk and religious artist.
(b) A Danish film of 1955 by Carl Theodor Dreyer about miracles; its five-letter title means 'The Word' in English.
(c) A 1928 French film, also by Dreyer, based on the trial of a 15th-century martyr? I need the full title either in English or French.

Your starter for ten:

3 An authority on surrealism, who wrote the script for the cult 1967 comedy slapstick film *Smashing Time*? As a jazz singer, he was associated with bands such as The Digby Fairweather Band and John Chilton's Feetwarmers.

Three questions on a bird:

(a) Alluding to Greek mythology, poets including Sir Philip Sidney and T.S. Eliot refer to which bird as 'Philomel' or 'Philomela'?

(b) In his 1835 poem 'The Progress of Rhyme', which English poet described the nightingale's song as: 'chew-chew chew-chew and higher still, cheer-cheer cheer-cheer, more loud and shrill'?

(c) In a work first published in 1819, which poet addressed the nightingale as 'thou, light-winged dryad of the trees'?

Your starter for ten:

4 In what Canadian province would one make landfall after sailing due west from St Ives in Cornwall?

Three questions on farce:

(a) In the story of a man whose life is disturbed by the ghost of his first wife, Elvira, what is the name of the eccentric medium in Noel Coward's 1941 farce *Blithe Spirit*?

(b) Joe Orton's *What the Butler Saw* concludes with the holding aloft of 'an intimate body part' of a statue of which public figure?

(c) The farce *Nothing On* is the play-within-a-play in which stage work by Michael Frayn, first performed in 1982?

Your starter for ten:

5 Which composer is this? At the age of 20, he walked more than 200 miles to hear Dieterich Buxtehude perform in the city of Lübeck. Compositions of his early twenties include the cantata 'God Is My King', and the Toccata and Fugue in D Minor, BWV 565.

Your bonuses are on a UNESCO World Heritage Site:

(a) Founded in London in 1759, which gardens are cited by UNESCO for their contribution to the study of plant diversity and economic botany?

(b) Born in 1830, which artist and traveller gives her name to a gallery that houses more than 800 of her botanical paintings, described as 'a perfect blend of beauty and science'?

(c) 'Kew Gardens' is a short story of 1919 by which author? It was published by Hogarth Press, the company that she and her husband founded in 1917.

Your starter for ten:

6 Give the four-letter name of the kingdom traditionally said to have been formed by the union of the Picts and Scots under Kenneth MacAlpin in 843. Consisting of much of the land north of the Forth, its name is also the modern Gaelic name for Scotland.

Three questions on people who were knighted in 1975:

(a) Which actor was knighted in the 1975 New Year's Honours at the age of 85? He had been living in Switzerland for more than twenty years.

(b) Which writer died, aged 93, in February 1975, a few weeks after he was awarded a knighthood? He had been living outside Britain since the Second World War and had held US citizenship since 1955.

(c) Who was knighted in a ceremony at a racecourse in Bridgetown in February 1975, a year after his retirement from professional sport?

Your starter for ten:

7 Answer promptly. The names 'Mississippi' and 'Tennessee' each contain three pairs of double letters. What is the only US state whose name contains exactly two pairs of double letters?

Your bonuses are on words that differ only by the addition of an initial letter 'c' to one of them. In each case, give both words from the definitions:

(a) A precious substance mined since ancient times in the Baltic region; and the angle made by the wheels of a vehicle?

(b) A collection of statistical models used to analyse the differences between group means in a sample; and an Italian Neoclassical sculptor whose works include *The Three Graces* and *Venus Victrix*?

(c) A large member of the corvid family; and a word meaning contemptibly cowardly?

Your starter for ten:

8 '[I] felt an obligation to get [him] away from a racial stereotype, and instead make him a crazy old Father Christmas gone wrong.' Those words of the actor Ron Moody summarize his portrayal of which of Dickens' characters?

Your bonuses are on the novelist J.L. Carr's *Dictionary of English Kings: Consorts, Pretenders, Usurpers, Unnatural Claimants and Royal Athelings*. Name each king from Carr's description; all three have the same regnal name:

(a) 'So virile that he holds the royal record for propagation – twenty-four undisputed offspring. Even so, after the wreck of the white ship, his sole legal heir was a daughter.'

(b) 'Partly buried in a gold cup at Westminster ... [he] enlarged the prosperity of barristers by abolishing trial by fire and water.'

(c) 'This cheerful-faced but unamiable ... miser, employing Morton's fork, left two million pounds.'

Your starter for ten:

9 Located around 60 kilometres northeast of Shiraz, which ancient city was founded by Darius the Great in the 6th century BC as the capital of his dynasty?

Your bonuses are on the novels of J.M. Coetzee. In each case, give the name of the novel from its description by the Nobel Prize committee:
(a) 'The novel deals with the flight of an insignificant citizen from growing disorder and impending war, to a state of indifference to all needs.'
(b) 'A paraphrase of Dostoevsky's life and fictional world.'
(c) 'The struggle of a discredited university teacher to defend his own and his daughter's honour.'

Your starter for ten:

10 Charlotte, Countess of Yarmouth; Charles Lennox, Duke of Richmond; and James Scott, Duke of Monmouth, were among the illegitimate children of which British monarch, who left no legitimate issue and was succeeded by his brother, James?

Three questions on particle physics:
(a) In the standard model of particle physics, the name of what broad class of subatomic particles derives from the Greek for 'heavy', the lightest among these heavy particles being the proton?
(b) Including baryons and mesons, what broader class of particles encompasses any composite of the fundamental particles whose name was inspired by James Joyce's *Finnegans Wake*?
(c) Baryons fall into another class that excludes mesons but includes electrons and other leptons, and is named after which physicist, born in Rome in 1901?

Your starter for ten:

11 Listen to the statement and answer the question that follows. In 1938, the BBC broadcast the first science fiction television programme: a live adaptation of Karel Capek's play *R.U.R.*; what five-letter word did this play introduce into the English language?

Three questions on botanical terms. In each case, identify the term from the description:
(a) First, what term denotes specialized structures of epidermal origin that are found on plant, lichen or algal surfaces? They are usually shaped like hairs, but can also appear as scales, buds or papillae.
(b) A term derived from the Greek for 'young shoot' and used to describe an undifferentiated plant-body. It can consist of a single cell in its simplest form.

(c) Also known as a 'root stock', a horizontal underground stem that can send out roots and leafy shoots; edible examples include ginger and turmeric?

Your starter for ten:

12 Give the fourth in this chronological sequence of Roman emperors: Galba, Otho, Vitellius and…?

Your bonuses are on British and Chinese history. In each case, I will name a British monarch or monarchs, and you will give me the Chinese dynasty that spanned the period of their rule:
(a) Rhodri the Great, King of Gwynedd.
(b) The Scottish kings Kenneth II, Macbeth and Alexander II. I need a single-word answer.
(c) The English monarchs Henry V, Richard III and Elizabeth I.

Your starter for ten:

13 Of the two types of nerve fibre in the human body, which type carries information away from the cell body, as opposed to towards it?

Three questions on tributaries:
(a) The Shenandoah joins which river at a confluence near Harper's Ferry in Virginia?
(b) The Balikh and the Sajur rivers join the Euphrates at different confluences in which country?
(c) The Ubangi and the Kasai are both tributaries of which major river, the world's deepest?

Your starter for ten:

14 The four-stroke cycle of the modern petrol engine, also called the Otto cycle, comprises the induction, power, exhaust and what other stroke, the introduction of which in 1876 greatly improved on earlier engine cycles?

Three questions on books set in US states:
(a) Which southern state is the setting of Fannie Flagg's 1987 novel *Fried Green Tomatoes at the Whistle Stop Cafe* and of Harper Lee's *To Kill a Mockingbird*?
(b) *Gilead* by Marilynne Robinson, *A Thousand Acres* by Jane Smiley and Bill Bryson's memoir *The Life and Times of the Thunderbolt Kid* are set in which midwestern state?
(c) The Pulitzer Prize-winning *Olive Kitteridge* by Elizabeth Strout and John Irving's novel *The Cider House Rules* are set in which New England state?

Your starter for ten:

15 What French term denotes a person variously described as: 'an ambivalent figure of urban affluence and modernity' who has 'no other purpose than to be an acute observer of industrialized, contemporary life'? The term is thought to derive from an Old Norse word meaning 'to wander aimlessly'.

Your bonuses are on performers who have won both the Academy Award for Best Actress and a Golden Raspberry:
(a) Who won a Razzie and an Oscar in the same weekend in 2010 for the films *All About Steve* and *The Blind Side*?
(b) Who won an Oscar for the 1976 satire *Network*, and a Razzie for playing Joan Crawford in the 1981 film *Mommie Dearest*?
(c) Halle Berry won an Oscar in 2002 and a Razzie three years later, marking her roles in which two films? I need both titles.

Your starter for ten:

16 I need a two-word term here. At Princeton University in the mid-20th century, John von Neumann and Oskar Morgenstern pioneered which branch of applied mathematics? It examines the interactions of participant choices, in, for example, economics or war.

Three questions on *travesti*, or 'trouser roles', in opera:
(a) Although originally performed by a castrato, Orfeo has often become a woman's role in a 1762 opera by which German composer?
(b) Count Oktavian, the youthful lover of an older princess, is a *travesti* role in which opera by Richard Strauss?
(c) In which opera by Mozart is the trouser-role character Cherubino sent away to join the army for flirting with female members of Count Almaviva's household?

Your starter for ten:

17 Moussaka, ratatouille and baba ganoush are among dishes that feature which vegetable of the nightshade family?

Three questions on the Arctic Ocean:
(a) The Svalbard archipelago and Franz Josef Land are two boundaries of which marginal sea of the Arctic Ocean, named after a 16th-century Dutch seafarer?
(b) Archangel is a port on which sea, connected to the Barents Sea by a narrow strait known as the Gorlo?
(c) The port of Honningsvåg on the Barents Sea is about 30 kilometres from the extremity of Europe known by what name?

Your starter for ten:

18 What plural noun appears in the titles of: a novel by E. Nesbit concerning Roberta, Peter and Phyllis; a dystopian novel by P.D. James; and the winner of special Booker Prizes in 1993 and 2008?

Three questions on marine ecosystems:

(a) The Great Barrier Reef, off the coast of Queensland, is located in which sea within the Pacific Ocean?

(b) Situated northwest of Jamaica, which British Overseas Territory consists of three islands each almost entirely surrounded by coral reefs?

(c) Consisting of a chain of more than a thousand coral islands and sandbanks, what country lies about 600 kilometres southwest of Sri Lanka?

Your starter for ten:

19 Champlevé and cloisonné are decorative techniques associated with what specific substance, made of powdered glass fused onto a surface by firing? It shares its name with one of the four tissues that make up human teeth.

Three questions on flags that are mainly green:

(a) The flag of which US state consists of a green field with the state seal, bearing the bust of a former president?

(b) A white curvilinear cross on a green field is the flag of which populous Italian region? Its provinces include Como, Bergamo and Cremona.

(c) A green flag with a green star in a white canton was adopted in 1905 as the flag of what international language?

Your starter for ten:

20 Featuring Catherine Deneuve and directed by Jacques Demy, which 1964 French musical film is noted for having all its dialogue sung rather than spoken? The title includes the name of a Channel port.

Your bonuses are on thought experiments in physics. In each case, name the scientist who gives their name to the following:

(a) After a physicist born in 1831, a hypothetical 'demon' that can apparently violate the second law of thermodynamics and enable perpetual motion.

(b) A paradox in quantum mechanics involving two observers; one is the so-called 'friend' of the eponymous physicist, and it investigates the timing of wave function collapse in the Copenhagen interpretation.

(c) A 'ship' that originated as a thought experiment, later carried out in reality, to demonstrate the classical principle of relativity.

Your starter for ten:

21 *Mimus polyglottos* is the binomial of which common North American songbird? The state bird of several southern states, it is mentioned in the lullaby 'Hush, Little Baby', and in the title of a 1960 novel by Harper Lee.

Your bonuses are on Latin legal terms. In each case, give the two-word term from the description:
(a) The right or ability to bring a legal action to court or to appear in a court, from the Latin for 'place of standing'?
(b) An act or situation that provokes or justifies a war, Latin for 'case for war'?
(c) With no appointed date for resumption, the Latin for 'without a day'?

Your starter for ten:

22 The newly married couples Elyot and Sybil Chase and Victor and Amanda Prynne are the principal characters of which play of 1930 by Noël Coward? Set in France, it is subtitled *An Intimate Comedy*.

Three questions on physics:
(a) 'It was almost as incredible as if you fired a fifteen-inch shell at a piece of tissue paper, and it came back and hit you.' Those words refer to the 'scattering' experiment of 1909, often named after which Nobel laureate?
(b) In the test, the nuclei in a thin foil of gold deflected alpha particles; to the nearest multiple of ten, how many times heavier than an alpha particle is a gold nucleus?
(c) The experiment led to the overthrow, in 1911, of which model of the atom, proposed in the previous decade by J. J. Thomson, with a name that suggests a seasonal food?

Your starter for ten:

23 The name of what mammal appears within the words that satisfy each of the following definitions: the official proving of a will; a Latin term meaning 'word for word'; and the bird that burdens the Ancient Mariner?

Your bonuses are on ski resorts. In each case, give the name from the description:
(a) A resort in southeast Switzerland; it is named after a 3rd-century commander of the Theban Legion who became the patron saint of the Swiss Guard.
(b) A resort in Colorado, named after an ore of gold; it hosts the film festival at which Jim Jarmusch and Michael Moore debuted their first films.
(c) An Italian resort in the Dolomites, north of Belluno, which hosted the 1956 Winter Olympic Games?

Your starter for ten:

24 Loosely based on a soldier who served under Louis XIV, which character appears in memoirs written by Gatien de Courtilz de Sandras that formed the basis for a series of novels by Alexandre Dumas père?

Your bonuses are on plants. In each case, give the alliterative, two-word common name of the plant described:

(a) First, *Buddleia davidii*, a showy flowering plant with cultivars including the Royal Red and the Pink Pearl. Its common name reflects its attractiveness to insects.

(b) *Caltha palustris*, also known as the kingcup, a perennial, typically yellow-flowering plant found in wetland habitats.

(c) *Salix babylonica*, a catkin-bearing deciduous tree with slender foliage that droops towards the ground.

Your starter for ten:

25 Automated external, or AED; implantable cardioverter, or ICD; and wearable cardioverter, or WCD. These are all types of what medical device?

Your bonuses are on trees in English poetry. In each case, identify the poet who wrote the following lines. The three questions are in chronological order:

(a) 'How vainly men themselves amaze / To win the palm, the oak, or bays / And their uncessant labours see / Crowned from some single herb or tree.'

(b) 'Willows whiten, aspens quiver, / Little breezes dusk and shiver / Thro' the wave that runs for ever / By the island in the river / Flowing down to Camelot.'

(c) 'Loveliest of trees, the cherry now / Is hung with bloom along the bough, / And stands about the woodland ride / Wearing white for Eastertide.'

The Answers

1 Seven (this is a neutralization reaction that will produce salt and water)
  (a) Nicholas
  (b) Lucia / Lucy
  (c) Andrew

2 Orangutan
  (a) *Andrei Rublev*
  (b) *Ordet*
  (c) *The Passion of Joan of Arc / La passion de Jeanne d'Arc*

3 George Melly
  (a) Nightingale (the maiden was transformed into one in Ovid's *Metamorphoses*)
  (b) John Clare
  (c) (John) Keats

4 Newfoundland (and Labrador)
  (a) Madame Arcati
  (b) Winston Churchill
  (c) *Noises Off*

5 (J.S.) Bach
  (a) Royal Botanic Gardens, Kew / Kew Gardens
  (b) Marianne North
  (c) Virginia Woolf

6 Alba
  (a) (Charlie) Chaplin
  (b) (P.G. / Pelham Grenville) Wodehouse
  (c) (Garry / Garfield) Sobers

7 Massachusetts
  (a) Amber and camber
  (b) Anova and Canova
  (c) Raven and craven

8 Fagin (Moody played Fagin in the film *Oliver!*, of course)
  (a) Henry I (his heir being Matilda, of course)
  (b) Henry III
  (c) Henry VII

9 Persepolis
  (a) *Life & Times of Michael K*
  (b) *The Master of Petersburg*
  (c) *Disgrace*

10   Charles II
     (a) Baryons (Greek: *barus*)
     (b) Hadrons (made up of quarks, of course)
     (c) (Enrico) Fermi (fermions, of course)

11   Robot (Rossum's Universal Robots)
     (a) Trichome(s)
     (b) Thallus / thallome (Greek: *thallos*)
     (c) Rhizome

12   Vespasian (AD 69, the Year of the Four Emperors)
     (a) Tang (618–907)
     (b) Song (960–1279)
     (c) Ming (1368–1644)

13   Axons (dendrites carry information towards the cell body)
     (a) Potomac
     (b) Syria / Syrian Arab Republic
     (c) (River) Congo

14   Compression (compresses the fuel before ignition)
     (a) Alabama
     (b) Iowa
     (c) Maine

15   Flâneur (Old Norse: *flana*)
     (a) Sandra Bullock
     (b) Faye Dunaway
     (c) *Monster's Ball* and *Catwoman*

16   Game theory
     (a) (Christoph Willibald von) Gluck
     (b) *Der Rosenkavalier*
     (c) *Le nozze di Figaro*

17   Aubergine / brinjal / eggplant
     (a) Barents Sea
     (b) White (Sea)
     (c) North Cape / Nordkapp (the northernmost point in Europe accessible by car)

18   Children (*The Railway Children*, *The Children of Men*, *Midnight's Children*)
     (a) Coral (Sea)
     (b) Cayman Islands
     (c) Maldives

19 Enamel
   (a) Washington
   (b) Lombardy / Lombardia
   (c) Esperanto

20 *The Umbrellas of Cherbourg / Les parapluies de Cherbourg*
   (a) (James Clerk) Maxwell
   (b) (Eugene) Wigner
   (c) Galileo (Galilei)

21 Mockingbird (i.e. common or northern mockingbird)
   (a) *Locus standi*
   (b) *Casus belli*
   (c) *Sine die*

22 *Private Lives*
   (a) (Ernest) Rutherford
   (b) Fifty
   (c) Plum pudding (accept Christmas pudding)

23 Bat (probate, verbatim, albatross)
   (a) St Moritz (St Maurice)
   (b) Telluride
   (c) Cortina (d'Ampezzo)

24 D'Artagnan
   (a) Butterfly bush
   (b) Marsh marigold
   (c) Weeping willow

25 Defibrillator
   (a) (Andrew) Marvell ('Thoughts in a Garden', of course)
   (b) (Alfred) Tennyson ('The Lady of Shalott')
   (c) (A.E.) Housman (the second poem of *A Shropshire Lad*)

Fry Day
Hull

VS

Queens' College, Cambridge
(1980)

On the face of it, the show broadcast on 4 February 1980 wasn't particularly notable. It was the beginning of a new series and the new teams of Hull and Queens' College, Cambridge were pitted against one another. On the Queens' side, however, was one Stephen Fry.

Below is the quiz they tackled. Stephen was key to getting a number of answers, including those on a 5th-century Roman leader, the musical version of a Shaw play and even the correct order of the coloured balls in snooker.

Hull
Andrew Ayton from Bournemouth, reading History
Clifton Snaith from Spalding, researching Victorian Literature
Matthew Diamond (captain) from Woodford Green, reading Drama
Barry Cameron from Harrow, reading Politics

Queens' College, Cambridge
Richard Barber from Shepperton, reading Natural Sciences
Stephen Fry from Booton, reading English
Steven Botterill (captain) from Worthing,
reading Modern and Medieval Languages
Mark Lester from Merton Park, reading Law

Your starter for ten:

1   What was said in the traditional story to be the benefit for the people
of Coventry which Lady Godiva intended to achieve by her naked ride
through the city?

Bonus questions:
(a) Between which two people is this farewell spoken? 'Forever, and forever,
farewell ... If we do meet again, why, we shall smile; if not, why, then this
parting was well made'?
(b) What were Hamlet's last four words before dying?
(c) Who was reputed to have said on his deathbed, 'Had I but served God as
diligently as I have served as the King, he would not have given me over in my
grey hairs'?

Your starter for ten:

2   What is the correct order of the six colours after all the reds have been
pocketed in snooker?

Bonus questions:
(a) What is particular about building blocks described as Cyclopean which are
in places as far apart as India, Greece and Peru?
(b) What is the correct name for a large object sometimes called a
Wellingtonia in this country out of respect for the great duke?
(c) What do the giants use as building materials to form a structure to scale
the Mount Olympus?

Your starter for ten:

3   Which future prime minister entered the House of Commons in 1922 as
representative of the Limehouse district of Stepney?

Bonus questions:
(a) What lies north of the Island of Rum in Scotland?
(b) What sea is called by the Arabs the Sea of Rûm?
(c) Rûm means or derives from Rome, but as a place meant somewhere
different to the early Muslims?

Your starter for ten:

4   Tell me all three types of deer that live in wild in Great Britain?

Bonus question:
(a) Dover and Sandwich were two of the five original Cinque Ports. What are
the other three?

Your starter for ten:

5 Which merchant of the 16th century founded a college which bears his name, did not in fact formulate the law which bears his name, but did found and build the Royal Exchange?

Bonus questions:

(a) What was the name of the Egyptian slave whom Abraham's childless wife Sarah gave to Abraham and whom, bearing him a son, then despised her mistress?

(b) What was the name of the son of Abraham and Hagar? It was foretold that his hand would be against every man, and every man's hand would be against him.

(c) Of what book is 'Call me Ishmael' the opening sentence?

Your starter for ten:

6 [This was a music starter, which neither team could answer]

Your starter for ten:

7 What is the everyday name for the type of container known, in its scientific form, as a Dewar vessel?

Bonus questions:

[The bonuses were music questions. Stephen Fry helped recognize Bizet's *Carmen*, the only answer Queens' got right in this round]

Your starter for ten:

8 Which Surrey town acquired a famous school one-mile to the north of it in 1872 when Charterhouse was transferred there from London?

Bonus questions:

(a) Who wrote the cautionary tale about Charles Augustus Fortescue who built The Cedars, Muswell Hill?

(b) An earlier Chatsworth House was begun in 1553 by Sir William Cavendish and was completed by his widow who went on to build another famous house which still stands. Who was she?

(c) Where did Job live, according to the opening verse of the book?

Your starter for ten:

9 Which inventor of a plot was born in 1648, the son of an Anabaptist preacher—?

[The question was successfully interrupted]

Bonus questions:

(a) What is the name of the old West African kingdom, at the height of its prosperity in the 14th to 17th centuries, which is famous for its quality of bronzes and woodwork?

(b) Benin still exists as a capital city in a province of a modern country. Which country?

(c) What was the European name for the part of the coast around the Bight of Benin?

Your starter for ten:

10 Which legendary Roman leader of the 5th century BC went over to the Volsci and betrayed his beloved—?
[The question was successfully interrupted]

Bonus questions:

(a) Which 5th-century Greek philosopher was the first of the Sophists, has a dialogue of Plato's named after him and beagn a work with the words, 'A man is the measure of all things'?

(b) Who in translation answered the question, 'What is property?' with the answer, 'Property is theft'?

(c) Who is reported in 1979 to have confronted the end of his life with the words, 'Oh Lord help me for I am innocent'?

Your starter for ten:

11 Which people were at risk from puerperal fever in the past and still are—?
[The question was successfully interrupted]

Bonus questions:

(a) What in Norse mythology is the name for the heaven where the Aesir, the chief gods, dwell?

(b) Whose wives were respectively Sif and Frigg?

Your starter for ten:

12 What is the name for the fast Italian dance in six-eight time?
Bonus questions:
In 1944 and 1945, there were three big conferences between Britain, the USA and the USSR. I'm going to give the dates and the people involved and I want you to tell me where they took place.

(a) November and December 1945 – Roosevelt, Stalin and Churchill.

(b) February 1945 – Roosevelt, Stalin and Churchill.

(c) July–August 1945 – Truman, Stalin and Churchill, followed later by Attlee.

Your starter for ten:

13 What is the precise electrical equivalent, as named after James Watt, of one horsepower as established by James Watt?
[Neither team answered correctly, so there was another starter]

Your starter for ten:

14 Who is the first major composer of Ragtime?

Bonus questions: In what manner did the following die?
(a) Adonis
(b) Achilles
(c) Agamemnon

Your starter for ten:

15 What substance before being applied is reduced from a thickness of one-eighth of an inch to one two-hundred-and-eighty-thousandth of an inch?

Bonus questions:
(a) Who created the first fictional detective, Auguste Dupin?
(b) Whose detective was Sergeant Cuff?
(c) What was the name of the story in which Sherlock Holmes made his first appearance?

Your starter for ten:

16 When one of Shaw's plays was made into a musical called *The Chocolate Soldier*, the change of title obscured what link between the play and Virgil's *Aeneid*?

Bonus questions:
(a) Which were the three original countries to sign the Holy Alliance in 1815?
(b) At the very lowest level of Inferno, Dante finds Lucifer with three heads gnawing at the three greatest betrayers. One is Judas Iscariot; the other two are which pair of friends?

Your starter for ten:

17 What is the name of the extinct shark-like reptiles of the Mesozoic era which, although descended from land creatures—?
[The question was successfully interrupted]

Bonus questions:
(a) Who was eaten up apart from her skull, her feet and the palms of her hands after being thrown from a window to the dogs?

(b) On which island were various pieces of prehistoric skeleton found, which have been categorized as *Pithecanthropus erectus*? The alternative name uses the name of the island.

(c) Who, in a gruesome cautionary tale, refused to eat his soup and gradually faded away until he died?

Your starter for ten:

18 [This starter was a picture question. Queens' correctly identified the base of the Statue of Liberty and, with the bonuses, failed to identify three bridges in New York but did correctly name Central Park as the location of a fourth]

Your starter for ten:

19 What custom, which later became widespread, is considered to have started with the item designed in 1843 by J.C. Horsley, which was printed in sepia on stiff cardboard and hand-coloured and was offered for sale in London with an addition 1,000 copies with an appropriate seasonal message beneath?

Bonus questions:

(a) In which city was the St Bartholomew's Day massacre?
(b) In which city was the St Valentine's Day massacre
(c) In or near which city was the Peterloo massacre?

Your starter for ten:

20 What is the name given to the short lines of shading drawn on a map to represent differences in the slope in the ground perpendicular to contour lines and unlike them giving no indicator of heights above sea level?
[Neither team answered correctly so another starter was asked]

Your starter for ten:

21 What is the name of the wife of the King of Lacedaemonia in Greek legend who finds herself in the embarrassing situation of laying eggs because of the unusual nature of the lover?

Bonus questions:
Some historical novels of the 19th century. What names are commonly given to the three main periods of English Gothic?

Your starter for ten:

22 What does the epithet *Khayyam* mean in the name Omar Khayyam?
[Neither team answered correctly so another starter was asked]

Your starter for ten:

23 Which city am I describing? In 1952 it was officially renamed Eva Perón in memory of the wife of President Perón. After his regime was overthrown, it resumed its original name. It is the capital of the province Buenos Aires and lies 33 miles southwest of the city of Buenos Aires and 3 miles from the river from which it takes its name.

Your starter for ten:

24 Who is the painter of religious paintings and landscapes who was born in Cookham in Berkshire?

Bonus questions:
(a) The feast of Candlemas on 2 February celebrates two related events connected with the temple – give me either.
(b) How many candles does the Menorah hold for Jews in ritual services for the festival of Hanukkah?
(c) How many branches did the great golden candelabra of the Tabernacle have, which appears frequently as a symbol for Judaism in art and which the Menorah of recent times loosely imitates?

Your starter for ten:

25 What is the title given by Bach to his 24 preludes and fugues of 1722 in all the major and minor keys and applied also to a further similar 24 of 1744 so that the title is given to the two sets together which were also known as the 48?

Your starter for ten:

26 What was the name of the Queen of Romania who was the author of several books in the 1920s and 1930s and whose father was the son of Queen Victoria and her mother the daughter of the Tsar Alexander II?
[Neither team answered correctly, so another starter question was asked]

Your starter for ten:

27 What right for authors was finally established after a long battle in a bill that was passed in the Commons in January 1979?

Bonus questions:
(a) Who played the lead in the 1972 film of *A Day in the Death of Joe Egg*?
(b) What happens in the *Punch* cartoon which gave the phase 'the curate's egg' to the language?
(c) The inhabitants of which fictional place disagreed profoundly on how to go to work on an egg?

Your starter for ten:

28 What is the name taken from that of a Roman general of the Socialist Society—?
[The question was successfully interrupted]

Bonus questions:
(a) One of the most poisonous flowering plants to grow in the northern temperate areas and one of the most ancient of poisons is a member of the parsley family. What is its name?
(b) What is the substance under the hairs of nettle leaves which cause irritation to the skin?
(c) Which wood carver's work has been traditionally held with the inclusion of a pea pod?

The gong sounds

Queens' won by an impressive 315 points to Hull's 120. They would reach the final, which then was a 'best of three' format. Queens' won the first and lost the second on a tie break. The final game went to the eventual champions, Merton College, Oxford.

The Answers

1   To reduce the taxes for the whole town
     (a) Cassius and Brutus
     (b) 'The rest is silence'
     (c) Cardinal Wolseley

2   Yellow, green, brown, blue, pink, black
     (a) They are an irregular shape – made to slot together
     (b) Sequoia
     (c) They were going to pile the mountain Pelion on Ossa

3   Clement Attlee
     (a) Skye
     (b) Mediterranean
     (c) Constantinople

4   Roe deer, fallow deer and red deer
     (a) Hythe
     (b) Hastings
     (c) Romney

5   (Sir Thomas) Gresham
     (a) Hagar
     (b) Ishmael
     (c) *Moby-Dick*

6   [Music starter]

7   Vacuum flask or thermos flask
     [Music bonuses]

8   Godalming
     (a) (Hilaire) Belloc
     (b) Bess of Hardwick
     (c) The land of Uz

9   Titus Oates
     (a) Benin
     (b) Nigeria
     (c) Slave Coast

10   Coriolanus
     (a) Protagoras
     (b) (Pierre-Joseph) Proudhon
     (c) (Zulfiqar Ali) Bhutto

11   Mothers in childbirth
(a) Asgard
(b) Thor and Odin

12   Tarantella
(a) Tehran
(b) Yalta
(c) Potsdam

13   746

14   Scott Joplin
(a) Gored by a boar
(b) Shot in the heel
(c) Murdered by his wife

15   Gold leaf
(a) Edgar Allan Poe
(b) Wilkie Collins (in *The Moonstone*)
(c) *A Study in Starlet*

16   The play was called *Arms and the Man*, which are the first words of Virgil's *Aeneid*
(a) Russia, Austria and Prussia
(b) Brutus and Cassius

17   Ichthyosaurs
(a) Jezebel
(b) Java (Java Man)
(c) Augustus

18   [Picture round]

19   Christmas cards
(a) Paris
(b) Chicago
(c) Manchester

20   Hachures

21   Leda
(a) Early English
(b) Perpendicular
(c) Decorative

22   A tent maker

23 La Plata

24 Stanley Spencer
(a) Purification of the Virgin Mary and the presentation of Christ in the temple
(b) Eight – for the eight days of the festival
(b) Seven

25 *The Well-Tempered Clavier*

26 Queen Marie of Romania

27 Public Lending Right
(a) Alan Bates
(b) A host says the curate has a bad egg and he retorts, 'Oh no, my Lord, I assure you! Parts of it are excellent!'
(c) Lilliput

28 Fabian Society
(a) Hemlock
(b) Formic acid
(b) Grinling Gibbons

Match

Your starter for ten:

1   I need a single-word name here. Thought to have been invented at the French court in the 17th century, which woodwind instrument has a double-reed mouthpiece and derives its name from the French for 'high wood'?

Three questions on rabbits and hares in Renaissance art:
(a) In the collection of the Louvre, *Madonna and Child with Rabbit* is a work of around 1530 by which Venetian artist?
(b) Related by marriage to the Bellini family, which artist includes rabbits in two versions of *The Agony in the Garden*? His other works include *Lamentation Over the Dead Christ*.
(c) Remarkable for its precise draughtsmanship, *Young Hare* is a watercolour of 1502 by which German artist?

Your starter for ten:

2   'It might be said that he had never been young.' Those words of the historian Macaulay refer to which British monarch? Born in 1650, he married a daughter of the Duke of York and was crowned at Westminster Abbey in April 1689.

Your bonuses are on the films of the US director Richard Donner, who died in 2021. Name each film from its summary on the IMDB website:
(a) This film of 1985: 'A group of young misfits … discover an ancient map and set out on an adventure to find a legendary pirate's long-lost treasure.'
(b) This 1987 film: 'Two newly paired cops who are complete opposites must put aside their differences in order to catch a gang of drug smugglers.'
(c) Finally, a film released in 1976: 'Mysterious deaths surround an American ambassador. Could the child that he is raising actually be the Antichrist?'

Your starter for ten:

3 Name either of the sports represented by initial letters in the abbreviation IBSF, this being an international governing body for two winter sports?

Three questions on dinosaurs:
(a) The dinosaur classifications *Saurischia* and *Ornithischia* are so called because of the resemblance of which skeletal joint to those of modern lizards and birds, respectively?
(b) Also known as the 'reptile bird', what bird of the South American swamplands is noted for the wing-claws of its young that resemble those of *Archaeopteryx* dinosaurs?
(c) Alive in the Cretaceous period and growing to a height of around eight feet, the dinosaur *Struthiomimus* was so named because of its superficial resemblance to what large bird?

Your starter for ten:

4 *The Marches*, *The Places in Between* and *Occupational Hazards* are among the works of which political figure? In 2010 he was elected MP for Penrith and the Border, and in 2019 he stood unsuccessfully for the leadership of the Conservative Party.

Your bonuses are on words that begin with the same four letters. In each case, give the word from the definition:
(a) A Sanskrit term meaning 'instrument of thought', denoting a word or sound repeated to aid concentration when meditating.
(b) A lace or silk scarf worn by Spanish women over the hair and shoulders.
(c) The part of a logarithm after the decimal point.

Your starter for ten:

5 The 1420 Battle of Vítkov Hill and the 1620 Battle of White Mountain took place near which present-day capital? The same city was looted by Swedish troops towards the end of the Thirty Years' War, and was occupied by Warsaw Pact forces in 1968.

Three questions on the deaths of saints:
(a) Killed in 258 during the persecution of the Emperor Valerian, which saint is traditionally believed to have met his death being grilled on a gridiron? Hagiographers claim that during the process he said, 'Turn me over, I'm cooked on that side.'
(b) According to tradition, the teacher Cassian, a former bishop of Brescia, was in 363 condemned to die by what process?

(c) Clubbed to death in Rome in 288 after recovering from being shot by archers, Saint Sebastian was a victim of the persecutions carried out under which emperor?

Your starter for ten:

6   Followers of which religion celebrate festivals known as *Gurpurabs* to commemorate events such as birthdays and martyrdoms in the lives of ten gurus, believed to have embodied a single eternal spirit? This spirit is now believed to reside in the religion's sacred book.

Three questions on an international agreement:
(a) To what international agreement was the French marshal Ferdinand Foch referring when he said: 'This is not peace. It is an armistice for twenty years'?
(b) Which former British prime minister said the Versailles treaty was 'not common sense, not the clean peace by which I always meant ... to end war with the war'?
(c) Which British economist and conference delegate resigned in protest at the treaty's terms, and later wrote: 'If we aim at the impoverishment of Central Europe, vengeance, I dare predict, will not limp'?

Your starter for ten:

7   A 1654 oil painting by Carel Fabritius plays a central role in, and gives its name to, which Pulitzer Prize-winning novel of 2013? It is a *Bildungsroman* whose characters include Pippa, Boris and Theo.

Your bonuses are on two-word French terms. Identify each term from the definition. All three answers end with the same three letters:
(a) First, an artistic or figurative depiction of the equalising power of death, such as that portrayed in a symphonic poem of 1874 by Camille Saint-Saëns.
(b) A description of late-19th-century works of poetry, such as those by Gustave Kahn, that are not restricted by traditional rules of prosody; the English translation of the term is sometimes also used.
(c) And finally, a lawsuit that attracts a large amount of public interest or notoriety.

Your starter for ten:

8   Similar to netball and basketball, which sport involves teams of eight, often mixed, and takes its name from the Dutch for 'basket'?

Your bonuses are on the pantheon of gods featured in the *Elder Scrolls* series of videogames:
(a) In the lore of the Elder Scrolls, the first emperor of Tamriel, Tiber Septim, ascended to godhood under what five-letter name? In Greek mythology, it is also the name of a bronze giant made by Hephaestus.
(b) Which of the seventeen Daedric princes that feature in the games shares his name with one of the four temperaments in humoral theory, alongside choleric, melancholic and phlegmatic?
(c) What five-letter name follows Mehrunes in the name of the Daedric Prince of Destruction? It is also the name of a Philistine god whose temple is destroyed by Samson in the Book of Judges.

Your starter for ten:
9 Which prominent political figure was fired from *The Times* after fabricating a quote from his godfather, the historian Colin Lucas? He subsequently became the Brussels correspondent of the *Daily Telegraph* and the editor of *The Spectator*.

Three questions on Schrödinger's cat in fiction:
(a) Described as a 'riff off Schrödinger's cat', *The Cat Who Walks Through Walls* is a 1985 novel by which leading US author of speculative fiction?
(b) 'Schrödinger's cat' is a short story by which author, who died in 2018? Her works include *The Dispossessed* and *The Left Hand of Darkness*.
(c) 'Wouldn't it be easier just to stomp on the … kitten?' This suggestion occurs in a discussion of Schrödinger's cat in which Booker Prize-winning novel by D.B.C. Pierre?

Your starter for ten:
10 Answer promptly, giving one year during the life of the Japanese haiku master Matsuo Bashō. He was born during the reign of the third Tokugawa shogun, and died in the year that saw the establishment of the Bank of England.

Your bonuses are on poems that include the theme of the New Year. In each case, name the poet:
(a) Born in Missouri in 1888, who wrote: 'For last year's words belong to last year's language / And next year's words await another voice'?
(b) Which poet, born in Boston in 1932, wrote: 'This is newness: every little tawdry / Obstacle glass-wrapped and peculiar, / Glinting and clinking in a saint's falsetto'?
(c) Finally, born in Lincolnshire in 1809, which poet wrote: 'Ring out the old, ring in the new, / Ring, happy bells, across the snow'?

Your starter for ten:

11 What precise five words appear on the banner that forms part of Gillian Wearing's statue of the suffragist Millicent Fawcett? Erected in Parliament Square in 2018, the statue was commissioned as part of the centenary of the 1918 Representation of the People Act.

Three questions on the US astronomer Carolyn Porco:
(a) Before she joined the imaging team on NASA's Voyager missions in 1983, Porco found evidence that magnetic fields were linked to the motion of the 'spokes' that Voyager had recently revealed, in what specific planetary feature?
(b) Porco was the principal investigator on the imaging team of which mission to Saturn and its moons, ending when the spacecraft plunged into Saturn's atmosphere in 2017?
(c) Using *Cassini*'s camera, Porco and her team discovered plumes erupting from the south pole of which of Saturn's icy moons?

Your starter for ten:

12 At atmospheric pressure near absolute zero temperature, what is the only element that does not freeze solid?

Three questions on fictional countries:
(a) In Meg Cabot's *Princess Diaries* series, the 15-year-old Mia Thermopolis discovers she is the sole heir to what kingdom?
(b) In which novel by Evelyn Waugh is the nature diarist for the *Daily Beast* mistakenly sent to report on a war in the East African state of Ishmaelia?
(c) In which novel of 1959 by Keith Waterhouse does the young Yorkshire-born protagonist invent other lives for himself, including one as the head of state of Ambrosia?

Your starter for ten:

13 In ornithology, what term is the opposite of sedentary? In Britain, for example, the annual habits of the sedentary partridge contrast with those of the flycatcher or house martin.

Your bonuses are on pairs of book titles. The last three letters of the first title are the first three letters of the second, as in *Zuleika Dobson* and *Sons and Lovers*. Give both titles in each case:
(a) The 1991 novel by Bret Easton Ellis, whose protagonist is Patrick Bateman; and the 1999 novel by Joanne Harris whose protagonist opens a sweetshop in a French village.

(b) A novel by Dickens published in book form in 1857, about the injustices of the English legal system; and the first novel in William Golding's *To the Ends of the Earth* trilogy.

(c) The 1959 novel by Günter Grass concerning Oskar Matzerath, who decides never to grow up; and a Tale first published by the Brothers Grimm in 1812 involving an imp who spins straw into gold.

Your starter for ten:

14 Answer as soon as your name is called, giving a fraction in its lowest terms. Using a randomly shuffled regular pack of playing cards, minus the joker, what is the probability that the top two cards are of the same suit?

Three questions on British seabirds:

(a) Belonging to the petrel family, which heavily built, short-tailed seabird has a name derived from the Old Norse for 'foul' and 'gull'?

(b) Usually breeding on sea cliffs, which bird has established an inland breeding site on part of the Baltic Centre in Gateshead? Its name is imitative of its call.

(c) Which black-and-white member of the auk family is characterized by the sharp edges of its upper beak, improving its ability to grasp fish and defend itself against predators?

Your starter for ten:

15 Derived from the Greek for 'a collection of flowers', what term denotes works such as *The Good Immigrant*, edited by Nikesh Shukla; *Being Alive*, edited by Neil Astley; and *The Zoo of the New*, edited by Don Paterson and Nick Laird?

Three questions on marine biology:

(a) The colossal and giant species of which sea animal have eyes up to 27 centimetres in diameter, the largest of any known living animal?

(b) The deep-sea dragon fish *Malacosteus niger* has a derivative of what pigment, normally found only in plants or bacteria, in the retina of its eye, enabling it to see both blue and red light?

(c) Having a thick internal calcified shell, which cephalopod has the most acute polarization vision of any animal, enabling it to see aspects of light invisible to humans?

Your starter for ten:

16 In the 9th and 10th centuries, Pliska and Preslav were capitals of which empire? Its rulers included Boris I and his son, Simeon the Great, the latter a major adversary of the Byzantines.

Three questions on faked correspondence:

(a) In 1972, the US novelist and journalist Clifford Irving was convicted of forging letters in order to be commissioned to produce an autobiography, also fake, ostensibly of whom?

(b) Which 8th-century forgery claimed to be a historical document transferring control of the Western Roman Empire to the papacy under Sylvester I?

(c) Describing the fabrication of a series of emails, the song 'Sincerely, Me' comes from which musical, the winner of a Tony Award in 2017?

Your starter for ten:

17 The 1898 publication *Tomorrow: A Peaceful Path to Real Reform* by Ebenezer Howard inspired which development in housing policy? These ideas led to the founding of the community of Letchworth, followed in 1920 by Welwyn.

Three questions on authors and banknotes:

(a) Born in 1862, the novelist and women's rights activist Fatima Aliye became the first woman to appear on which country's banknotes? She features on the 50 lira note introduced in 2009.

(b) The author Ichiyō Higuchi appears on a Japanese 5,000-yen note. She died aged 24 in 1896, during the reign of which emperor?

(c) The Bank of England £10 note introduced in 2017 features Jane Austen and an image of which cathedral, her final resting place?

Your starter for ten:

18 Developed during the Middle Ages and mentioned, for example, in Milton's poem *L'Allegro*, the rebeck is generally held to be the forerunner of which modern musical instrument?

Three questions on the Nobel Prize in Literature:

(a) On awarding the 2013 prize to which Canadian author did the Swedish Academy say, 'She has taken an art form, the short story ... and cultivated it almost to perfection'?

(b) *The Good Earth* and *A House Divided* are novels by which US author, who won the 1938 prize 'for her rich and truly epic descriptions of peasant life in China'?

(c) Both banned in South Africa, *Burger's Daughter* and *July's People* are works by which Nobel laureate?

Your starter for ten:

19 Formed by a confluence near Kulmbach in Bavaria, which river flows

westwards through Würzburg, joining the Rhine at the capital of Rhineland-Palatinate? Its name appears in that of Germany's largest financial centre.

Three questions on diseases with names that usually appear in a plural form:
(a) Which infectious disease caused by a paramyxovirus is characterized by swelling of the parotid glands, sometimes in conjunction with pancreatitis or orchitis?
(b) Also known as framboesia, what infectious tropical disease manifests itself as a series of crusted tumours or ulcers on the surface of the skin?
(c) Caused by the decalcification of bone, what condition is associated with a deficiency of vitamin D?

Your starter for ten:
20 Taroko Gorge, Sun Moon Lake and the National Palace Museum are noted attractions on what island, a little larger than Belgium and situated to the north of Luzon?

Three questions on the moon in 20th-century art:
(a) Featuring three bowler-hatted men and three crescent moons, *The Mysteries of the Horizon* is a work by which Surrealist?
(b) The title object appears suspended on a turquoise sky in *Ladder to the Moon*, a work of 1958 by which US artist?
(c) Featuring an astronaut and a US flag in translucent colours, *Moonwalk* is a series by which artist, who died in 1987?

Your starter for ten:
21 In 1719, who wrote: 'One may find a great deal of pleasure in building a palace for another; when one should find very little in living in it ones self'? At about this time he began work on Eastbury in Dorset and Seaton Delaval in Northumberland, his earlier works having included Castle Howard and Blenheim Palace.

Three questions on the universe:
(a) By number of atoms, which element makes up about 8 per cent of the solar system, and about 8 per cent of the baryonic matter in the universe?
(b) After hydrogen and helium, what is the third most abundant element in the solar system and the universe, whether reckoned by mass or number of atoms?
(c) What is the fourth most abundant element in the universe? It is also the most abundant element to form a solid, rather than a gas, at standard temperature and pressure.

Your starter for ten:

22 What initial letter links all of these place names: the county towns of Tyrone and Rutland; a town to the north of Dartmoor; the metropolitan borough southeast of Rochdale; and the river that flows through Selby and York?

Three questions on trees:

(a) Which evergreen tree has a species known as the 'Italian' or 'funeral', often having an extremely narrow and tapering crown, and so called because it is frequently found in cemeteries in the Mediterranean?

(b) Taken from a character described in Fitzgerald's *Rubaiyat of Omar Khayyam* as a 'cypress-slender minister of wine', what four-letter pen-name was used by the author of short stories including 'The Open Window' and 'Sredni Vashtar'?

(c) The title of Agatha Christie's novel *Sad Cypress* is taken from the lines: 'Come away, come away, death; / And in sad cypress let me be laid', sung in which of Shakespeare's plays?

Your starter for ten:

23 'I find ecstasy in living. The mere sense of living is joy enough.' Which 19th-century poet wrote those words in response to a friend's concern about the 'narrowness' of her life in the Massachusetts town of Amherst?

Your bonuses are on pieces of popular music written wholly or partly in the unusual time signature seven-four, or septuple time:

(a) Released by Peter Gabriel in 1977 as his solo debut, which single takes its name from the location of an Iron Age fort in Somerset?

(b) 'Unsquare Dance' was written in 1961 by which jazz musician? The track ends with unscheduled laughter from the group's drummer Joe Morello.

(c) Taken from the Pink Floyd album *The Dark Side of the Moon*, which song begins with a seven-beat bass guitar rhythm and the sound of cash register bells?

Your starter for ten:

24 Having a name that fits its standing, what has the highest mass among all the elementary particles in the standard model of particle physics?

Three questions on representations of the Trojan War and its aftermath:

(a) 'Was this the face that launch'd a thousand ships, / And burnt the topless towers of Ilium?' These words appear in which play by Christopher Marlowe?

(b) In an oil painting of about 1610, which artist of the Spanish Renaissance depicted the Trojan priest Laocoön?

(c) Based on the story of Dido and Aeneas, *Les Troyens* is an epic opera of the 1850s by which French composer?

Your starter for ten:

25 Born in 1845, which German mathematician gives his name to the following theorem? 'For any set "a", the cardinal number of "a" is less than the cardinal number of the power set of "a".'

Three questions on English history:
(a) Which residential district near Staines in Berkshire gave its name to the 1973 political agreement that aimed to establish a power-sharing executive in Northern Ireland?
(b) Named after a Berkshire village near Newbury, what financial relief system was introduced in 1795 as a means of supplementing the wages of agricultural labourers?
(c) Which prominent town in Berkshire gives its name to the treaty of 1386 that established a longstanding alliance between England and Portugal?

The Answers

1   Oboe (fr: *haut*, high; *bois*, wood; bassoon also double-reed)
   (a) Titian
   (b) (Andrea) Mantegna
   (c) (Albrecht) Dürer

2   William III (accept William of Orange)
   (a) *The Goonies*
   (b) *Lethal Weapon*
   (c) *The Omen*

3   Bobsleigh / skeleton (International Bobsleigh and Skeleton Foundation)
   (a) Hip (Greek: *iskhion*, 'hip joint')
   (b) Hoatzin (*Opisthocomus hoazin*; aka the skunk bird, stinkbird or Canje pheasant)
   (c) Ostrich (roughly from the Greek meaning 'ostrich mimic')

4   Rory Stewart
   (a) Mantra
   (b) Mantilla
   (c) Mantissa

5   Prague
   (a) St Lawrence
   (b) Hacked to death by his own students (supposedly using their own styli)
   (c) Diocletian

6   Sikhism
   (a) (Treaty of) Versailles
   (b) (Herbert Henry) Asquith
   (c) (John Maynard) Keynes

7   *The Goldfinch* (by Donna Tartt)
   (a) Danse macabre
   (b) Vers libre
   (c) Cause célèbre

8   Korfball
   (a) Talos
   (b) Sanguine
   (c) Dagon

9   (Alexander) Boris (de Pfeffel) Johnson
   (a) (Robert A.) Heinlein
   (b) (Ursula K.) Le Guin
   (c) *Vernon God Little*

10   1644 to 1694
    (a) T.S. Eliot ('Little Gidding')
    (b) Sylvia Plath ('New Year on Dartmoor')
    (c) Alfred, Lord Tennyson (*In Memoriam*)

11   'Courage Calls to Courage Everywhere'
    (a) Rings of Saturn
    (b) *Cassini–Huygens* (accept *Cassini*, as it is commonly known, correcting it)
    (c) Enceladus

12   Helium
    (a) Genovia
    (b) *Scoop*
    (c) *Billy Liar*

13   Migratory
    (a) *American Psycho* and *Chocolat*
    (b) *Little Dorrit* and *Rites of Passage*
    (c) *The Tin Drum* and 'Rumpelstiltskin'

14   Four-seventeenths (not 12/51 as we've asked for the lowest term)
    (a) Fulmar (Old Norse: *full*, 'foul'; *már*, 'gull')
    (b) Kittiwake
    (c) Razorbill (*Alca torda*)

15   Anthology
    (a) Squid
    (b) Chlorophyll
    (c) Cuttlefish

16   Bulgarian (i.e. the First Bulgarian Empire)
    (a) Howard Hughes
    (b) Donation of Constantine / Donatio Constantini
    (c) *Dear Evan Hansen*

17   Garden city (movement)
    (a) Turkey
    (b) Emperor Meiji / Mutsuhito
    (c) Winchester (Cathedral)

18   Violin
    (a) Alice Munro
    (b) Pearl (S.) Buck
    (c) (Nadine) Gordimer

19 Main
    (a) Mumps
    (b) Yaws
    (c) Rickets

20 Taiwan
    (a) (René) Magritte
    (b) (Georgia) O'Keeffe
    (c) (Andy) Warhol

21 (Sir John) Vanbrugh
    (a) Helium
    (b) Oxygen
    (c) Carbon

22 O (Omagh, Oakham, Okehampton, Oldham, Ouse)
    (a) Cypress
    (b) Saki (Hector Hugh Munro, 1870–1916)
    (c) *Twelfth Night*

23 Emily Dickinson
    (a) 'Solsbury Hill'
    (b) Dave Brubeck
    (c) 'Money'

24 Top quark (even heavier than the Higgs boson, by almost 50 GeV/c^2)
    (a) (*The Tragical History of*) *Doctor Faustus*
    (b) El Greco
    (c) (Hector) Berlioz

25 (Georg) Cantor
    (a) Sunningdale
    (b) Speenhamland (system)
    (c) Windsor

Famous Contestants

Part 2

Of course, to viewers of a certain age the most memorable parody of *University Challenge* was broadcast in May 1984. The first episode of Series Two of the cult classic comedy series *The Young Ones* was called 'Bambi', a play on the name of Bamber Gascoigne. 'Bambi' was played by Griff Rhys Jones. Scumbag College – Rik Mayall, Adrian Edmondson, Nigel Planer and Christopher Ryan as Rick, Vyvyan, Neil and Mike, respectively, were up against Footlights College. In terrific casting, the Footlights team was made up of Hugh Laurie, Ben Elton (*The Young Ones*' co-writer), Emma Thompson and Stephen Fry as Lord Snot. Fry, of course, had competed himself while at university and also went on to appear in later special editions.

After leaving Manchester University, **Adrian Edmondson** made a name for himself alongside comedy partner, Rik Mayall, whom he met at Manchester, on the alternative comedy scene of the early 1980s and later as a prolific actor. 'When I used to write with Rik Mayall, we had a little routine with which to end any prolonged silence during the creative process. We would say, "Buzz – Edmondson, Bradford" or "Buzz – Mayall, Droitwich" and then go on to reveal whatever it was we'd thought of. *University Challenge* is ingrained in our psyches.'

Adrian appeared on an alumni special edition of *University Challenge* in December 2020 representing the University of Manchester with actor Justin Edwards, author Juliet Jacques and war surgeon David Nott. They reached the final but were beaten by the Courtauld Institute of Art, London.

Adrian says he never applied to go on *University Challenge* when he was a student at the University of Manchester, just down the road from where the programme was filmed, because he thought he was 'too stupid'. He did agree, however, to appear for his old university on the alumni special: 'I thought I'd learned a lot since leaving university. Like everyone else I play along when the show is on the telly and some weeks I can't answer any of the questions, but on my best week I scored 17 correct answers. And I had spotted that the alumni specials were slightly less challenging – especially in terms of maths and the sciences.'

This particular alumni Christmas special was filmed during the COVID pandemic. 'Despite the COVID restrictions it was a fun, convivial experience. Jeremy was his usual curmudgeonly, rather unpleasant self – I would have hated it if he were any different. I think the whole team was nervous, mostly at the thought of everlasting humiliation. The absolute thrill of buzzing in – "Buzz – Edmondson, Manchester" – and then getting the answer right will be hard to top. The team came out of the first game as high as if we'd just come from an opium den.

'I was very proud of spotting a Monet snow scene. And also of spotting a piece by Beethoven – classical music is not my forte but my dad had eight records when I was a kid, and that was one of them. I went on to lose all the bonus classical music questions, though. Swings and roundabouts – and part of the game is to stop the other team from scoring.

'In the final I thought we were going to do it. About three-quarters of the way through we were well ahead, but a lucky couple of art-specific questions – the Courtauld Institute were our opponents – allowed the score to slip away.'

Which appearance did Adrian find the most fun, *The Young Ones*' spoof version or appearing for real? 'I think I preferred appearing on it for real. The excitement was genuine. Just pressing the buzzer and getting Roger Tilling to say my name made the day very special. And we made a good fist of it. If we'd lost very badly, I would probably think the other way round.

'It's strange, but I think *University Challenge* is still popular because the questions are so hard. As you watch on your sofa, there's such a sense of achievement in getting one right. The students, especially the younger ones (in my view it should be undergraduates only – these days you can see a team with four old men), are fascinating, because they are generally so guileless. You get the ones who know a lot in the middle seats, and the specialists on the outsides – sometimes you can wait nearly a whole programme before someone gets one, and it'll be something really obscure.

'Watching brainy people think hard – the nerds, the weirdos, the confident, the timid, the ones who try to be cool, the ones who know they will never be cool – is entertainment!'

*

Journalist, author and television presenter **David Aaronovitch** has written for *The Independent*, *The Guardian* and *The Times*, among others, and won the Orwell Prize for Political Journalism in 2001. As a student, he was part of the University of Manchester team that in 1975 made headlines for their disruptive 'protest' appearance on the programme (see page 70). He has also appeared in the Paxman era.

David believes the secret to *University Challenge*'s ongoing success is that 'everyone loves to see a whizz kid who knows everything. But I also think if you get three or four questions right that's part of the appeal. I think it lost that silly "gonk and scarf" stuff which was really dated; it was a kind of picture of student life in the 1950s which they maintained well into the 1970s, and I think that was what threatened to kill it off in the first instance, and changing and updating it and stripping it back to the essence of what it was and not what it had become maybe worked as well.'

David returned to the *University Challenge* floor for a Christmas special in 2018 as part of a Manchester alumni team facing a University of Sheffield team featuring former Home Secretary David Blunkett. They won but not by enough to progress in the competition. 'There was a kind of low level of competitiveness. It was half a new thing and half a trip down memory lane. I knew Jeremy Paxman; I'd been asked questions by him before when I'd appeared as a pundit on *Newsnight*, so to me it wasn't terrifying – he's someone I've known for a long time.

'As you get older, you might know the answer, but you're slow to get there, you're not as quick on the buzzer. It's like watching 40-year-old men who still insist on playing football and imagine themselves in some way to be as athletic as their younger selves, but the fact is, they're just slower. We just lumbered to the buzzer. It's a strange thing to do in your sixties. I really do think quickfire quizzes are a young person's game.'

Try Your Luck
Match

Your starter for ten:

1   In April 2018, which singer was commissioned to contribute material for a project celebrating the Brontë sisters? 2018 also saw the 40th anniversary of her number one single based on one of their works.

Three questions on books published in 1973:
(a) *Rubyfruit Jungle* was the first novel of which US author?
(b) Which US writer published the 1973 poetry collection *Diving into the Wreck*?
(c) Published in 1973, *The Rachel Papers* was the first novel of which British author?

Your starter for ten:

2   What two-word expression did *The Times* coin in 1896 to describe the foreign policy of the incumbent coalition government? Joseph Chamberlain popularized the phrase in a speech proclaiming that 'the Empire stands secure in the strength of her own resources.'

Three questions on commemorative poems:
(a) Written in July 2019, Simon Armitage's poem 'Conquistadors' commemorates the 50th anniversary of what event?
(b) Carol Ann Duffy wrote 'The Wound in Time' for a commemoration of the centenary of what event?
(c) Andrew Motion's poem 'Spring Wedding' was written to mark the wedding of which two people in April 2005?

Your starter for ten:

3   In musical performances, what French word describes the position of the mouth and lips when playing a wind instrument?

Three questions on fortresses:

(a) A centre of cheese-making, which town near Cardiff is home to Britain's largest castle after Windsor?

(b) Meaning 'fortress' or 'stronghold', Caer is the Welsh name of which English city, a former Roman legionary base?

(c) The legionary fortress of Caerleon is situated on the River Usk a few miles from which Welsh city?

Your starter for ten:

4   'Binsey Poplars' and *The Wreck of the Deutschland* are among the notable works of which poet? Received into the Catholic Church by John Henry Newman, he is noted for his development of 'sprung rhythm'.

Three questions on sculpture:

(a) 'I think my sculptures are about what a human being or an animal feels like, not what they necessarily look like.' These are words of which 20th-century sculptor, whose works include *Horse and Rider* and the *Goggle Head* series?

(b) What single word completes the phrase coined by the critic Herbert Read to describe the work of sculptors including Bernard Meadows, whose use of spindly and angular forms influenced Frink's early work: 'the geometry of ...' what?

(c) Frink's *Warhorse* and *Walking Madonna* may be seen in the gardens of which stately home in Derbyshire?

Your starter for ten:

5   Give one of the common names of *Dracaena trifasciata*, a houseplant with decorative sword-shaped leaves and small, fragrant flowers. One common name includes that of a reptile, another that of a person related by marriage.

Three questions on film adaptations of 19th-century works:

(a) *The Castle of Thornfield* and *The Orphan of Lowood* are among several silent film versions of which 19th-century novel?

(b) Starring Emma Stone, the 2010 high-school comedy *Easy A* is an adaptation of which novel by Nathaniel Hawthorne?

(c) Starring Deborah Kerr as a governess, the 1961 black-and-white film *The Innocents* is based on which novella by Henry James?

Your starter for ten:

6   In the mid-19th century, which group of artists was named after a village near the forest of Fontainebleau to the southeast of Paris? Painters associated with this school include Millet and Corot.

Three questions on Aneurin Bevan:

(a) In the early 1940s, Bevan was editor of which publication? Its current website describes it as 'Britain's oldest democratic socialist publication'.

(b) In 1934, Bevan married which Scottish politician? As minister for the arts in Harold Wilson's cabinet, she was prominent in the founding of the Open University.

(c) Bevan was MP for Ebbw Vale from 1929 until his death in 1960. Which future Labour leader succeeded him as MP for this seat? He retired from Parliament in 1992.

Your starter for ten:

7 What given name links: the creator of the *Isenheim Altarpiece*; a 15th-century king of Hungary with the byname Corvinus; and, in the Book of Acts, the person selected to replace Judas Iscariot among the Apostles?

Three questions on a style of architecture:

(a) Stourhead House in Wiltshire is an example of what architectural style? Characterized by symmetry and strict proportion, it is named after a 16th-century Venetian.

(b) One of the three principal orders of ancient Greek and Roman architecture, which style of column is a characteristic of Palladian design? It is typically decorated with stylized motifs based on the leaves of the acanthus plant.

(c) Which architect is credited with introducing the Palladian style to England? His works include the Queen's House in Greenwich and the Banqueting Hall at Whitehall.

Your starter for ten:

8 Built by the French in 1754, Fort Duquesne is a historical site in which US city? Situated about 100 miles south of Lake Erie, its sports teams include the Penguins, the Pirates and the Steelers.

Your bonuses are on consorts of British monarchs. In each case, name the person from their predecessor and successor as consort. A single given name is sufficient in each case:

(a) Which consort came after Isabella of France and before Anne of Bohemia?

(b) Who came after Katherine of Valois and before Elizabeth Woodville?

(c) Who came after Adelaide of Saxe-Meiningen and before Alexandra of Denmark?

Your starter for ten:

9 Used in both track athletics and equestrian sport, what term has its origins

in impromptu races held from the late 18th century over natural country, in which churches served as course landmarks?

Your questions are on place names that contain within them the surname of a starship captain from the *Star Trek* franchise. In each case, give the place name from the description:
(a) A town in Fife across the Firth of Forth from Edinburgh; it was the birthplace of the economist Adam Smith?
(b) A Mediterranean island roughly halfway between Barcelona and Algiers?
(c) The historical region of France which in 2016 merged with the Nord-Pas-de-Calais to form the Hauts-de-France region?

Your starter for ten:

10 Born in Birmingham, William Wyon served at what government body from 1816 until his death in 1851? His designs include 'Una and the Lion' and the much-reproduced 'Young Head', both depicting Queen Victoria.

Three questions on films of 1970:
(a) Glenda Jackson won the Best Actress Academy Award for her role as Gudrun Brangwen in Ken Russell's adaptation of which novel by D.H. Lawrence?
(b) Elio Petri's *Investigation of a Citizen Above Suspicion* won the Academy Award for Best Foreign Language Film. In what language was it originally released?
(c) Which historical film of 1970 won the Academy Award for Best Picture? George C. Scott refused the Best Actor award for his performance in the title role.

Your starter for ten:

11 An early European depiction of a kangaroo, along with celebrated racehorses such as Whistlejacket and Hambletonian, are among paintings by which artist, born in Liverpool in 1724?

Your bonuses are on people who, since 2004, have appeared in *Forbes* magazine's annual list of the world's most powerful women. In each case, give the name from the description:
(a) A politician who served as US Secretary of State from 2005 to 2009.
(b) An Italian-born politician who assumed leadership of the Indian National Congress Party in 1998. I need forename and surname.
(c) Finally, a French lawyer and politician who was appointed managing director of the International Monetary Fund in 2011?

Your starter for ten:

12 Answer promptly. Expressed as a power of ten, what is the square root of a googol?

Your bonuses are on physics and astronomy. In each case, I want you to give me the term defined. All three begin with the same letter, and end with the letters '-tion'.
(a) A nine-letter term for the gathering of matter by an astronomical body; it often precedes the word 'disk' to describe structures through which gas and dust fall onto stars and black holes.
(b) A term for the wearing away of material from the surface of an object travelling at high speed through a planetary atmosphere, through vaporization, melting and other processes; it differs by only one vowel from a word meaning 'washing'.
(c) Finally, transport by bulk motion, usually used of transport perpendicular to the direction of gravity.

Your starter for ten:

13 Yong Ler was the third emperor of which Chinese dynasty? He moved the capital from Nanjing to Beijing, and ordered naval expeditions to expand Chinese influence in Southeast Asia, India and East Africa.

Three questions on scientists:
(a) The experiments conducted by Alfred Hershey and Martha Chase in 1952 showed that DNA is the genetic material, rather than what other biological macro-molecule?
(b) The Chinese-American scientist Chien-Shiung Wu provided the first experimental proof that what property of fundamental particles is not conserved in weak subatomic interactions?
(c) Along with Fritz Strassmann and Otto Hahn, the Austrian scientist Lise Meitner made key contributions to the discovery of what phenomenon in uranium?

Your starter for ten:

14 I need the name of an artist here. *Judith and Holofernes*, *The Fates* and *The God Saturn* are among the title figures of a series of works produced from about 1819 by which artist, born near Zaragoza?

Three questions on the former names of chemical elements:
(a) 'Columbium' was the original name given by the British chemist Charles Hatchett to which shiny, white metal with the atomic number 41? Having similar properties to tantalum, it is now named after the daughter of Tantalus.

(b) With the atomic number 85, the name 'alabamine' was originally proposed in the 1930s for what naturally occurring rare halogen?

(c) Known since antiquity and derived from the ore stibnite, which grey metalloid with the atomic number 51 was formerly known as 'stibium'?

Your starter for ten:

15 In the English names of geographical features, what short word follows Denmark, Palk, Cook, Menai and Bering? All are narrow passages of water that connect two seas or other larger bodies of water.

Three questions on gulfs:

(a) In the mid-1960s, which Asian gulf gave its name to a resolution adopted by the US Congress to support increased American involvement in the Vietnam War?

(b) The Strait of Hormuz separates the Persian Gulf from which other gulf, named after a present-day country?

(c) The Saronic Gulf, also called the Gulf of Aegina, is situated to the east of which narrow isthmus?

Your starter for ten:

16 Which Japanese city is a setting in Kazuo Ishiguro's *A Pale View of Hills*, Kamila Shamsie's *Burnt Shadows* and David Mitchell's *The Thousand Autumns of Jacob de Zoet*? For more than 200 years it was the only Japanese port where Europeans were permitted to trade.

Three questions on a play by Shakespeare:

(a) 'If this were played upon a stage, now, I could condemn it as an improbable fiction.' This line appears in which play by Shakespeare, first known to have been performed at Candlemas, 2 February 1602?

(b) Which ancient region of the northwestern part of the Balkan Peninsula shares its name with the setting of *Twelfth Night*?

(c) In the Royal National Theatre's 2017 production of the play, Malvolio became Malvolia and was played by which actress, also known for her TV comedy roles?

Your starter for ten:

17 Born in 1861, which French engineer gives his name to a tendency or 'effect' in psychology in which individuals in a group become less productive as group size increases? It was originally noted by observing participants in a rope-pulling exercise.

Your bonuses are on physics. In each case, name the person after whom the given phenomenon is named. All three answers begin with the same letter:
(a) Electromagnetic radiation is emitted when charged particles moving in a dielectric medium exceed the local speed of light.
(b) Linked to quantum field theory, which effect causes a force between two uncharged conducting plates in a vacuum?
(c) Often noted in weather patterns, which inertial force causes a sideways deflection of objects moving in a rotating reference frame?

Your starter for ten:

18 Beginning with the same four letters, what two words mean: a mixture of corundum and iron oxides used as an abrasive, and a green variety of beryl, prized as a gemstone?

Three questions on species of crab:
(a) The Norwegian Red King Crab is found to the north of Russia in which area of the Arctic Ocean, also known as the Murmean Sea?
(b) What demonym or nationality precedes 'spider crab' in the name of the world's largest crustacean by size?
(c) What common name is given to crabs such as *Dardanus calidus* that continually outgrow their shells and line up in size order to occupy vacated carapaces?

Your starter for ten:

19 At 479 metres, Ward Hill, about five miles southwest of Stromness, is the highest point of which island group? Its summit gives views of the Pentland Firth and Scapa Flow.

Three questions on astronomical symbols:
(a) A depiction of what is thought to be an ancient scythe or sickle is the symbol of which planet, named after the Roman god of seed-sowing?
(b) The symbol for Pluto is made up of the 'P' and 'L' in the former planet's name. These are also the initials of which astronomer, who predicted its discovery? I need only the surname.
(c) The symbol for Uranus combines the symbol of the sun – a shield with a circle inside – with the spear from the symbol of what other planet?

Your starter for ten:

20 In the context of diagnostic and screening tests, for what do the letters PPV stand?

Three questions on Charlotte Brontë's *Jane Eyre*:

(a) In the first chapter of *Jane Eyre*, the narrator refers to the *History of British Birds* by which engraver and naturalist? A species of swan is named after him.

(b) Jane describes a novel by Samuel Johnson as having 'a name that struck me as strange, and consequently attractive'. Which prince is the title figure of the novel?

(c) To what novel is Jane referring with the words: 'the cornfields forest-high, the mighty mastiffs, the monster cats, the tower-like men and women'?

Your starter for ten:

21 Writing in Diderot's *Encyclopaedia*, the philosopher D'Alembert listed painting and sculpture as the first two of the five 'fine arts'. Name two of the other three.

Three questions on Gertrude Stein:

(a) Stein is credited with coining what two-word term, often associated with the post-First World War generation? Hemingway popularized it through his novel *The Sun Also Rises*.

(b) Stein's 1914 poetry collection *Tender Buttons* was especially influenced by which artistic movement, whose exponents include Georges Braque?

(c) 'Overshadowing her in death, just as much as in life'; those words of one observer refer to Stein's tombstone in Père Lachaise, which also bears what other name, albeit on the back of the stone, and in much smaller letters?

Your starter for ten:

22 Sometimes known as the Shining Prince, who is the title figure of the 11th-century Japanese work that has been described as the world's first novel? The author was Murasaki Shikibu.

Three questions on physics:

(a) How many quantum numbers determine the quantum state of an electron in an atom?

(b) Referring to an angular measurement, what alternative name is sometimes used for the orbital angular momentum quantum number?

(c) What letter of the Roman alphabet is used to represent the principal quantum number?

Your starter for ten:

23 James, an ex-actor; his morphine-addicted wife Mary, and their two sons Jamie and Edmund are characters in which four-act drama? Published posthumously in 1956, the play takes place over one summer day in Connecticut.

Three questions on a work of non-fiction:

(a) *The Birth of Britain, The New World, The Age of Revolution* and *The Great Democracies* are the four volumes of which major historical work of the 1950s by Winston Churchill?

(b) 'For ten years he had led the armies of the Grand Alliance; he never fought a battle he did not win, or besieged a town he did not take.' Churchill uses these words to describe which of his ancestors?

(c) Of whom did Churchill write: 'He ranks with Marlborough as the greatest English man in the century between 1689 and 1789 ... the first great figure of British imperialism'?

Your starter for ten:

24 In chess, what four-letter word denotes a tactic in which a single piece attacks two or more pieces at the same time?

Three questions on the films of Buster Keaton:

(a) A stunt in the 1928 film *Steamboat Bill Junior*, in which the façade of a house falls around Keaton, inspired the 1997 short film *Deadpan* by which artist and film director?

(b) Keaton's 1923 film *Three Ages* featured interwoven love stories set in three different eras. It was a satire on which D.W. Griffith movie of 1916?

(c) What name is given to the steam locomotive in the title of Buster Keaton's 1926 film set during the American Civil War?

Your starter for ten:

25 In a Cartesian coordinate system, what is the term for the distance of a given point from the y-axis?

Three questions on a Nobel laureate:

(a) Born in Sweden in 1858, who was the first woman to win the Nobel Prize in Literature?

(b) According to her Nobel biography, Lagerlof's enduring work, *Gosta Berling's Saga*, went unnoticed until its translation into which closely related language?

(c) Telling the historical tale of twelve so-called Cavaliers, *Gosta Berling's Saga* bore the influence of which Scottish writer, born in 1795?

The Answers

1   Kate Bush (along with Jeanette Winterson, Jackie Kay and Carol Ann Duffy)
    (a) Rita Mae Brown
    (b) Adrienne rich
    (c) Martin Amis

2   Splendid isolation
    (a) (The first / Apollo 11) moon landing
    (b) The Armistice / end of the First World War
    (c) Prince of Wales / Prince Charles and Camilla Parker-Bowles

3   Embouchure
    (a) Caerphilly
    (b) Chester
    (c) Newport / Casnewydd

4   Gerard Manley Hopkins
    (a) (Elisabeth) Frink
    (b) Fear
    (c) Chatsworth

5   Snake plant / mother-in-law's tongue or nose
    (a) *Jane Eyre*
    (b) *The Scarlet Letter*
    (c) *The Turn of the Screw*

6   Barbizon (school)
    (a) *Tribune*
    (b) Jennie Lee
    (c) (Michael) Foot

7   Matthias (Grünewald; from the raven (Latin: *corvus*) on his escutcheon)
    (a) Palladian (Andrea Palladio)
    (b) Corinthian
    (c) Inigo Jones

8   Pittsburgh
    (a) Philippa (of Hainault; wife of Edward III)
    (b) Margaret (of Anjou; wife of Henry VI)
    (c) (Prince) Albert (of Saxe-Coburg-Gotha)

9   Steeplechase
    (a) Kirkcaldy (Captain James Tiberius Kirk from the original series)
    (b) Mallorca (Captain Gabriel Lorca of *Star Trek: Discovery*)
    (c) Picardie (Captain Jean-Luc Picard from *Star Trek: The Next Generation*)

10   Royal Mint (Second then Chief Engraver)
     (a) *Women in Love*
     (b) Italian (*Indagine su un cittadino al di sopra di ogni sospetto*)
     (c) *Patton*

11   (George) Stubbs
     (a) Condoleezza Rice
     (b) Sonia Gandhi (born Edvige Antonia Albina Maino; married Rajiv Gandhi in 1968)
     (c) Christine Lagarde

12   10^{50}
     (a) Accretion
     (b) Ablation
     (c) Advection

13   Ming (reigned 1402–1424; personal name Zhu Di)
     (a) Protein
     (b) Parity
     (c) (Nuclear) fission

14   (Francisco de) Goya (1746–1828)
     (a) Niobium
     (b) Astatine
     (c) Antimony (hence its atomic symbol Sb)

15   Strait(s)
     (a) (Gulf of) Tonkin
     (b) (Gulf of) Oman
     (c) (Isthmus of) Corinth

16   Nagasaki
     (a) *Twelfth Night*
     (b) Illyria
     (c) Tamsin Greig

17   (Maximilian) Ringelmann (the Ringelmann effect; research in 1913)
     (a) Cherenkov (radiation)
     (b) Casimir (effect)
     (c) Coriolis (force)

18   Emery and emerald
     (a) Barents Sea
     (b) Japanese
     (c) Hermit (crabs)

19 Orkney (Islands)
   (a) Saturn
   (b) (Percival) Lowell
   (c) Mars

20 Positive predictive value (accept 'predictive positive value')
   (a) (Thomas) Bewick
   (b) Rasselas (accept 'the Prince of Abyssinia')
   (c) *Gulliver's Travels*

21 Architecture / poetry / music
   (a) Lost Generation
   (b) Cubism
   (c) Alice B. Toklas

22 Genji / Hikaru Genji (meaning 'Shining Prince')
   (a) Four
   (b) Azimuthal
   (c) N

23 *Long Day's Journey into Night* (Eugene O'Neill, of course)
   (a) *A History of the English-Speaking Peoples*
   (b) (Duke of) Marlborough (accept but qualify John Churchill)
   (c) (William) Pitt the Elder (accept but qualify Earl of Chatham)

24 Fork
   (a) Steve McQueen
   (b) *Intolerance* (not *Birth of a Nation*, released in 1915)
   (c) *The General*

25 Abscissa (not ordinate, which is the distance to the x-axis)
   (a) Selma Lagerlof
   (b) Danish
   (c) Thomas Carlyle

Remake/Remodel

Royal Holloway

vs

Dundee
(1986)

In 1986, the show experimented with new formats. The teams had already faced each other in a regular format and Royal Holloway were leading 230 points to Dundee's 120. The form of this game was like a relay race; each player carried a baton (symbolized by a tube with six lights, each of which lit up every time a contestant got an answer right) for a lap which consists of two correct answers. The baton would light up in six stages (three laps of two correct answers) and when the entire baton was lit up the team won the round and the right to a bonus question. Each lap was worth 15 points. The person that was behind at any point, first on aggregate and then within the round, got to choose the subject.

1   Religion
    (a) Which people's gods included Xochipilli, Tonatiuh and Quetzalcoatl?
    (b) Which great compilation of law and tradition consists of the Mishna and the Gemara?
    (c) With which larger church have the Maronites been formally in union since the 16th century?
    (d) In which place or culture was Nut worshipped as the Mother Goddess, the curve of whose body was the arch—?
    [The question was correctly interrupted]

    (e) What word is used for the sacred books of which the most foremost examples are known as *Yajur*, *Sama*, *Atharva* and *Rig*?

[With two answers right, Dundee passed the baton to the next contestant and scored 15 points]

2   Ancient Worlds
(a) Which historian wrote *The March Upcountry* about the mercenary soldiers—?
[The question was successfully interrupted; Royal Holloway reached two right answers and got 15 points, passing the baton to the next opponent]

3   General Questions
(a) Who in 1947 became India's first prime minister after Independence?
(b) Which castle in Cornwall has traditionally been held to the be the birthplace of King Arthur?
(c) Give me either of the two South American countries which do not have a coastline?
[Royal Holloway passed the baton with another two correct answers]

4   Technology
(a) What fixes the image in xerography or the dry copying process?
(b) What is the term for a girder that is hollow and neither square nor rectangular in shape and a particular type of bridge uses it as a component?
[Dundee passed their baton, having completed a 'lap']

5   General Questions
(a) What is the usual English name for the great conqueror known more correctly as Timur – the phrase used correctly as Tamurlane or Timur the Lame explaining the English version?
(b) What does 'Bad' mean in such places as Bad Homburg?
(c) What more evocative name was apparently suggested by Churchill himself for the Local Defence Volunteers and became the name by which our defence force in the Second World War is now known?
(d) The name of which German guidebook led to a series of air raids?
[Dundee completed the baton's lights and got to confer over bonus questions]

Bonus Questions
(a) What is the language of Walloon?
(b) Which Spanish dialect is the standard form of European Spanish?
(c) Which TV character said very characteristically, 'They have sounds for things, the Jocks and Irish, which is no good to them apart from talking amongst themselves. They want to talk to other people, they need to talk English'?
[The baton was handed on with no lights on]

6 Sport

(a) Who won the women's' singles title at Wimbledon six times in the period from 1919 to 1925 and was French?

(b) Which great runner established more than 20 world records in the 1920s, won 12 Olympic medals and was a native of Finland?

(c) What was the middle name of Jack Hobbs or, more formally, of Sir John B. Hobbs?

(d) What was the year of the Olympic Games dominated by Jesse Owens?

[Dundee passed the baton]

7 History

(a) Which two of his wives were executed by Henry VIII?

(b) Members of which family were victims of an assassination attempt in a cathedral on 26 April 1478? The plot became known as the Pazzi conspiracy?

(c) Whose purgatories in the autumn of 1668 led to the deaths of about 35 innocent people in England?

(d) At which port a few miles northeast of Belfast did William III land his expedition of 1690?

(e) What was the final battle of the English Civil War in 1651 where Charles II was defeated?

8 General Questions

(a) What is the German for a trout, as in Schubert's Quintet?

(b) What is the capital of Malaysia?

[Dundee passed the baton]

9 Music

(a) The title role in Britten's *Rape of Lucretia* was especially written for a great English contralto who died in 1953 at the age of 41. Who was she?

(b) Give me the English title for Prokofiev's ballet *Zolushka*, the equivalent of which in other European languages would be *Aschenputtel, La Cenerentola* or *Cendrillon*?

(c) How is a glass harmonica played?

(d) What is the term for a triad of which the fifth is perfect, the notes G, B and D forming it for G major?

(e) Which composer's works were given catalogue numbers all preceded by 'BWV', which stands for his name?

[Royal Holloway passed the baton]

10 Ancient World

(a) Which Latin poet of the 1st century BC had as his mistress Clodia?

(b) In which modern country is Susa, the administrative capital of Darius I?

(c) Who with Marc Antony and Octavian was the third member—?
[The question was correctly interrupted; Royal Holloway passed the baton]

11 Mythology
(a) Who completes a quartet, together with Clytemnestra, Castor and Pollux, the four of them being children of Leda?
(b) The story of which great hero was found on twelve incomplete tablets at Nineveh?
[Royal Holloway completed the round and advanced to the bonus questions]

Bonus Questions
(a) Which two large rivers flow into the Aral Sea?
(b) Into what two countries is the island Hispaniola divided?
(c) Which cathedral sixty miles southwest of Paris has two spires in two different styles?

12 Medicine
(a) For what condition is epistaxis the medical term?
(b) Give me either of the painful skin conditions which have been popularly known as St Anthony's fire, one an infectious disease and the other poisoning by diseased cereals?
(c) What is the colour of erythrocytes?
[Dundee passed the baton]

13 Geography
(a) Which strait lies between the Persian Gulf and the Gulf of Oman?
[Royal Holloway passed the baton]

14 General Questions
(a) Which northwestern city played host to a major snooker tournament in its Guild Hall in the last two months of 1984?
(b) What type of birds are called 'passenger' if caught when immature and 'haggard' if caught while adult?
(c) Whose books include *The Overloaded Ark*, *The Bafut Beagles* and *My Family and Other Animals*, one other animal in the family being the author of *The Alexandria Quartet*?
(d) Of which country is Amharic the official language and the Derg the name for the government?
(e) According to the *Punch* cartoon, whose boiled egg for breakfast was good—?
[The question was successfully interrupted; Royal Holloway passed the baton]

15 Broadcasting
(a) Which Ronnie Barker series was the sequel to *Porridge*?
[Dundee passed the baton]

16 General Questions
(a) Which singer and long-serving president of the Boys Club Association had number 1 hits early in his career with 'Garden of Eden' and 'Tower of Strength'?
(b) In what century did the doctrine known as the 'priesthood of all believers' become a major point of issue between differing branches of the Reformation?
(c) 'Though I sit down now the time will come when you will hear me.' Which great politician ended his maiden speech with those words in 1837, having been howled down, but later amply justified his prophecy?
(d) Which of Edward I's great castles stands on the island of Anglesey?
[Royal Holloway took the round]

Bonus Questions
(a) What word is used for a former Hindu practice of a widow's self-immolation on her husband's funeral pyre?
(b) Give me the title and first word of the book the opening sentence of which continues: '... light of my life, fire of my loins'.
(c) What peace was being celebrated by the royal display of fireworks for which Handel wrote his suite?

17 The Bible
(a) In what language is the *Codex Sinaiticus*, which contains an incomplete Old Testament and a complete New Testament in a 4th-century manuscript?
(b) What article of Jesus's clothing is mentioned by John the Baptist in the first chapters of Mark as an indication of John's relative unworthiness?
(c) Who wrote, 'Of the Jews five times received I forty stripes save one'?
(d) Who painted her face and tied her hair and looked out of the window?
[Royal Holloway passed the baton]

18 Geography
(a) In what sense is marginal land marginal?
(b) Which two countries are separated by the Kattegat?
[Dundee passed the baton]

19 General Questions
(a) Which dramatic ancient site among the cragged peaks of the Andes in south-central Peru and has a name meaning 'lost city of the Incas'?

(b) What is the official title of the chief officer of the cities of Aberdeen, Dundee and Edinburgh?

(c) What was the profession of the man born in 1904 as William Brandt, who was always known by a shorter version his name? He studied in the 1930s under Man Ray, and his books include *Perspective of Nudes*?

(d) What two words are used for the 26 members of the House of Lords consisting of 21 senior incumbents around the country plus those of London, Durham, Winchester, York and Canterbury?

[Dundee passed the baton]

20 Spelling

(a) It means in one sense a release from life, and it is 'quietus'.

(b) A word for a strange but characteristic mannerism, which is 'idiosyncrasy'.

(c) It means a state of disrepair, and it is 'dilapidated'.

(d) It means the condition of not being in use, and it is 'desuetude'.

(e) It means to disconcert or fluster, and it is 'embarrass'?

[Royal Holloway passed the baton]

21 Mixed Bag

(a) Marble Arch was designed to be the main entrance to what?

[Dundee won the round]

Bonus Questions

(a) What number is indicated by the symbol 'T' standing for terawatt-hour?

(b) What is the special characteristic of Italian flooring known as *terrazzo*?

(c) In biology, what is the special subject of teratology?

22 Geography

(a) What in northern English dialect is a 'pike', as in Scafell Pike?

(b) Which firth separates Nairn from Cromarty, the name of the firth being the Scottish District Council with its headquarters in—?

[The question was interrupted]

23 General Questions

(a) What is studied in dactylography?

Royal Holloway beat Dundee by 385 points to 290.
They went on to play St Catherine's College, Oxford for a place in the quarter-finals.
Jesus College, Oxford won the series, beating Imperial College London.

The Answers

1 Religion
(a) Aztecs
(b) *Talmud*
(c) Roman Catholic
(d) Egyptians
(e) Veda

2 Ancient Worlds
(a) Xenophon

3 General Questions
(a) (Jawaharlal) Nehru
(b) Tintagel
(c) Bolivia or Paraguay

4 Technology
(a) Heat
(b) Box girder

5 General Questions
(a) Tamburlaine
(b) 'Bath' or 'Spa' – a watering place
(c) The Home Guard
(d) *Baedeker*

Bonus Questions
(a) French
(b) Castilian
(c) Alf Garnet

6 Sport
(a) Suzanne Lenglen
(b) Paavo Nurmi
(c) Berry
(d) 1936

7 History
(a) Anne Boleyn and Catherine Howard
(b) Medici
(c) Titus Oates
(d) Carrickfergus
(e) Worcester

8 General
(a) *Die Forelle*
(b) Kuala Lumpur

9 Music
(a) Kathleen Ferrier
(b) *Cinderella*

(c) With wet fingers on the rim of glasses of different heights filled with water

(d) A common chord

(e) (Johann Sebastian) Bach

10 Ancient World
(a) Catullus
(b) Iran
(c) Lepidus

11 Mythology   Bonus questions:
(a) Helen of Troy   (a) Amu Darya and Syr Darya
(b) Gilgamesh   (b) Haiti and Dominican Republican
                                           (c) Chartres

12 Medicine
(a) Nosebleed
(b) Ergotism (ergot poisoning)
(c) Red (blood cells)

13 Geography
(a) Hormuz

14 General Questions
(a) Preston
(b) Falcon
(c) Gerald Durrell
(d) Ethiopia
(e) The Curate's

15 Broadcasting
(a) *Going Straight*

16 General Questions   Bonus Questions
(a) Frankie Vaughan   (a) Suttee
(b) 16th century   (b) *Lolita*
(c) Benjamin Disraeli   (c) Aix-la-Chapelle
(d) Beaumaris

17 Bible
(a) Greek
(b) His sandal (or shoe)
(c) St Paul
(d) Jezebel

18 Geography
(a) It's only just going to make a profit from cultivation

(b) Denmark and Sweden

19   General Questions
(a) Machu Picchu
(b) Lord Provost
(c) Photographer
(d) Lords Spiritual

20   Spelling
(a) Quietus
(b) Idiosyncrasy
(c) Dilapidated
(d) Desuetude
(e) Embarrass

21   Mixed Bag
(a) Buckingham Palace

Bonus Questions
(a) 10^{12}
(b) Bits of marble which are ground smooth
(c) Study of abnormalities

22   Geography
(a) A peak
(b) Moray Firth

23   General Questions
(a) Fingerprints

Challenging Tales
The Return

Many TV quiz shows have been revived after a break from our screens – lately *Fifteen to One*, *Catchphrase* and *Blockbusters*. When *University Challenge* reappeared in 1994 after a seven-year break, quiz fans were delighted.

During its first incarnation, the programme was shifted around the schedules by the different regional ITV companies, moving from late at night to afternoons or weekends. The lack of a regular slot inevitably meant falling audience figures, and in 1983 London Weekend Television stopped broadcasting the programme altogether. The programme's format was altered in 1986, introducing a relay leg where contestants selected questions from set categories. It was fully networked at this point but shown in the mornings throughout the summer and, failing to really make a mark in terms of viewing figures, it was axed.

The resurrection of *University Challenge* by the BBC, although eagerly anticipated, attracted some concern that the benign supervision of Bamber Gascoigne was to be replaced by the acerbic Jeremy Paxman. It was noted that, when the programme began in 1962, Gascoigne wrote many of the questions himself; he was seen as the guardian of *University Challenge*, a programme he loved. Could Paxman compete?

He did, admirably. Members of the production team and former contestants speak highly of his stewardship, and his likeability and sense of humour. Viewing figures were healthy and the return to the original format and the new presenter meant the slightly tired show was reinvigorated. There was excitement in student circles and teams quickly applied in growing numbers.

University Challenge was still made by ITV, for the BBC. The current executive producer Peter Gwyn joined the production team for the second series with Jeremy Paxman in the chair. He recalls: 'I didn't do the first one, but I took over as producer and then, after a few years, became executive producer.'

Peter's pedigree in television is solid. He joined the BBC in the mid-1980s as a researcher across several shows. He worked with Jasper Carrot and then Bob Monkhouse on *Bob's Full House*, which was his first experience of being a questions verifier. 'That stood me in very good stead; I learned a great deal there.' He worked for Hat Trick Productions on *Clive Anderson Talks Back* and the pilot for *Have I Got News for You*. A move to Granada Television in 1990 saw Peter work across several programmes including several series of *Stars in Their Eyes*. He has also executive-produced *Countdown* for fifteen years.

Try Your Luck
Match

Your starter for ten:

1 In geometry, what term defines a conic section whose eccentricity is equal to zero?

Three questions on a shared name:
(a) The *Epodes* and the *Ars Poetica* are among the works of which lyric poet and satirist, born in 65 BC?
(b) Horace Walpole was the author of which Gothic horror tale of 1764, featuring the characters Manfred, Theodore and Isabella?
(c) The journalist Horace Greeley unsuccessfully opposed which Republican incumbent in the United States presidential election of 1872?

Your starter for ten:

2 The most abundant isotope of which actinoid element has a half-life slightly greater than the age of the universe, at about 14 billion years? It has been used as a fuel in experimental nuclear reactors, and is named after a Norse god.

Three questions on literary works:
(a) Give the two title characters of the 19th-century poem that includes the words 'honey', 'money', 'small guitar', 'mince', 'quince' and 'runcible spoon'?
(b) *The Owl Service* is a 1967 work by which Cheshire-born author, also noted for *Red Shift* and *Elidor*?
(c) 'Owl Post' is the first chapter of what fictional work, first published in 1999, and one of a series of seven novels?

Your starter for ten:

3 Meaning an elevated tract of open country, and appearing in the opening lines of *The Lady of Shalott*, what short word designates chalk uplands on either side of the Humber Estuary in East Yorkshire and Lincolnshire?

Three questions on psychology:

(a) Born in 1878, the American John B. Watson is regarded as a pioneer of which field of experimental psychology, in which all actions are viewed as being conditioned by observable external experience?

(b) The developer of the 'air crib', in which an infant could be raised in a controlled, artificial environment, which US psychologist is particularly noted for his work in the branch of behaviorism known as operant conditioning?

(c) What is the title of Skinner's utopian novel of 1948, based on a concept of social engineering? It shares the first part of its name with a work by Henry David Thoreau.

Your starter for ten:

4   Answer as soon as your name is called, giving your answer in degrees. Consider a sample of an optical medium placed in a vacuum: if the refractive index of the material is two, what is the critical angle for light travelling in the sample?

Your bonuses are on characters in Homer's *Odyssey*, according to the scholar and translator Emily Wilson:

(a) Which character in *The Odyssey* does Wilson describe as 'canny, strong-willed [and] loyal; a competent, mostly single mother who shows deep love for her difficult, moody son'?

(b) Wilson contrasts Penelope with 'élite wives who do scary things'. She cites which two sisters, one of whom 'abandons her husband for another man', while the other 'helps her lover murder her husband'. I need both names.

(c) According to Wilson, who is 'a wonderfully gender-fluid goddess, who protects and saves her favourite human [Odysseus]'?

Your starter for ten:

5   Answer promptly, naming the two North American lakes linked by the Welland Canal, to the south of Toronto? The natural waterway between these two lakes is the Niagara River.

Your bonuses are on shipwrecks – specifically, those listed as protected wreck sites by Historic England:

(a) The *Association*, the flagship of the fleet led by Sir Cloudesley Shovell, was one of four royal navy ships wrecked in 1707 on the Gilstone Rocks, part of which island group?

(b) Which warship was captured from the French navy during a battle at Cape Finisterre in 1747 but was wrecked eleven years later on a sandbank in the Solent? It was rediscovered in 1979.

(c) Which ship was raised from the seabed of Spithead, near Portsmouth, in 1982, having capsized while fighting a French invasion fleet 437 years earlier?

Your starter for ten:

6   What is the sole three-digit integer with the following two characteristics: firstly, that reversing the order of its first two digits gives its square root; and secondly, its last digit is also its cube root?

Your bonuses are on novels since 1890. In each case, name the work from the description. The same adjective appears in all three answers:
(a) A novel of 1921 by Aldous Huxley; set in a country house, it satirizes the intellectual pretensions of the 'bright young things' staying there.
(b) The 2012 debut novel of Kevin Powers; it takes its title from a marching song learnt by Powers whilst serving with the US army.
(c) An 1890 novella by Charlotte Perkins Gilman; it details the breakdown suffered by a young woman confined as part of a strict 'rest cure'.

Your starter for ten:

7   I need the name of an SI unit. What unit is used to express the physical quantity that is a homophone of a heavy item of jewellery worn around the neck and associated with Celtic civilizations? In its most usual form, it has the abbreviation 'N·m'.

Three questions on New York's Chelsea Hotel:
(a) During a six-year residence in the Chelsea Hotel following his divorce from a prominent actress, who wrote the stage work *After the Fall*, which premiered in 1964?
(b) Which literary figure was a resident in 1953 when he died after a series of extensive drinking bouts in the nearby White Horse Tavern?
(c) Also a resident at the hotel, who wrote the 1959 novel *Naked Lunch*?

Your starter for ten:

8   Since the early 16th century, all male monarchs of which country have borne the regnal names 'Frederick' or 'Christian'? Christian II was the last to rule over Sweden, while Frederick VI was the last to rule over Norway.

Your bonuses are on the 2019 British Book Awards, also known as the 'Nibbies'. In each case, give the title from the description:
(a) First, the memoir that won Audiobook of the Year, written and narrated by Michelle Obama?
(b) The novel that won the award for Crime Fiction and Thriller of the Year? It was the twelfth novel by the South London author Louise Candlish.

(c) The novel by Sally Rooney that won the award for Overall Book of the Year? I need the two-word title here.

Your starter for ten:

9   In the 1950s, the Duke and Duchess of Windsor, Richard Nixon and Brigitte Bardot were among the subjects asked to perform what action by the photographer Philippe Halsman? The action also features in the titles of hits from the 1980s for The Pointer Sisters and Van Halen.

Three questions on an American author:
(a) In 1921, who became the first woman to win a Pulitzer Prize for fiction with her novel *The Age of Innocence*?
(b) What is the title of Wharton's second novel, published in 1905? The four words complete a quotation from Ecclesiastes that begins: 'The heart of fools is in …'?
(c) Highly regarded among Wharton's short stories, which work of 1934 concerns two American women on holiday in Europe with their daughters? It was adapted as an opera by the US composer Philip Hagemann in 1989.

Your starter for ten:

10 What name is shared by a figure in Greek mythology who took part in the pursuit of the Calydonian boar, and a football club from Bergamo in Lombardy that reached the UEFA Champions League quarter-finals for the first time in 2020?

Your bonuses are on events which took place in years that are multiples of 100. Give me the number of centuries that separate the two events in each question:
(a) The crowning of, respectively, Charlemagne as Holy Roman Emperor and Stephen I as King of Hungary, both on Christmas Day.
(b) The battle of Catraeth, in which the invading Angles won a victory against the Brythonic Gododdin people, and the battle of Seki-Gahara, which saw a decisive victory for the future Tokugawa shogun?
(c) The deaths of England's Richard II, arguably leading to the Wars of the Roses, and Spain's Charles II, sparking the War of the Spanish Succession?

Your starter for ten:

11 '[She] portrayed the world from a mouse's or rabbit's or small child's-eye view. The vantage point in her exquisite watercolours varies from a few inches to a few feet from the ground, like that of a toddler.' Those words of the novelist Alison Lurie refer to which author and illustrator, born in London in 1866?

Your bonuses are on countries that have a larger land area than the UK but are smaller than any of their neighbours. Name each country from the description:
(a) One of the most sparsely populated countries in the world, its two neighbours both have populations of more than 100 million; copper mining accounts for about 10 per cent of GDP.
(b) A landlocked country with one of Africa's highest literacy levels; following years of hyperinflation, its official currency was suspended in 2009.
(c) The world's largest producer of copper; contiguous regions of this country extend over more than thirty-five degrees of latitude.

Your starter for ten:

12 With his partner Juman Malouf, who opened the exhibition *Spitzmaus Mummy in a Coffin and Other Treasures* in Vienna in 2018? The person in question directed the films *Rushmore* and *The Grand Budapest Hotel*.

Three questions on a Latin word:
(a) What seven-letter Latin word means 'truth', 'fact' or 'accuracy'? In a set expression, it follows the words 'in vino'.
(b) 'Veritas' appears on the seal of which US university, founded in 1636?
(c) The political party Veritas was founded in 2005 by which public figure and TV host?

Your starter for ten:

13 What five-letter name links: the US astronomer who discovered Pluto; a football club that moved from Glasgow to Cumbernauld in 1994; and an outlaw played by Warren Beatty in a 1967 film, co-starring Faye Dunaway?

Three questions on astronomy:
(a) Which red super-giant star is the brightest in the constellation Scorpius? Its name contains the letters of the word 'star', though not in that order.
(b) About 25 light years away, which star of spectra type A is the brightest in Piscis Austrinus? This name contains the letters of the word 'hot', though not in that order.
(c) Finally, visible from the southern hemisphere, and the second brightest in the night sky, the name of which star contains the letters of the word 'sun', again, not in that order?

Your starter for ten:

14 Which element of the periodic table links the names of all the following: a wingless insect of the order Zygentoma; a US statistician and author of *The Signal and the Noise*; and the 2012 film for which Jennifer Lawrence won the Academy Award for Best Actress, starring alongside Bradley Cooper?

Three questions on a West African city:

(a) A centre of Trans-Saharan salt and gold trade in the 14th century, which city in Mali is home to Sankoré University, an ancient centre of learning?

(b) Which Berber-speaking pastoralists founded Timbuktu? In 2012, separatist rebels of this ethnic group took control of northern Mali and claimed Timbuktu as part of the independent state of Azawad.

(c) Set in 1361, the musical *Timbuktu!* by Roger Wright and George Forrest is a retelling of which stage work, set in Baghdad and based on the music of Borodin?

Your starter for ten:

15 The f-number or focal ratio of a lens is the ratio of which two quantities?

Three questions on 19th-century novels:

(a) *Moeurs de province*, meaning 'Provincial Customs', was the subtitle to which 1856 French novel, first serialized in the *Revue de Paris*?

(b) Which novel of 1826 has the subtitle, *A Narrative of 1757*? Its title refers to the character Chingachgook.

(c) *The Parish Boy's Progress* was the subtitle of which novel by Dickens, originally published in serial form from 1837?

Your starter for ten:

16 Which composer's piano sonatas include those known by the names *Les adieux, The Tempest, The Hunt, Appassionata* and *Waldstein*?

Three questions on plant families:

(a) Artichoke, lettuce and salsify belong to the aster or *Compositae* family, also known by the name of what common garden flower?

(b) Kale and radish are part of the cabbage or *Brassica* family, also known by the name of what other culinary plant, with the binomial *Sinapis alba*?

(c) Apricot, cherry and apple are all members of which plant family?

Your starter for ten:

17 What is the only consonant in all of the following: the title of an Oscar-winning musical of 1958 starring Leslie Caron; a narrow, S-shaped curve; a measure, for example, in railway construction; and a Greek goddess who personifies the Earth?

Three questions on similar words:

(a) Which element of the periodic table is the least dense solid and as a salt is used medically to treat bipolar disorder?

(b) In geology, the outer rigid lithosphere consists of the crust and the solid, outermost layer of what part of the Earth, lying between the crust and the central core?

(c) Lithography, a form of surface printing, was discovered in 1798 and, in its earliest and most common form, used a block of what porous rock as a plate?

Your starter for ten:

18 A factor of 10 to what power is denoted by the prefix Yotta?

Three questions on a two-dimensional shape:

(a) Comprising two shuttles with fixed separation moving along perpendicular paths, the trammel of Archimedes is a mechanism used to generate what specific shape?

(b) What process in laser physics often uses a cavity with elliptical cross-section to reflect light into a solid-state rod, in order to create a population inversion? I need a two-word term.

(c) An ellipse centred at the origin with width 2a and height 2b has the equation $x^2/a^2 + y^2/b^2$ = what?

Your starter for ten:

19 I need a six-letter word here. In a mechanism for converting rotary into linear motion, for example in vehicle steering systems or mountain railways, what term denotes a small cog or gear wheel that engages with a toothed bar known as a 'rack'?

Three questions on people who have opened Olympic Games:

(a) Which head of state opened a late-20th-century summer games, having earlier competed in sailing at the 1972 Olympics?

(b) In the absence of Jimmy Carter, which vice president opened the 1980 Winter Olympics in Lake Placid?

(c) The head of state of which country opened the summer games in 1964, and the winter games in 1972?

Your starter for ten:

20 The US architect Walter Burley Griffin won a 1911 competition to design which capital city, whose name is derived from an indigenous word for 'meeting place'? It is surrounded by the political entity known as ACT.

Three questions on a Roman poet:

(a) 'Love conquers all things.' This line appears in which work by the poet Virgil? The same work prophesies the birth of a child who will bring a new golden era.

(b) Meaning 'the working of the earth', which long poem by Virgil is ostensibly a guide to agriculture, animal husbandry and beekeeping?

(c) The opening of Virgil's *Aeneid* refers to the 'never-forgetting anger' of which 'fierce' Roman goddess, the female counterpart of Jupiter?

Your starter for ten:

21 'His whole body was responding to a kind of wonder at himself ... A narcissistic orgy of some kind. An orgy of one.' Those words of the photographer Richard Avedon describe which dancer, who sat for him after his defection to the West in 1961?

Three questions on John Keats:

(a) Which ode by Keats contains the line: 'Thou wast not born for death, immortal bird!'?

(b) The 'Ode to a Nightingale' begins: 'My heart aches, and a drowsy numbness pains / My sense'. The name of what poisonous plant, here regarded as a sedative, appears in the second line?

(c) In the same poem, the line 'Full of the true, the blushful Hippocrene' alludes to a fountain on Mount Helicon, associated with what mythological group?

Your starter for ten:

22 Sometimes known by a three-letter abbreviation, which hormone is produced by the hypothalamus and stimulates the reabsorption of water by the kidneys, thus regulating urine production? A lack or malfunction of this hormone causes diabetes insipidus.

Your bonuses are on enzymes used in molecular cloning:

(a) What specific single word is applied to bacterial enzymes that recognize and cut DNA at specific sites, and so are used to isolate gene-containing fragments?

(b) The abbreviation ALP represents which enzyme? Purified from E. coli or calf intestine, it is used to prevent recircularization of vectors in cloning.

(c) Isolated from the bacteriophage T4, among others, which enzyme connects blunt and cohesive DNA ends resulting from restriction enzyme digestion?

Your starter for ten:

23 Described as 'a small fleshy excrescence', the structure called the lacrimal caruncle adjoins the innermost external edge of which organ of the human body?

Three questions on physics:

(a) In one formulation, the first law of thermodynamics states that the change in internal energy of a system is equal to the sum of what two quantities? Two single-word answers are sufficient.

(b) In one version, the second law of thermodynamics states that no process is possible whose sole result is the transfer of heat from a colder to a hotter body. This statement of the law is attributed to which physicist, born in 1822?

(c) The third law of thermodynamics describes a limiting behaviour of entropy, and implies among other things the unattainability of what state?

Your starter for ten:

24 Choreographed by Matthew Bourne and premiered in 1992, a modern version of which ballet begins one Christmas Eve at Dr Dross's Orphanage and features the Gobstopper Boys and the Marshmallow Girls performing to a score by Tchaikovsky?

Three questions on tennis:

(a) In 1919, which French player became the first from a country other than Britain and the USA to win the Wimbledon women's singles title? She went on to win it six times, and a court at the Roland Garros Stadium is named after her.

(b) Born in Czechoslovakia, Jaroslav Drobny became in 1954 the first player to win a Wimbledon singles title representing an African country: which country?

(c) In 1959, which Brazilian became the first South American player to win the women's singles title at Wimbledon?

Your starter for ten:

25 Published in 1934, what novel is divided into three parts entitled 'The Facts', 'The Evidence' and 'Hercule Poirot Sits Back and Thinks'? The last chapter of the final part has the title 'Poirot Propounds Two Solutions'.

Three questions on the social reformer Eglantyne Jebb:

(a) Born in Shropshire in 1876, Jebb witnessed the plight of refugees on a visit in 1913 to which present-day country, a part of the Ottoman Empire partitioned after the Balkan Wars?

(b) Jebb co-founded which charitable organization in 1919, in response to the plight of young refugees displaced by the First World War?

(c) Jebb's five-point document 'The Declaration of the Rights of the Child' was officially endorsed and adopted in 1924 by which international body?

The Answers

1   Circle
(a) Horace (Quintus Horatius Flaccus)
(b) *The Castle of Otranto*
(c) (Ulysses S.) Grant

2   Thorium (i.e. thorium-232)
(a) The Owl and the Pussycat (by Edward Lear, of course; first published 1871)
(b) (Alan) Garner
(c) *Harry Potter and the Prisoner of Azkaban*

3   Wold(s) ('Long fields of barley and of rye / that clothe the wold and meet the sky')
(a) Behaviorism
(b) (B.F. / Burrhus Frederic) Skinner
(c) *Walden Two*

4   Thirty (degrees) (sin c = ½; this gives c = 30°)
(a) Penelope
(b) Helen and Clytemnestra
(c) Athena (accept Pallas Athena)

5   (Lakes) Erie and Ontario
(a) (Isles of) Scilly
(b) (HMS) *Invincible*
(c) *Mary Rose*

6   729 (27^2 and 9^3)
(a) *Crome Yellow*
(b) *The Yellow Birds*
(c) *The Yellow Wallpaper*

7   Newton metre (accept kilogram metres squared per second squared)
(a) Arthur Miller
(b) Dylan Thomas
(c) William Burroughs

8   Denmark
(a) *Becoming*
(b) *Our House*
(c) *Ordinary People*

9   Jump (Halsman's *Jumpology* series; 'Jump' by Van Halen released 1983; 'Jump (For My Love)' by The Pointer Sisters released 1984)
(a) Edith Wharton
(b) *The House of Mirth*
(c) *Roman Fever*

10   Atalanta (Atalanta Bergamasca Calcio)
     (a) Two centuries / 200 years (AD 800 and AD 1000)
     (b) Ten centuries / 1000 years (AD 600 and 1600)
     (c) Three centuries / 300 years (1400 and 1700)

11   Beatrix Potter
     (a) Mongolia (borders China and Russia and has a population of about 3 million)
     (b) Zimbabwe (borders South Africa, Botswana, Mozambique, Zambia)
     (c) Chile (borders Peru, Bolivia, Argentina)

12   Wes Anderson
     (a) Veritas
     (b) Harvard
     (c) (Robert) Kilroy-Silk (accept Kilroy)

13   Clyde (Tombaugh, 1906–1997; Clyde FC.; Barrow, 1909–1934)
     (a) Antares
     (b) Fomalhaut
     (c) Canopus

14   Silver (silverfish, Nate Silver and *Silver Linings Playbook*)
     (a) Timbuktu
     (b) Tuareg
     (c) *Kismet*

15   Focal length and diameter of the aperture
     (a) *Madame Bovary* (Flaubert, of course)
     (b) *The Last of the Mohicans* (Fennimore Cooper)
     (c) *Oliver Twist*

16   (Ludwig van) Beethoven (Nos. 26, 17, 18, 23 and 21)
     (a) Daisy
     (b) Mustard
     (c) Rose / *Rosaceae*

17   G (*Gigi*, ogee, gauge, Gaia / Gē)
     (a) Lithium
     (b) Mantle
     (c) (Bavarian) limestone

18   24 (i.e. 10^{24})
     (a) Ellipse (if 'oval' given, prompt for more specific answer)
     (b) Optical pumping (light source at one focus, laser medium at the other)
     (c) One (ellipse in standard configuration)

19 Pinion
    (a) King Juan Carlos (of Spain)
    (b) Walter Mondale
    (c) Japan (Hirohito, of course)

20 Canberra (Australian Capital Territory, of course)
    (a) (The) *Eclogues*
    (b) (The) *Georgics*
    (c) Juno (not Hera, her Greek equivalent, of course)

21 (Rudolf) Nureyev
    (a) '(Ode to a) Nightingale'
    (b) Hemlock
    (c) The Muses

22 Vasopressin (accept arginine vasopressin / AVP / anti-diuretic hormone / ADH / argipressin)
    (a) Restriction (enzyme)
    (b) Alkaline phosphatase (accept alk phos / basic phosphatase)
    (c) (DNA) ligase

23 Eye (i.e. the little pink blob in the inner corner of the eye)
    (a) Heat and work (i.e. heat transfer into the system, and work done on the system, or negative of work done by the system as the equation often has work as a negative quantity.)
    (b) (Rudolf) Clausius
    (c) Absolute zero (temperature; accept zero kelvin / -273.15°C)

24 *The Nutcracker* (accept Bourne's title, *Nutcracker!*)
    (a) (Suzanne) Lenglen
    (b) Egypt
    (c) (Maria) Bueno

25 *Murder on the Orient Express* (Agatha Christie, of course)
    (a) North Macedonia (accept Macedonia, correcting it)
    (b) Save the Children
    (c) League of Nations

The Hosts

Part 2
1994–present

Jeremy Dickson Paxman
(born 11 May 1950)

After Bamber Gascoigne's 28 years at the helm of *University Challenge*, it's difficult to think of a better successor than Jeremy Paxman, or a more different one. The former *Newsnight* inquisitor, famed for his incisive and sometimes aggressive questioning of often unforthcoming politicians on the BBC's key news programme, fronted both shows until 2014 when he left *Newsnight* after 25 years.

Born in Leeds in 1950 and educated at Malvern College, Jeremy Paxman read English at St Catharine's College, Cambridge, where he was editor of the university newspaper, *Varsity*. He joined the BBC at Radio Brighton on its graduate trainee scheme and, after moving to Belfast to report on the Troubles, transferred to London and eventually worked on *Panorama*, reporting from trouble spots around the world. After a spell reading the *Six O'Clock News*, he moved to BBC One's *Breakfast Time*, becoming presenter of *Newsnight* on BBC Two in 1989.

Currently the longest-serving quizmaster on British television, Paxman's trademark acerbic manner – the raised eyebrow and humorously dismissive reaction when someone proffers what he deems a ridiculous answer – has won him many fans. Yes, he's not Bamber but that has been the key to his successful stewardship. Paxman has the knowledge and the news-based gravitas to make it compelling viewing.

The father of three appeared as himself in an episode of the satirical political comedy *The Thick of It*, interviewing a hapless junior minister named Ben Swain, played by actor Justin Edwards who, by coincidence, appeared as a celebrity contestant on a *University Challenge* special in December 2020 for the University of Manchester.

But Paxman isn't noted for interrogating just politicians: his interviews with David Bowie, Vivienne Westwood and Russell Brand all made headlines.

Another bizarre headline-making occurrence happened in 2000 when the Enigma machine, stolen from Bletchley Park, was posted to Paxman, who promptly returned it to the museum. He has an affinity with the Scottish Highlands and, as a lover of whisky, recently invested in an organic distillery.

Paxman is also a respected author. He has written books about, among other things, chemical warfare, volcanoes, Victorian paintings, politics… and fishing (he's a keen fly fisher). His memoir, *A Life in Questions*, was published in 2016, while his latest book is *Black Gold: The History of How Coal Made Britain*, published in 2021. He is also a vice-president of the London Library, the trustees of which have included Bamber Gascoigne.

Paxman's onscreen persona may be brusque but members of the *University Challenge* production team and the contestants speak highly of him, citing his knowledge and humour. He chats easily to the teams before each recording, putting them at ease. The mutual respect is evident – as long as someone doesn't overstep the mark. Ralph Morley, captain of Trinity College, Cambridge's 2014 team, remembers Paxman calling his foursome 'smartarses' when he had declared, 'What else could it be?' after swiftly answering a starter question on Margaret Thatcher. But then, as Morley remembers, 'Jeremy Paxman was very nice to us … he was much less grumpy [than his reputation].'

In 2000, Paxman was made an Honorary Fellow of St Catharine's College, Cambridge, his alma mater, and St Edmund's Hall, Oxford, and has an honorary LLD from the University of Leeds and DLitt from the University of Bradford. He has won a plethora of awards over the years including two Richard Dimbleby Awards and five Royal Television Society Awards.

Try Your Luck
Match

Your starter for ten:

1 After Arabic, which Semitic language has the most speakers? Written in the Ge'ez script, it is the national language of Ethiopia.

Three questions on people who have held Seat Number 1 in the Académie Française:
(a) Elected in 1944, which Nobel physics laureate gives his name to the hypothesis that electrons have wave-like properties?
(b) Elected in 1753, which writer produced a 36-volume work on natural history? He gives his name to a principle of biogeography.
(c) Michel Debré, the first prime minister of the Fifth Republic, joined the Académie in 1988. Who preceded him as head of government?

Your starter for ten:

2 Which SI-derived unit of radioactivity has the same dimensions as the SI unit of frequency?

Three questions on a novel:
(a) *Oil!* is a 1927 novel by which US author, noted for his polemics on social and labour issues?
(b) *Oil!* was loosely based on which scandal that engulfed the administration of President Warren Harding in the early 1920s?
(c) *Oil!* also served as the loose inspiration for which Academy Award-winning film of 2007?

Your starter for ten:

3 Which King of Scots gained possession of Orkney and Shetland as a consequence of his marriage to Margaret of Denmark? He was among four kings with the same regnal name who died violently, his father having been killed by an exploding cannon, while his son died at the Battle of Flodden.

Three questions on place names:
(a) Associated with the early church historian St Eusebius, Caesarea Maritima is an archaeological site in which Eastern Mediterranean country?
(b) Nova Caesarea is a Latin name applied to which US state? It was admitted to the Union in 1787, and is known as the Garden State.
(c) Birthplace of St Basil the Great, the city once known as Caesarea in Cappadocia is in which present-day country?

Your starter for ten:
4   Clement Clarke Moore's poem 'A Visit from St Nicholas' and Lewis Carroll's 'Jabberwocky' both begin with what four-letter contraction?

Three questions on fungi:
(a) What large genus of fungi is characterized by thick stems and an absence of gills on the underside of the cap? Examples in Britain include the Cep, or Penny-bun, and the Old man of the woods.
(b) What is the common name of fungi of the genus *Lactaria*, so called because they exude a latex-like fluid when damaged?
(c) Having a fruiting body with a distinctive pitted head, what name is commonly given to edible fungi of the *Morchella* genus?

Your starter for ten:
5   Assuming that everyone in the line of succession to the British crown chooses to reign under their primary given name, what will be the regnal number of the person currently third in line for the throne?

Your bonuses are on US national forests:
(a) The Daniel Boone National Forest lies in which state, to the west of the Cumberland Gap?
(b) The Mark Twain National Forest lies mostly in the Ozark Highlands in which state, his birthplace in 1835?
(c) Which large state is the location of several national forests, including Lewis and Clark, Custer and Helena?

Your starter for ten:
6   Formed from a number of Tungusic Jurchen tribes by Nurhaci and his son in the early 17th century, which people overthrew the Ming empire, capturing Beijing in 1644? Their name appears in a historical term for Northeast China.

Three questions on geometry:
(a) What is the highest-order regular polygon that can be used to create a perfect tessellation, or tiling, of the plane?
(b) The dual of the regular hexagonal tiling, formed by lines that connect the centres of neighbouring hexagons, creates a new tiling comprised solely of what regular polygons?
(c) A feature of Islamic decoration, the pattern made by overlapping rows and columns of elongated pentagonal tilings is named after which major city in North Africa?

Your starter for ten:
7   What form of artistic expression is most associated with the names Martha Cooper, Francesca Woodman, Berenice Abbott, Nan Goldin and Diane Arbus?

Your bonuses are on novels that have won the Prix Goncourt. Give the authors of:
(a) The 2016 winner, *Lullaby*, published in the USA as *The Perfect Nanny*.
(b) The 1984 winner, *The Lover*, set in pre-war Indochina.
(c) The 1954 winner, *The Mandarins*, concerned with the intellectual and political climate of post-war France?

Your starter for ten:
8   What five-letter word links: an Oscar-winning film of 1973, starring Robert Redford and Paul Newman; the Wallsend-born singer-songwriter Gordon Sumner; and a fictional sword used by Bilbo and Frodo Baggins?

Three questions on artists and murder:
(a) Born in Milan in 1571, which painter was forced to flee Rome in 1606 after killing a man?
(b) Born in 1500 in Florence, which Mannerist sculptor, goldsmith and writer claimed in his somewhat fanciful autobiography to have stabbed his brother's murderer to death, killed a rival goldsmith and fatally shot an innkeeper?
(c) Born in 1860 and a member of the Camden Town Group, which painter had a keen interest in the Jack the Ripper murders? The writer Patricia Cornwall has suggested that he himself was responsible for them.

Your starter for ten:
9   Which three letters all begin the following? The surname of the creator of Randle Patrick McMurphy; a Sikh religious doctrine regarding uncut hair; the town at the northern end of Derwentwater; and the small falcon sometimes known as the 'windhover'.

Three questions on a French author:
(a) Born in 1873, which French author's works include *Ripening Seed* and *The Last of Chéri*? She was played by Keira Knightley in a film of 2018.
(b) Set partly in the Parisian dance halls, which novella by Colette has a title meaning 'Homeless Wanderer', or 'Unsettled Person'?
(c) Which novel by Colette was adapted into an Oscar-winning film with Leslie Caron playing the title role?

Your starter for ten:
10 Large populations of the Wolof and Serer ethnic groups are found in which country in West Africa? It is named after a river that rises in neighbouring Guinea.

Three questions on British Overseas Territories:
(a) Inscribed as a UNESCO World Heritage Site in 1988, Henderson island is a coral atoll that is part of which island group in the South Pacific?
(b) The Tristan da Cunha group contains two islands that were together named as a World Heritage Site in 1995: Gough Island and which other?
(c) St George, whose town and related fortifications were named as a World Heritage Site in 2000, is in the north of which Overseas Territory?

Your starter for ten:
11 Rose quartz, cadet, marengo, Spanish, platinum, nickel and glaucous are among the thirty or so shades of what colour, named on a popular online reference source?

Three questions on laboratory equipment named after scientists:
(a) Named after a 19th-century German scientist, what device combines a flammable gas with controlled amounts of air before ignition, to produce a hotter flame than would be possible using air and gas alone?
(b) Born in 1584, which French mathematician gives his name to the small, movable, graduated scale for obtaining subdivisions of a main fixed scale on a measuring instrument?
(c) Named after a German chemist born in 1825, what flat-bottomed container with a cylindrical neck is often used for titration or growing microbiological cultures?

Your starter for ten:
12 Concatenating the fourth and fifth primes gives the name of what international retail chain?

Your bonuses are on Carolingian rulers. In each case, I need the regnal name, which is the same for all three, and the uncomplimentary byname by which they are commonly known:

(a) Which grandson of Charlemagne became king of the West Franks in 843, and was crowned emperor in 875?

(b) Which nephew of Charles the Bald became emperor in 881? He bought off the Vikings when they besieged Paris, and was deposed soon afterwards.

(c) Which son of Louis the Stammerer became king of France in 893? The territory he ceded to the Vikings later became known as Normandy.

Your starter for ten:

13 Born in North Africa in the early 3rd century BCE, which Greek polymath is credited with the first accurate estimate of the circumference of the Earth?

Three questions on a gift of the Magi:

(a) Who was prime minister when the United Kingdom abandoned the gold standard in 1931?

(b) The Klondike Gold Rush occurred in Canada in which decade of the 19th century?

(c) Finally, which play by Shakespeare includes the line, 'All that glisters is not gold'?

Your starter for ten:

14 Born in Picardy in 1869, who depicted his wife in the 1905 painting *Woman with a Hat*? It is an early example of Fauvism.

Three questions on physics:

(a) The time taken for light to travel three millimetres in a vacuum is roughly equal to what prefixed SI unit?

(b) What electrical constant is equal to 8.85 pico-farads per metre?

(c) Expressed as a power of ten, how many picograms make up a metric tonne?

Your starter for ten:

15 Name either of the two moons of Pluto that are named after multi-headed mythological creatures.

Three questions on an economic system:

(a) From the Greek for 'self-sufficient', what term is applied to an economic system of limited or no trade with neighbouring countries?

(b) Often cited as a contemporary example of autarky, what country, established in 1948, follows the policy of *Juche*, or self-reliance?

(c) Born in 1772 and considered the founder of modern international trade theory, which British economist argued the advantages of free trade over autarky?

Your starter for ten:

16 I need the name of a chemical element here. The two-letter symbol of which chemical element begins words meaning or naming: the subject of Virgil's *Georgics*; universal, unconditional love; the mother of the Emperor Nero; and a 1st-century governor of Britain with a name meaning 'farmer', the subject of a biography by Tacitus?

Three questions on a philosopher:
(a) Nicknamed Doctor Mirabilis, which 13th-century English Franciscan friar was a prominent, though unconventional, scholar of mathematics, astronomy and optics?
(b) In his *Opus Majus*, Bacon calculated the maximum elevation of the red ray of light in a rainbow to appear at what angle above the horizon at sunrise or sunset? You may have three degrees either way.
(c) Bacon is thought to have been the first European to give precise instructions for the making of what commodity, although its origins are credited to the Chinese over 200 years earlier?

Your starter for ten:

17 What number results from adding together the number of towers of the cathedrals of Gloucester, Worcester and Lincoln?

Three questions on colloids:
(a) What three-letter term describes a colloid formed from a solid dispersed in a liquid such that the suspension does not solidify, as it does in a gel?
(b) A colloid composed of a gas in either a liquid or a solid is generally known by what four-letter name?
(c) A suspension of one liquid in another is generically described as what?

Your starter for ten:

18 Known scientifically as *Mustela putorius*, which member of the weasel family has recolonized extensive parts of England, after being pushed to the brink of extinction 100 years ago? It is the ancestor of the domesticated ferret.

Your bonuses are on shorter words that can be formed from the letters in the word 'nutcracker':
(a) First, a word meaning 'straying' or 'wandering'; it may follow the word 'knight' or precede the word 'husband'.
(b) A powerful poison obtained from *Strychnos toxifera* and other plants of tropical South America.
(c) A diacritical mark on a letter, used, for example, to indicate stress or different qualities of sound.

Your starter for ten:

19 In 1884, the Scottish zoologist William Hay Caldwell sent a telegram that read: 'Monotremes oviparous, ovum meroblastic.' This related to his study in Australia of which mammal, not previously well understood by science?

Three questions on comic verse about big cats:
(a) A noted monologue of the comedian Stanley Holloway, a boy comes to grief in the Marriott Edgar poem 'The Lion and Albert' during a visit to which seaside town?
(b) 'The tiger, on the other hand, is kittenish and mild, / He makes a pretty playfellow for any little child.' Who wrote those lines in a poem of 1896?
(c) 'If you're attacked by a lion / Find fresh underpants to try on'. Which author and comedian wrote this? He was the last surviving member of the comedy team the Goons.

Your starter for ten:

20 What short name links the daughter of Charles the Bad of Navarre who became the wife of Henry IV of England in 1402 and the Fair Maid of Kent, the mother of Richard II?

Three questions on geologists:
(a) Born in Copenhagen in 1638, which early geologist indicated the true origin of fossil animals and differentiated between stratified and volcanic rocks?
(b) In the early 20th century, the British geologist Gertrude Elles became known for her pioneering research into which fossil marine invertebrates, named from the Greek for 'marked with letters'?
(c) Born in 1785, Adam Sedgwick calculated the stratigraphic succession of fossil-bearing rocks in North Wales and assigned the oldest of them to what geological period?

Your starter for ten:

21 What short given name links: Mrs Helmer in Ibsen's play *A Doll's House*; the wife of the author James Joyce, and the screenwriter of films including *You've Got Mail* and *When Harry Met Sally*?

Three questions on National Character Areas (NCAs), subdivisions of England based on a combination of landscape, bio- and geo-diversity, and economic activity, as defined by Natural England:
(a) Meaning 'hilly open country', what plural word follows 'Lincolnshire' and 'Yorkshire' in the names of two national character areas?
(b) What is the short name of the East England NCA described as 'a distinctive historic and human-influenced wetland landscape lying to the west of the Wash Estuary'?
(c) What short word follows 'Dark' and 'White' in the names of two NCAs that together form part of a national park?

Your starter for ten:

22 Which poet wrote these lines? 'Does my sassiness upset you? / Why are you so beset with gloom?/ 'Cause I walk like I've got oil wells / Pumping in my living-room.' They appear in the title poem of the writer's third volume of poetry, *And Still I Rise*.

Three questions on chemical engineering:
(a) Developed by Chaim Weizmann, later the president of Israel, the ABE fermentation process uses an acid-resistant bacterium to produce which volatile chemical compound, with by-products of butanol and ethanol?
(b) Acetone is used in the acetate process for the production of acetate rayon, a fibre composed of what naturally occurring polysaccharide?
(c) A major industrial use of acetone during the First World War was the production of which explosive, a mixture of cellulose nitrate and nitrolycerin?

Your starter for ten:

23 Give the name of the s-block element that has a symbol comprising the initial letters of the SI unit of inductance and the human organs of vision?

Three questions on the ancient Indian work known as the 'Eight Chapters':
(a) In the 'Eight Chapters', Pānini defines the morphology and syntax of which language, describing the differences between its usage in spoken language and sacred texts?
(b) Pānini sums up Sanskrit phonetics and grammar in about 4,000 brief rules known by what term, meaning 'thread' or 'string'? The same word often appears in the titles of Buddhist texts.

(c) Pānini's grammar has been likened to what eponymous idealized mathematical model, introduced in 1936, that reduces the logical structure of any computing device to its essentials?

Your starter for ten:

24 Which play by Shakespeare is referenced in the title of Daniel Gardner's 1775 group portrait of Georgiana, Duchess of Devonshire, Elizabeth, Viscountess Melbourne, and the sculptress Anne Seymour Damer? The painting is said to hint at the political influence held by the three women.

Three questions on astronomy:
(a) In the official nomenclature set by the International Astronomical Union, for what does the letter 'P' stand in the designations 'P/Tempel', '2P/Encke' and '1P/Halley'?
(b) Halley, Encke and Tempel are comets that return periodically. What condition is indicated by a letter 'D' in a comet's designation, for example '5D/Brorsen' and '3D/Biela'?
(c) Indicating another class of comet-like objects that cannot return, for what does the letter 'I' stand in the names '2I/Borisov' and '1I/Oumuamua'?

Your starter for ten:

25 In 2020, a new type of mineral was discovered by scientists analysing a rock mined in Cornwall about 220 years earlier. It was given what name, in part after the Cornish name for Cornwall?

Three questions on Renaissance art:
(a) In the early 16th century, which artist created the murals in the four rooms known as the Stanze, part of the Vatican accommodation of Pope Julius II?
(b) What name is given to Raphael's mural on the main wall of the Stanza della Segnatura that depicts a perspective of a group of philosophers of ancient Greece?
(c) Which figure is depicted towards the centre of *The School of Athens*, in conversation with Aristotle and holding a copy of the dialogue *Timaeus*?

The Answers

1   Amharic (accept Amhara)
    (a) (Louis) de Broglie
    (b) (Comte de) Buffon
    (c) Charles de Gaulle

2   Becquerel (seconds-1, or per second; i.e. as the hertz)
    (a) Upton Sinclair
    (b) Teapot Dome (scandal)
    (c) *There Will Be Blood*

3   James III (reigned 1460–1488, killed at the Battle of Sauchieburn)
    (a) Israel
    (b) New Jersey
    (c) Turkey (Kayseri)

4   'Twas (''Twas the night before Christmas' and ''Twas brillig', of course)
    (a) Boletes / boletus
    (b) Milk-caps
    (c) Morels

5   Seven(th) (Prince George as King George VII)
    (a) Kentucky
    (b) Missouri
    (c) Montana

6   Manchu (not Qing / Ch'ing, alternative names for the dynasty but not for the area)
    (a) (Regular) hexagon
    (b) (Equilateral) triangles
    (c) Cairo

7   Photography (accept photojournalism, street photography)
    (a) (Leila) Slimani
    (b) Marguerite Duras
    (c) Simone de Beauvoir

8   Sting
    (a) Caravaggio
    (b) (Benvenuto) Cellini
    (c) Walter Sickert

9   Kes (Ken Kesey in *One Flew Over the Cuckoo's Nest*, kesh, Keswick, kestrel)
    (a) (Sidonie-Gabrielle) Colette
    (b) *La Vagabonde*
    (c) *Gigi*

10 Senegal
    (a) Pitcairn (Islands)
    (b) Inaccessible (Island)
    (c) Bermuda

11 Grey
    (a) Bunsen burner
    (b) (Pierre) Vernier
    (c) Erlenmeyer flask (Emil Erlenmeyer, 1825–1909)

12 7-eleven
    (a) Charles the Bald / Charles le Chauve / Karl der Kahle
    (b) Charles the Fat (not usually counted among the kings of France)
    (c) Charles the Simple (i.e. Charles III of France, grandson of Charles the Balds)

13 Eratosthenes (of Cyrene / Alexandria)
    (a) (Ramsay) MacDonald
    (b) 1890s (1896–1899; not 1840s, which saw the California Gold Rush)
    (c) *The Merchant of Venice*

14 (Henri) Matisse
    (a) Picosecond
    (b) Permittivity of the vacuum (or permittivity of free space)
    (c) 10^{18}

15 Hydra / Kerberos
    (a) Autarky (Greek: *autarkēs*)
    (b) North Korea / Democratic People's Republic of Korea / DPRK)
    (c) (David) Ricardo

16 Silver (i.e. Ag; agriculture, agape, Agrippina the Younger, Agricola)
    (a) (Roger) Bacon
    (b) 42 degrees (so accept 39 to 45 degrees)
    (c) Gunpowder (accept black powder)

17 Five (Gloucester: 1; Worcester: 1; Lincoln: 3)
    (a) Sol
    (b) Foam
    (c) Emulsion

18 (European) polecat (NB not the stoat, *Mustela erminea*)
    (a) Errant
    (b) Curare
    (c) Accent

19 (Duck-billed) platypus
    (a) Blackpool
    (b) Hilaire Belloc
    (c) Spike Milligan

20 Joan
    (a) (Nicolaus / Niels) Steno (accept Stensen or Stenonius)
    (b) Graptolites (Greek: *graptos*)
    (c) Cambrian

21 Nora
    (a) Wolds
    (b) (The) Fens
    (c) Peak

22 Maya Angelou
    (a) Acetone (accept 'propanone', correcting it)
    (b) Cellulose
    (c) Cordite

23 Helium (He: henry, eye)
    (a) Sanskrit
    (b) Sutra(s) (accept Sutta)
    (c) Turing machine

24 *Macbeth* (*The Three Witches of Macbeth*)
    (a) Periodic
    (b) Destroyed (accept disappeared, deceased, dead and similar)
    (c) Interstellar

25 Kernowite
    (a) Raphael (Raffaelo Sanzio)
    (b) *The School of Athens*
    (c) Plato

Where Are They Now?

Part 2

Sean Blanchflower was a member of Trinity College, Cambridge's 1995 winners, a team which also included Kwasi Kwarteng who went on to become Secretary of State at the Department of Business, Energy and Industrial Strategy. They were the first winning team after the programme was revived, the first in the Paxman era.

Sean is a manager for a major software company based in Cambridge and in his spare time curates a website that details much of the history of *University Challenge*. He is also a winner of the quiz show *Only Connect*.

'When I was in secondary school the show was on in the daytime, so it wasn't possible to watch, and when it was being revived, we'd heard of it but very few of us had actually seen it. We knew very little about it, just that it was a long-running quiz show with extremely hard questions. They put up a poster around the college saying, "Does anybody want to come along to a quiz trials evening to form a team?" Robin [Bhattacharyya, captain] and I were friends, we liked quizzes, so we thought we'd give it a go.'

The team chosen after a relatively informal trial – 'The head of the Students' Union had bought a kind of "my first pop quiz" book for a pound and asked a load of questions' – was made up of Sean and Robin, who were both reading Mathematics, Kwasi Kwarteng, who was reading Classics, and Erik Gray, an English undergraduate.

The *University Challenge* producers came to Cambridge to whittle down the teams with written questions and then face-to-face interviews. 'We knew that it was a TV show. We knew they needed people who weren't going to freeze up under pressure. They needed people who would come across as lively and talkative on television. Their last question was, "If you had to describe yourself as a food dish, what would it be and why?"'

The Trinity team took on Brasenose College, Oxford in their first-round match, winning by five points (185–190), decided on the final starter question. 'The first round and our semi-final [against Aberdeen that went down to a tie-break which Sean won] were very, very close, and the other games we won strongly. People say it's easy when you're sitting at home, but that it's very different when you're there under the lights. I never found that. When the cameras turned on and I was under pressure, my mind came to life and I was coming up with answers that I began to think I wouldn't have got at home. The other three, on the other hand, said they didn't enjoy it one bit.

'When we returned to Manchester several months later for the later rounds, we felt we were kind of old hands. We were all able to relax and enjoy it, and then it went really smoothly.'

Following the nerve-jangling semi-final against the strong Aberdeen side, Sean's team faced New College, Oxford in the final. They were 200 points up after only 10 minutes and eventually won 390–180. They were awarded their trophy by Bamber Gascoigne who told them their winning score was the highest he could remember.

'It's a testament to how much the show means to people in that the college got dozens of letters from old students saying congratulations and how much it meant to them and reminded them of their student days, so it felt like we'd done something that meant something to people around the country. There have been times over the years since when I began to think that nothing I could do could ever match winning *University Challenge*. I'd done the first line of my obituary. The rest of my life was going to be an anti-climax. Twenty-five years on I'm still introduced to people as a *University Challenge* champion.

'I think the reason *University Challenge* is still so popular is that it hasn't really changed; it's a reassuring constant in a fast-changing world. If you went to university, you automatically have a team to support and follow through the rounds. But the thing I think that keeps it most relevant is the contestants. The students are a mirror of society, and they show the diversity of society and the ambitions of society. And the characters on the show rarely disappoint.'

Sean believes the questions have got harder over the years. 'There's no doubt there. Every now and again, there's an article in the papers about how in Bamber Gascoigne's day the questions were impossible and nowadays there are questions about pop music and football and *Coronation Street*. But that's just nonsense. The questions change with how society's changed and how universities have changed. In Bamber Gascoigne's day there were more questions on Classics, more esoteric literature and things like that, whereas questions on nuclear physics were a bit too tricky for then. Nowadays they're absolutely standard. The quality of science questions has just gone up and up.

'But also the quality of contestants really has gone up. I'd like to say that we were the heyday of the team and you'll never see anything like 1994 but that's just not true. The teams now are fantastic.

'Because of this show, quizzing is now seen as a sporting discipline. The winners of the 1996 series, Imperial, organized the first British student quiz championships and that has snowballed.'

What advice would Sean have for anyone considering putting themselves forward for *University Challenge* these days?

'Everybody asked me how you prepare to go on the show and what revision I did and the answer is you just can't revise. You can brush up on a couple of areas but you have to spend the previous 18 years preparing for it, really. If you do go on, you just have to try to enjoy it. I'd say go on and have a bit of fun.'

*

Elizabeth Mitchell was the captain of the 2014 University of Manchester team, who were semi-finalists against Trinity College, Cambridge, when Ralph Morley was the Trinity captain. Elizabeth studied Politics, Philosophy and Economics from 2011 to 2014. After university, she worked for Manchester City Council, and in April 2021 joined the Department for Levelling Up, Housing and Communities as a senior policy adviser.

'I actually applied in my first year. I watched the programme growing up with my family. I'd done a little bit of quizzing at school. There's a thing called *Schools Challenge*, so I thought I'd give it a go. Obviously, I didn't expect to get on or anything, but I was selected as the reserve. As a reserve you get a bit of exposure to it, and if you're helping the team practise, it's probably no bad thing. And then having been the reserve during my first year, I applied again the following year and got on the team proper. In my third year I helped out with the selection process, and we got over a hundred applicants that year.'

The year Elizabeth was reserve was at the old Granada Studios; it was the last series that was made there. 'So we trundled off there to be interviewed. By chance, a match featuring the Manchester team from the year before was being shown on TV that night. So we all went to the pub to watch it, which was quite fun.'

The filming itself is a bit nerve-racking, Elizabeth remembers. 'I found it really exciting seeing behind the scenes. You know the seats aren't on top of each other, but it still feels weird to see them side by side. And the whole process of being in the green room, meeting other teams, going to get your make-up put on, I found it really, really enjoyable. Although it is quite intense. I don't remember the actual filming of the matches themselves brilliantly. I kind of remember the bits around them. It's probably a lot of adrenalin.

'One question that sticks in my mind was to do with ABBA, whom I really dislike, and in our first-round match I buzzed in after about one second and could identify Colin Firth singing [an ABBA song] and I feel like that did nothing for my credibility!

'I think we did feel a bit of pressure after Manchester's success in the previous two years, but I wouldn't say we felt pressure from the former teams or anything. We just wanted to do everyone proud. It definitely felt like we were there representing the university and the city to an extent. I think when we got to the semis and we were playing Trinity Cambridge again – we'd already played them once – I don't think that result was a surprise. The better team won.

Elizabeth says she didn't really have a particular specialism. 'I was kind of a jack of all trades, master of none. We did have people on our team who did have unexpected specialism, so Joe Day was a physics student but his knowledge of politics and political history was incredible. I felt one of my jobs was to work out where my teammates' unexpected knowledge was. Joe would obviously get physics questions right but if there was a politics question, I could also ask him, "What's the answer?" So I hope I brought a bit of that to the table, trying to try to draw the answers out of others.'

What does Elizabeth think it is about *University Challenge* that keeps it so popular? 'Everyone loves a quiz, right? And I feel like *University Challenge* does test you; it's not easy. You feel the satisfaction when you get a question right. Jeremy's always been a very charismatic presenter. I've certainly always found it very enjoyable to watch it with other people. It's quite an interactive show to watch in that sense. I used to watch it growing up with my family. And I remember getting the first question right and being a really smug kid. And now I watch it and I'm like, "Oh God, I can't remember anything because I can't get any of these." I think it does work across generations as well. I always enjoy when you hear the contestants conferring and you get to see their personalities coming through.'

Elizabeth is still in touch with Manchester contestants across the different series and she even met her partner through it. 'I would tell anyone to give it a go. I think even the application process itself is a fun thing to go through. What's there to lose?

'The main thing I'd want to get across is just how much fun it was. I think people think that quizzing is super intense, especially on there, especially on that one. And I think people think you've got to sit there, revising quiz books or something, and my experience was the complete opposite of that. It was everyone having a laugh and then going for drink afterwards, and that extended to the other teams we were interacting with during filming as well.

'There's a real community in quizzing. I feel like sometimes the kind of caricatures of *University Challenge* that you might see in the press, it's not quite like that in real life. It's much more fun.'

*

Stephen Pearson was a member of the 1997 University of Manchester team who were semi-finalists. Although Stephen's team were narrowly beaten in the semi-finals, Stephen is an important figure in the recent history of the programme. Described as the 'Alex Ferguson of *University Challenge*', he set up a selection and training structure at the University of Manchester that produced four winning teams in a short space of time.

He recalls: 'I was working as a librarian at Manchester University, and doing a master's degree in Old English Literature in my spare time. When I was doing my undergraduate degree in the 1980s, *University Challenge* with Bamber Gascoigne was one of my favourite programmes, and I'd have liked to have appeared on it but my Oxford college wasn't invited to apply during the time I was there. Then *University Challenge* went off the air and I thought I'd lost my chance to be on.

'About a year after I started doing my master's, the programme came back and I thought, "Ah, this has worked out nicely, I can try to be on *University Challenge* now."' Stephen had always been keen on quizzes, having taken part in *Ask the Family*, presented by Robert Robinson, with his parents and younger sister when he was 15 and *Schools Challenge* a couple of years later. He had set up an informal quiz league at Oxford and similar competitions between the halls of residence at Manchester. Before *University Challenge*, he took part in BBC Radio 4's *Counterpoint* music quiz and appeared on *Mastermind*. Stephen's team stormed to a 360–40 point win over Birkbeck College, London in their first round and progressed to the semi-finals where they lost by 15 points to Magdalen, Oxford, the eventual champions of the 1996–1997 series.

After their appearance, Stephen approached the Students' Union and asked if he could take on the job of recruiting and training the next *Challenge* team. He got the go-ahead and set about refining his training techniques. Speedy buzzer skills are vital, he says, and the training consisted of regular practice sessions using buzzers and replicating as far as possible the environment of the show, with Stephen acting as both quizmaster and name caller.

Selecting the teams is something of an art, too. A mix of specialisms including Classics, science and mathematics is ideal, but even the most knowledgeable group of students has to get through the programme's audition process. 'I really enjoyed the experience of taking part in *University Challenge* and I thought, "I want to continue being involved in this because I like the quiz culture." The next year, the team I selected didn't get through the audition process but the following year's did, although they were beaten in the second round by Oriel, which was, ironically, my old Oxford college.' But the dedication and hard work paid off and, under Stephen's stewardship, the Manchester team have won four times – in 2006, 2009 (when Manchester won by default after the original winners, Corpus Christi College, Oxford, were disqualified) 2012 and 2013, and reached the semi-finals in 2005, 2008 and 2010.

Team captain of the first winning Manchester team, politics postgraduate student Joseph Meagher, told the *Manchester Evening News* at the time: 'We didn't just meet over the university bar and decide to enter. There was quite a rigorous process to get in the team. Stephen was putting us through our paces with practice every week and then twice a week when we were in the competition. We took it seriously. It was hard work but it paid off.'

*

On the first winning team from Manchester University in 2006, **Gareth Aubrey** was studying for a master's in Nuclear Science and Technology when he was selected by Stephen Pearson. Gareth eventually qualified as a solicitor, worked in the Welsh Assembly and was a city councillor for Cardiff.

'The big thing from our perspective was that Stephen [Pearson] would arrange regular practice sessions playing actual buzzer quiz questions,' he remembers. 'We'd play against a combination of people who had already been on the show before. By the time we were preparing, we had practice opponents who had been on the show recently and had done pretty well. So the teams we were playing at that point were as strong or potentially stronger than anybody we were going to be going to be facing.'

Manchester's first winning run through the competition was nearly derailed on the day of the quarter-final. Gareth remembers: 'One of the team members was from Blackpool and was travelling from Blackpool to Manchester on the morning of the recording. However, his train was delayed and the programme got as far as making a nameplate for our stand in. Our teammate arrived just in time, though.' The team, which included captain Joseph Meagher, a Politics postgraduate student, Chris Holmes, a Material Science undergraduate, and Mathematics student Adrian Anslow, went on to beat Trinity Hall College, Cambridge in a tight final with Manchester winning by just 10 points.

Gareth believes the type of person who makes a good *University Challenge* player is someone who keeps up with the news, does lots of non-fiction reading, and happens to have the type of mind that retains information. 'Obviously there are plenty of people who do like the formalized way of learning with hundreds of flashcards with different questions, but even then I don't think there's anybody in that category who doesn't have a genuine enjoyment of knowing about the world.' He says the secret to *University Challenge*'s long-running popularity is the history of the show. 'It's been around since 1962, and you get that sense of how knowledge has evolved.'

Following *University Challenge*, Gareth became interested in the wider world of competitive quizzing and is now captain of the Wales national team. They take part in the annual European Championships and a Celtic nations tournament each year. He has also appeared on *Only Connect*. 'By coincidence, the *Only Connect* production office was in the ward I represented when I was on Cardiff City Council, so I applied and my team went on as the County Councillors.' He also took part in a special 'champion of champions' *University Challenge* match in April 2014 to mark 50 years of BBC Two. It pitted members of each of the four winning teams from Manchester and Magdalen College, Oxford against each other, with Manchester winning 230–80.

*

Freya McClements also appeared in the 2014 'champions' match, for her old Oxford college. She was the captain of the winning team in 2004, which was the third win for Magdalen. Now an author, documentary-maker, radio panellist and journalist – she is Northern Editor of the *Irish Times* – she remembers her time on *University Challenge* with pride.

'My journey with *University Challenge* probably started way before university because *University Challenge* came back on television when I was a teenager. It was one of those things that you always watched. I had been involved in school quizzes in Northern Ireland where there's a really big tradition of school quizzes. I remember sitting at home and watching it every week. I remember actually watching Magdalen, which had done really well in 1998, when I was applying for universities. I went to an ordinary school in Northern Ireland [Dalriada Grammar School], and we didn't have a big connection with Oxbridge or anything. And this is before the internet so there wasn't the availability of information. Magdalen was the one that I knew because they had just won *University Challenge* and also it had a female captain [Sarah Fitzpatrick]. She was absolutely an inspiration for me.'

Freya, who was reading Modern History, applied and was selected for her college team but that first team were not selected for the programme. A year later, with Freya as captain, they were successful. 'The hardest thing is actually getting on because when you think of the number of teams, I mean, it was way over 100 that applied to get on and they select 28. I don't know why we got picked the second time but we did.'

Freya had appeared on televised quizzes before, thanks to her involvement in schools quizzing. 'I had a bit of experience being in the TV studio but there's nothing like *University Challenge*. It has this key place in our culture, in our society. There have been films made about it, books, TV shows… It's in songs. It's a remarkable thing to have been part of. When you're actually there and you see the set and you see the *University Challenge* logo you suddenly realize that – wow – this is really happening. It's a strange mixture of excitement and nerves. I don't think anybody goes into it thinking that they're going to win. I mean, obviously, you would like to win. That's the dream.'

Magdalen moved comfortably through the rounds, despatching Nottingham, Sussex, the Royal Northern College of Music and St Andrews before meeting Gonville and Caius, Cambridge in the final which they won 190–160 before collecting their trophy from author Bill Bryson. 'I remember the final really, really clearly. It was nerve-racking because, at that stage, it's within touching distance and Gonville and Caius were a really strong team. I had developed this really bad habit in previous rounds of being too keen to get on the scoreboard and buzzing too early so I remember consciously thinking, "Right, take a minute, think about it…"'

'Although I was reading Modern History, geography was kind of one of my specialisms so I realized there was a geography question. It was something about some geopolitical entity which I had never heard of, something which was apparently spelt GUUAM. And you had to say what this stood for. So I remember buzzing in and, in my head, I'd got as far as I think, Georgia, Ukraine… So I buzzed in and went, "Georgia, Ukraine…" and then I was desperately trying to think and I said, "Uzbekistan, Armenia, and er, maybe Moldova?" I sort of stumbled through, just making them up off top my head, and it was right!'

'I'd been keeping an eye on the time with my watch under the desk as I knew the final was a slightly shorter quiz in order to accommodate the prizegiving and I'll never forget the moment that the gong went and there was this moment of realization that, "Oh my God, we've won!" I'll never forget that moment. There was this realization that this is something that I'm going to have for the rest of my life. You're up against such brilliant teams. I mean, some of the teams in it were fantastic, so you needed skill, but you absolutely needed luck as well. You needed all the things to fall right for you on the day.'

Because Magdalen were the first team to win the competition three times, they were allowed to keep the trophy. 'We can go and see it whenever we like, and I've actually I've brought people to see it – they have a lovely display cabinet in the library. So it's a really special thing.'

Appearing on *University Challenge* was beneficial for Freya's career. She wanted to become a journalist and after the programme was broadcast she was invited to do work experience with the BBC. It led to working for the corporation for several years and also to a respected career in newspapers. She has written books, created documentaries, and although she 'retired' from competitive quizzing after *University Challenge*, she is now one half of the Northern Ireland team on BBC Radio 4's *Round Britain Quiz* which is 'an absolute delight'.

Challenging Tales
Bottoming Out

Just sometimes, it can all get a bit too much… There was one contestant who asked to go to the loo towards the end of filming a round – and refused to return.

'I think it was around the second or third series we had with Jeremy,' recalls executive producer Peter Gwyn. 'We were about a couple of minutes to the gong. One contestant put her hand up and asked to go to the toilet and then she wouldn't come out!

'We completed the recording without her on the basis that there was no possible way her team could have won. And then we edited her back into the programme in post-production. I think she just had a panic attack or decided she didn't want to go back on or something.'

*

The Sincerest Form

The 1984 *Young Ones* spoof of *University Challenge* has gone down in cult comedy history, but it isn't the only time the programme has been (mis) represented on screen. In the 1990s, long-running soap *Coronation Street* was filmed in the same Granada Studios building and, in a 1997 sketch for Comic Relief, Jeremy Paxman was confronted with 'a team of ordinary people' from Weatherfield. Pitted against a fictional St Luke's, Cambridge team, Gail (then) Platt (played by Helen Worth), Jim McDonald (Charles Lawson), Vera Duckworth (Liz Dawn) and Norman 'Curly' Watts (Kevin Kennedy) wound up winning, to the delight of viewers and a wry smile from the quizmaster. *University Challenge* has also sent itself up a number of times for TV charity events such as Children in Need.

And in 2006 the film *Starter for Ten*, about a student played by James McAvoy desperate to compete on *University Challenge*, saw *League of Gentlemen* co-creator and *Sherlock* and *Doctor Who* writer Mark Gatiss star as Bamber Gascoigne. When Gascoigne died, Gatiss tweeted: 'Very sorry to hear that Bamber Gascoigne has died. An ever-cheerful icon of our collective TV upbringing who made knowledge and intelligence seem fun. That's how boffins should be, I always thought. It was a great joy to play him.'

Try Your Luck
Match

Your starter for ten:

1 Almost 800 kilometres in length, the Southern Buh, or Boh, is a major river in which European country? It flows into the Black Sea about 50 kilometres west of the Dnieper.

Three questions on poisonous plants, as described in Maud Grieve's 1931 book *A Modern Herbal*:

(a) Known in German as *Fingerhut*, which flower does Grieve describe as 'perhaps the handsomest of our indigenous plants'? She identifies its several glucoside compounds that act as cardiac stimulants, including digitoxin.

(b) Which tall, yellow-flowering tree has seeds that contain the poisonous alkaloid cytisine? Grieve recommends that it 'should not be allowed to overhang a field used as a pasture'.

(c) Of which climbing plant does Grieve state that when the leaves or flowers are applied to the skin 'they produce inflammation and vesication, hence the name *Flammula jovis*'? Alternative names include virgin's bower and traveller's joy.

Your starter for ten:

2 Regarded as a showcase for new Nordic cuisine, what is the four-letter name of the Copenhagen restaurant founded in 2003 by Claus Meyer and head chef René Redzepi?

Three questions on schoolmasters in the novels of Charles Dickens:

(a) Mr M'Choakumchild appears in which novel? He is a teacher at an experimental school in northern England, run on Utilitarian principles.

(b) Bradley Headstone is a schoolmaster in which novel? A mentor to Charley Hexam, his passion for Charley's sister Lizzie leads to his destruction.

(c) First serialized in 1849, which novel features Salem House school, run by the sadistic Mr Creakle?

Your starter for ten:

3   Born in 1879, the author Stella Miles Franklin bequeathed her estate to fund a literary award in what country? Winners have included Melissa Lucashenko, Tim Winton, Thea Astley and Patrick White.

Your bonuses are on winners of the Academy Award for Best Picture. In each case, give the title of the film from the date of its release and the author of the source material on which it is based:
(a) 2013 and Solomon Northup.
(b) 1948 and William Shakespeare.
(c) 1963 and Henry Fielding?

Your starter for ten:

4   In a common laboratory procedure, the addition of an equal mixture of phenol and which other compound is used to purify nucleic acids from proteins and lipids? Having the chemical formula $CHCl_3$, it was pioneered as an anaesthetic in 1847 by the Scottish physician James Young Simpson.

Three questions on French art in the 1830s:
(a) Exhibited in 1833, *View of the Forest of Fontainebleau* is an early work by which prolific French landscape painter, associated with the Barbizon school?
(b) Published in the mid-1830s, *Reminiscences of My Life* is a memoir by which Parisian artist, noted for her numerous portraits of Marie Antoinette?
(c) *Women of Algiers in Their Apartment*, *Fanatics of Tangier* and *Jewish Wedding* are among the works of the 1830s by which major French Romantic painter?

Your starter for ten:

5   Known as the 'dean of Arab diplomacy', Sheikh Sabah al-Ahmed al-Sabah died at the age of 91 in 2020, having ruled which country since 2006?

Three questions on constellations. In each case, I need the Latin name or names of the constellations described:
(a) I need two names here. Which two constellations have names differing in just two of their letters? One contains the alpha-designated star Dubhe, the other, Polaris?
(b) Similarly, name two constellations, one containing the alpha-designated star Sirius, the other, Procyon.
(c) The name of which constellation of the zodiac precedes the word 'minor' in the name of another constellation which lies adjacent to Ursa Major in the night sky?

'Scholarly, gentle and yet commanding', *University Challenge*'s
original host, Bamber Gascoigne, is pictured at the helm
during the third show of the first series in 1962. In those
early days, Gascoigne not only presented the programme
but also researched and wrote some of the questions.

VYVYAN   RICK   NEIL   MIKE

SCUMBAG COLLEGE

Cult comedy *The Young Ones'* famous parody of *University Challenge*, in which Vyvyan, Rick, Neil and Mike, representing 'Scumbag College' take on 'Footlights College, Oxbridge', was first broadcast in 1984. In 2020, actor Adrian Edmondson (who played punk Vyvyan) delighted fans when he appeared as himself as part of a University of Manchester alumni team in a Christmas special.

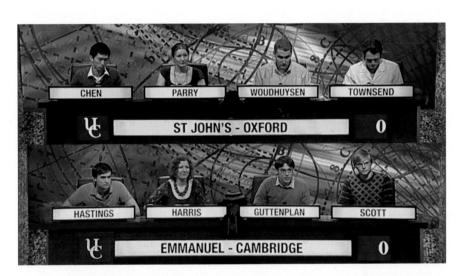

St John's College, Oxford and Emmanuel College,
Cambridge prepare to do battle at the beginning of the
2010 final. Emmanuel emerged victorious scoring 315
points to 100 for St John's. Emmanuel's high-scoring captain,
Alex Guttenplan (second from right), was described in
the Press at the time as 'an unlikely sex symbol'.

WOUDHUYSEN · DAY · MITCHELL · COLLINGS

MANCHESTER · 0

Elizabeth Mitchell (second from right) captained the University of Manchester's 2014 team which reached the semi-finals, losing out to that series' eventual champions, Trinity College, Cambridge. Elizabeth had been the team reserve player the previous year, which she said stood her in good stead to lead the team.

Bobby Seagull (second from right), who admits to never having seen the show before he went on it, captained the Emmanuel College, Cambridge team in the 2017 series. His team reached the semi-final, where they were beaten by Wolfson College, Cambridge, headed up by Eric Monkman. The two captains have since gone on to star in their own TV show and write a book together.

In one of the many Oxbridge battles, Eric Monkman's Wolfson College, Cambridge were pitted against Balliol College, Oxford in the 2017 final. Balliol won by 190 points to 140 and received their trophy from the celebrated theoretical physicist Stephen Hawking just five months before his death.

Lucy Clarke (far left) had wanted to appear on *University Challenge* since she first watched it, aged seven, with her father. In 2020, she achieved her ambition as a member of Jesus College, Oxford's team. They reached the quarter-finals, losing out to Trinity College, Cambridge.

Imperial took on Reading in 2022's final, beating them by only
10 points (shown here just before Hutchinson lost his team
5 points seconds before the final gong). Imperial's victory
meant they joined Magdalen College, Oxford and Manchester
in having won the trophy an impressive four times.

Jeremy Paxman settles in to present his very first
University Challenge in 1994. He has now presented the
programme for longer than Bamber Gascoigne and is
one of the world's longest-serving quiz show hosts.

Your starter for ten:

6   Answer promptly, naming any two of the four contiguous countries whose post-independence leaders have included Thomas Boni Yayi, Yakubu Gowon, Paul Biya and Omar Bongo.

Three questions on novels:

(a) *Thieves in the Night* is a 1946 work by which Hungarian-born author, who had earlier written *Darkness at Noon*?

(b) Teju Cole's 2007 novel *Every Day Is for the Thief* is set in which major African city?

(c) *The Lightning Thief* by Rick Riordan is the first in a series featuring which fictional schoolboy?

Your starter for ten:

7   Proclaiming himself emperor in 1802, Gia Long unified which present-day Asian country, founding its last ruling dynasty before its conquest by France?

Three questions on fruit:

(a) What fruit has varieties named Comice, Williams and Anjou?

(b) Originally grown by Thomas Rivers of Hertfordshire, which dessert pear gained its common name after it won a prize at a meeting of the National British Pear Growers in 1885?

(c) The Hass cultivar is a major variety of what fruit, also known as the alligator pear?

Your starter for ten:

8   Name either of the films for which Ingrid Bergman won the Academy Award for Best Actress. Both have single-word titles: one is a word that has come to mean 'to manipulate someone into questioning their own sanity', and the other is the name of a daughter of Tsar Nicholas II.

Your bonuses are on Tove Jansson, the Finnish-born creator of the Moomins:

(a) In 2017, which international organization used Jansson's Moomin products in a worldwide campaign to help women and girls fight inequality and escape poverty?

(b) Reissued in 2003, which of Jansson's novels for adults tells the story of a grandmother and granddaughter's holiday on a remote island?

(c) When suffering from Alzheimer's, which prolific British author was reportedly comforted by his daughter reading the Moomin books aloud to him? He died in 2015.

Your starter for ten:

9   In eukaryotic cells, an important part of the maturation of messenger RNA involves the addition of a long repeating stretch of which nucleic acid base to its three-prime end?

Three questions on literary terms used in poetry:
(a) After an organ of the body, what two-word term denotes pairs of words that end in the same letters, but do not rhyme? Examples include 'laughter' and 'daughter', and the name of the actor Sean Bean.
(b) An example being a work of 1595 by Edmund Spenser, an epithalamium is a poem in celebration of what event?
(c) Etymologically related to the name of a type of pasta, what adjective denotes verse that mixes words in more than one language, notably Latin and English?

Your starter for ten:

10 The 1960 science fiction film *Village of the Damned*, about a group of sinister telepathic children, is based on which 1957 book by the British author John Wyndham?

Your bonuses are on glacial features and landforms. Give each term from the description, as found on the *National Geographic*'s website:
(a) What term denotes a rock, deposited by a glacier, that differs from the geology or landscape in which it is found?
(b) What name is given to a long earthen mound shaped by the movement of glaciers?
(c) What term denotes material, such as earth, sand and gravel, transported by a glacier?

Your starter for ten:

11 Kisumu, Mwanza, Bukoba and Kampala are among cities on or near the shore of which inland body of water?

Your bonuses are on William Hazlitt's *Spirit of the Age*, a collection of contemporary biographical essays published in 1825. Identify the writer described in each case:
(a) '[His] genius is a pure emanation of the spirit of the age; if he can assuage the pain or close up the wound with the balm of solitary musing, or the healing power of plants and herbs and "skyey influences", this is the sole triumph of his art.'
(b) 'He is undoubtedly the most popular writer of the age – the "lord of the ascendant" for the time being; his is a mind brooding over antiquity – scorning "the present ignorant time".'

(c) '[He] is the spoiled child of fame as well as fortune. He has taken a surfeit of popularity, and is not contented to delight, unless he can shock the public.'

Your starter for ten:

12 Answer as soon as your name is called. Given three cups, one red, one blue and one yellow, and three saucers, also one red, one blue and one yellow, how many ways are there of putting each cup on a saucer so that none of the colours match?

Three questions on a science fiction novel:
(a) Which novel of 1989 by Dan Simmons follows pilgrims travelling to the Time Tombs on the title planet? The title also refers to a poem by Keats, who appears in the novel in the form of an android named Johnny.
(b) While travelling, the pilgrims tell tales of their life in the Hegemony of Man, a galactic empire centred on which star? A popular setting in science fiction, it is the second-closest spectral class G star to the sun.
(c) The Time Tombs are guarded by a fearsome creature that kills people by impaling them on a metal tree, and is therefore named after which bird of the family Laniidae?

Your starter for ten:

13 Used by Chaucer to distinguish planets from stars, what word is used in Earth science to mean a stray mass of rock transported from its place of origin by glacial action? In everyday speech, it is an adjective meaning 'unpredictable' or 'inconsistent'.

Your bonuses are on the small number of pre-20th-century figures who have had a separate Wikipedia page dedicated to their deaths; name each person from the date and place it occurred. All three are associated with the arts:
(a) Vienna, on 26 March 1827?
(b) Baltimore, on 7 October 1849?
(c) Auvers-sur-Oise, on 29 July 1890?

Your starter for ten:

14 Answer as soon as your name is called, giving your answer in decimal. What is the sum of the binary numbers 1-0-1 plus 1-0-0-1?

Your bonuses are on sports grounds with shared names. Give the shared name from the descriptions:
(a) A Test cricket ground in Hobart, Australia, and a golf course in Missouri that hosted the 2018 PGA championship. The name translates from the French meaning 'beautiful shore'.

(b) A Test cricket ground in Roseau, Dominica; and the home ground of the Northern Ireland national football team.

(c) A Test cricket ground in Kolkata; and a multi-sports venue in Auckland that hosted the 2011 Rugby World Cup final.

Your starter for ten:

15 I need the name of a chemical element here. The symbol for what element is obtained by concatenating the letters of the alphabet that represent the universal gas constant and the Planck constant?

Three questions on astronomy:

(a) What name is given to small bodies in the solar system orbiting between Neptune and Jupiter, which often show characteristics of both asteroids and comets?

(b) In 1989, astronomers observed a faint cometary coma around which object, with a diameter of about 200 kilometres? In 1977, it was the first centaur to be discovered.

(c) The largest known centaur, Chariklo, was reported in 2014 to have what feature, in common with the solar system's giant planets, detected through stellar occultation?

Your starter for ten:

16 I need an eight-letter term. Chloral and vanillin are examples of what class of organic compound that differs from hydrocarbons by the presence of the carbonyl group? The simplest of the class has the formula HCOH, and is often used to preserve biological specimens.

Three questions on chemical compounds:

(a) What single-word term describes either of a pair of chemical compounds whose molecular structures are mirror images of each other, and are not superimposable simply by reorientation?

(b) In terms of physical properties, enantiomers differ from each other only in the direction in which they are able to rotate what type of light, which consists of waves vibrating in the same direction?

(c) What word describes a mixture containing equal amounts of the enantiomers, that is, equal amounts of the right- and left-handed isomers?

Your starter for ten:

17 What two words follow 'Three Places in' to complete the title of an orchestral work by US composer Charles Ives? The three places in question are Stockbridge, Boston Common and Redding, Connecticut.

Three questions on composers of videogame music:

(a) Yoko Shimomura is best known for her scores for which series of videogames, set in a crossover universe populated by Disney, Pixar and Square Enix characters?

(b) Between 1992 and 2011, Rika Muranaka was a house composer at which major game company? Her work there included music for the *Castlevania* and *Metal Gear Solid* series.

(c) First released on the Nintendo Switch in 2017, which game in the *Legend of Zelda* series was the first to feature Manaka Kataoka as lead composer, taking over from Koji Kondo?

Your starter for ten:

18 National parks near which major Commonwealth city include Ku-ring-gai Chase, Thirlmere Lakes and the Blue Mountains?

Three questions on recipients of the Presidential Medal of Freedom:

(a) A computer programmer who wrote code for the Apollo space project, Margaret Hamilton popularized what two-word term to describe her profession?

(b) Katharine Graham received a posthumous medal in 2002, having transformed which US newspaper and supported its investigation into a major political scandal of the 1970s?

(c) The architect and sculptor Maya Lin is perhaps best known for designing part of the memorial in Washington, DC. To veterans of what conflict?

Your starter for ten:

19 What phenomenon may be measured in the ZHR, or zenithal hourly rate, this being the number that would be seen under ideal observing conditions? The phenomenon may occur sporadically, or in showers, or occasionally storms, with a ZHR that may reach tens of thousands.

Three questions on Channel 4's Alternative Christmas Message:

(a) Who, in 1993, gave the first Channel 4 Christmas Message? Born on Christmas Day 1908, he was an author and raconteur who styled himself as 'one of the stately homos of England'.

(b) Appearing in an animated series that had been acquired by Channel 4, which character read the message in 2004, comparing her marriage to that of the Beckhams?

(c) Having revealed the existence of the NSA's information-gathering programmes in 2013, which US National Security Agency contractor read the message that year?

Your starter for ten:

20 Similar in meaning to 'pastoral', what word derives from the Greek for 'herdsman' and denotes a form of literature that includes Virgil's *Eclogues* and Shakespeare's *The Winter's Tale*?

Three questions on the physicist Maria Goeppert-Mayer:
(a) Born in Katowice in 1906, Goeppert-Mayer shared the Nobel Prize in 1963 for her work on which description of the nucleus, linked to the concept of 'magic numbers'?
(b) Her PhD thesis predicted two-photon absorption, a third-order optical effect where which property of a dielectric varies non-linearly with electric field?
(c) In 1961, two-photon absorption was first observed using a europium-doped crystal, in which laboratory in Murray Hill, New Jersey?

Your starter for ten:

21 Meanings of what term include: in biology, the surface on which a sedentary organism occurs or grows; and, in biochemistry, the molecule that a particular enzyme acts on, bringing about a specific transformation?

Three questions on joints of the human body:
(a) The popliteus is a flat triangular muscle at the back of which joint?
(b) Köhler's disease results in inflammation of which bone of the ankle, named after its approximate resemblance to the shape of a boat?
(c) What short word follows 'rotator' to give the name of a part of the shoulder that is commonly injured?

Your starter for ten:

22 The last line of Charles Causley's poem 'Innocent's Song' refers to which historical figure, described in the second chapter of Matthew's Gospel as having died shortly after the birth of Jesus?

Three questions on operatic heroines:
(a) In which Italian opera of 1816 does Rosina lay 'a hundred traps' to thwart her guardian Dr Bartolo, who plans to marry her in order to claim her dowry?
(b) In which opera by Tchaikovsky does Tatyana, in the course of a twelve-minute aria, write a love letter to the title character, who then rejects her?
(c) In Mozart's *The Marriage of Figaro*, what is the name of the maid, betrothed to Figaro, who sings the aria 'Come, kneel down' as she dresses Cherubino as a woman?

Your starter for ten:

23 Which national park lies on a straight line connecting Liverpool and Newcastle upon Tyne?

Your bonuses are on astronomy. All three answers begin with the same four letters:
(a) Distinguished by a group of five bright stars forming a slightly irregular letter 'W', which constellation is named after the queen of Ethiopia whose daughter was Andromeda?
(b) Born in about 1629, which French priest gives his name to the design of a two-mirror reflecting telescope?
(c) A director of the Paris Observatory under Louis XIV, which Italian-born astronomer discovered four satellites of Saturn and the division in that planet's rings?

Your starter for ten:

24 Born in California in 1920, which pianist fronted a quartet known for *Time Out*, the first jazz album to sell more than a million copies, and 'Take Five', the bestselling jazz single of all time?

Three questions on serendipity:
(a) In 1754, which English author coined the word 'serendipity' in a letter analysing a Persian tale entitled 'The Three Princes of Serendip'?
(b) 'Serendip' derives from the classical Persian name of which island, somewhat smaller than Scotland?
(c) The novelist William Boyd created the word 'zemblanity' to mean an 'unpleasant un-surprise'. It derives from the name of a cold, barren archipelago that is part of what country?

Your starter for ten:

25 In surveying, what term denotes a mark placed permanently on a building or an outcrop of rock as a reference point? In a more general sense, it indicates an accepted standard by which other things are evaluated.

Three questions on the German mathematician Emmy Noether:
(a) Born in 1882, Noether gives her name to a theorem that has become a central pillar of theoretical physics. It connects symmetries with what specific class of physical laws?
(b) According to Noether's theorem, symmetry in time requires the conservation of what quantity?
(c) 7001 Noether, with a perihelion of just over two astronomical units, is an example of what type of object?

The Answers

1 Ukraine
(a) Foxglove
(b) Laburnum
(c) Clematis

2 Noma (an acronym for 'nordisk mad', i.e. Nordic food)
(a) *Hard Times*
(b) *Our Mutual Friend*
(c) *David Copperfield*

3 Australia (the Miles Franklin Award)
(a) *12 Years a Slave*
(b) *Hamlet*
(c) *Tom Jones*

4 Chloroform / trichloromethane
(a) (Jean-Baptiste-Camille) Corot
(b) (Élisabeth) Vigée-Lebrun
(c) (Eugène) Delacroix

5 Kuwait (he was succeeded by his 83-year-old half-brother)
(a) Ursa Major and Ursa Minor
(b) Canis Major and Canis Minor
(c) Leo (Minor)

6 Benin, Nigeria, Cameroon, Gabon
(a) (Arthur) Koestler
(b) Lagos
(c) Percy Jackson

7 Vietnam (the Nguyen dynasty)
(a) Pear
(b) Conference
(c) Avocado

8 *Gaslight* / *Anastasia* (1944 and 1956 respectively)
(a) Oxfam
(b) *The Summer Book*
(c) Terry Pratchett

9 Adenosine / adenine
(a) Eye rhyme
(b) Marriage
(c) Macaronic

10 *The Midwich Cuckoos*
   (a) (Glacial) erratic
   (b) Drumlin
   (c) (Terminal) moraine

11 Lake Victoria / Victoria Nyanza (in Kenya, Tanzania, Tanzania and Uganda)
   (a) (William) Wordsworth
   (b) (Sir Walter) Scott
   (c) (Lord) Byron

12 Two
   (a) Hyperion
   (b) Tau Ceti
   (c) The shrike (shrikes impale insect bodies on thorns)

13 Erratic (in *Troilus and Criseyde*)
   (a) (Ludwig van) Beethoven
   (b) (Edgar Allan) Poe
   (c) (Vincent) van Gogh

14 14 (101 = 5, 1001 = 9; 9 + 5 = 14)
   (a) Bellerive (Bellerive Oval; Bellerive Country Club)
   (b) Windsor Park
   (c) Eden (Eden Gardens; Eden Park)

15 Rhodium (Rh; not rhenium, symbol Re)
   (a) Centaurs
   (b) Chiron
   (c) Ring system / rings

16 Aldehyde (formaldehyde, of course)
   (a) Enantiomer / enantiomorph (not isomer or stereoisomer – these are broader classes)
   (b) (Plane) polarized light
   (c) Racemic (mixture) / racemate

17 New England
   (a) *Kingdom Hearts*
   (b) Konami
   (c) *Breath of the Wild*

18 Sydney
   (a) Software engineer (medal awarded in 2016; term coined in the late 1960s)
   (b) *Washington Post* (Watergate, of course; she died in 2001)
   (c) Vietnam War

19 Meteor showers (accept meteors)
    (a) Quentin Crisp (born Denis Charles Pratt)
    (b) Marge Simpson
    (c) Edward Snowden

20 Bucolic (Greek: *boukolos*)
    (a) Shell model
    (b) Polarization / polarization density
    (c) Bell (laboratories / labs)

21 Substrate
    (a) The knee
    (b) Navicular (or tarsal navicular bone)
    (c) Cuff (i.e. a rotator cuff tear)

22 Herod (the Great)
    (a) *The Barber of Seville / Il barbiere di Siviglia* (Rossini)
    (b) *Eugene Onegin*
    (c) Susanna

23 Yorkshire Dales
    (a) Cassiopeia
    (b) (Laurent) Cassegrain (the Cassegrain reflector)
    (c) (Gian Domenico) Cassini

24 Dave Brubeck (1920–2012)
    (a) (Horace) Walpole
    (b) Sri Lanka (accept Lanka, as the main island is known)
    (c) Russia

25 Benchmark
    (a) Conservation (laws)
    (b) Energy
    (c) Asteroid (accept minor planet, correcting it)

'Oh, do come on!'
Trinity College, Cambridge

VS

New College, Oxford
(1995)

This was the first final hosted by Jeremy Paxman. It was an Oxbridge affair, with Trinity getting through the semi-final on a tie break and New coming from behind in many of their heats to get through. It proved to be a pointsfest, with a colossal aggregate score of 570 points between the two teams.

The Trinity team contained two notable members: Kwasi Kwarteng, who in 2021 was appointed Secretary of State for Business, Energy and Industrial Strategy, and Sean Blanchflower, who is not only Vice President of Engineering at a major software company, but also has an in-depth and fascinating website on *University Challenge* where he recounts his experience on the show.

New College were notable for the fact that each of their contestants came from a different continent. They have made more comebacks than Frank Sinatra. They have beaten the universities of North London, St Bennetts Hall, Oxford, Birmingham University and Edinburgh. In each case, they rose from the apparently dead.

Trinity College, Cambridge
Sean Blanchflower from Quinton in Birmingham, reading Mathematics
Kwase Kwarteng from London, reading Classics
Robin Bhattacharyya (captain) from Stockport, reading Mathematics
Erik Gray from Charlottesville, Virginia, reading English

New College, Oxford
Alec Dinwoodie from Maryland, USA, reading Modern Poetry
Darren Smyth from Wakefield, West Yorkshire, studying Organic Chemistry
John Danesh (captain) from New Zealand, studying Etymology
Aran Balasudramanian from Madras, India, reading Law

*

Your starter for ten:
1 Which museum is a painstaking replica of the *Villa dei Papiri* in Herculaneum built on the West Pacific Coast Highway at Malibu and containing many world-famous works of art?

Your bonuses are on capital cities:
(a) Which European capital city was known as Kristiania from 1624 to 1925 after King Christian IV?
(b) Which administrative capital city was founded in 1855 by the son of the Dutch settler from whom the city took its name?
(c) Which capital city, founded in 1541, was named in honour of a patron saint of Spain?

Your starter for ten:
2 Constructed with an ape's jaw and human cranium, the fake remains of early—?
[The question was successfully interrupted]

Your bonuses are on numeric names or terms:
(a) Which numeric term was applied to the extremist religious sector of the Cromwellian period, which was led by Thomas Harrison and John Venner among others?
(b) Which battle was known as the Battle of the Three Emperors?
(c) Which numeric name is given to the eroded chalk pits on the Sussex coast between Cuckmere Haven and Beachy Head?

Your starter for ten:
3 Which science fiction writer in an article for the *Scientific Magazine* in 1945 predicted in detail a satellite system would relay—?
[The question was successfully interrupted]

Your bonuses are on exiles:

(a) In May 1994, the former first secretary of the East German Communist Party, Erich Honecker, died in exile, in which country?

(b) Who lived in exile for 20 years before returning home in 1680 as John Clarke?

(c) The deposed Shah of Iran died in exile in 1980, in which country?

Your starter for ten:

4 Which sea in the South West Pacific extending east of Australia and New Guinea—?

[The question was successfully interrupted]

Your bonuses are on fictional diaries and journals:

(a) Which fictional journal was published in 1722, more than half a century after the events it catalogued?

(b) Which fictional diarist, whose diary covers 15 months of his life in the early 1890s, lived with his wife Carrie in Brickfield Terrace, Holloway?

(c) Which Booker Prize-winning novel takes the form of a journal for his guardian, kept by Edmond Talbot on a voyage to Australia in the early 19th century?

Your starter for ten:

5 Acknowledging the receipt of an honorary degree in 1879 from Breslau University, which composer wrote the *Academic Festival Overture*, first performed there in 1881?

[No one answered the starter question correctly]

Your starter for ten:

6 Which of Shakespeare's characters says to her husband, 'But screw your courage to the sticking-place and we'll not fail'?

Your bonuses are on physics:

(a) Which French physicist discovered the phenomenon of radioactively through his investigations of uranium and other substances?

(b) The two radioactive series that begin with uranium-235 and uranium-238 respectively both end on stable isotopes of which element?

(c) The ratio of uranium to lead in certain rocks and minerals can be used to estimate the age of the Earth. To the nearest billion, how many years old is the Earth according to these measurements?

Your starter for ten:

7 [This was a picture round. Trinity correctly identified Gainsborough as the artist who painted the Linley sisters. They identified the subjects and artists of two out of three bonus pictures, the last of which being Holbein's portrait of Henry VIII, a copy of which, as Sean Blanchflower points out, hangs in the dining hall of Trinity College]

Your starter for ten:

8 Which Scottish explorer made two expeditions to plot the course of the river Niger. The first, which began in 1795, and the second that began in—? [The question was successfully interrupted]

Your bonuses are on French history:
(a) What name is given to the series of uprisings which took place in France in 1648 and 1653, which ended in a clear victory for Mazarin?
(b) Known from 1789 until 1792 as the Society of the Friends of the Constitution, what was the popular name for the extreme revolutionary group that ruled France from mid-1793 to mid-1794 and were so called because they met in a poor Dominican convent?
(c) What name did the Parisian radicals who rebelled against the government in 1871 after the Franco-Prussia War give themselves in emulation of the Jacobins of the French Revolution?

Your starter for ten:

9 What name is given to the phenomenon which occurs when the frequency of the driving force applied to an oscillatory system—? [The question was interrupted correctly]

Bonus questions:
(a) In the film *Play Misty for Me*, Clint Eastwood played a disc jockey, Dave Garland, who worked in which Californian town and later had non-acting significance for Eastwood?
(b) Which prophet persuaded King Ahab to assemble 450 priests of Baal on Mount Carmel and stage a competition in igniting a sacrificial bullock, the priests failing miserably?
(c) Who composed the oratorio *Elijah*, first performed in Birmingham in 1846 and in the composer's birthplace, Hamburg, the following year?

Your starter for ten:

10 Which American actress appeared with Jack Lemon in the 1988 film *Missing*, starred in the 1980 film *Coal Miners Daughter* and received an Academy Award nomination for her 1976 role in *Carrie*? [No one answered the question correctly]

Your starter for ten:

11 Which sporting body's initials appear to read 1200 in roman numerals?

Bonus questions:
(a) There are 20 full ones and 6 half ones, and among their number are Vaud, Valais, Tichino and Neuchâtel. What are they?
(b) What are the 20 administrative areas into which central Paris is divided called?
(c) What in Paris are Petit, Royal, Carrousel and Saint Michel?

Your starter for ten:

12 Which American, statesman, scientist and essayist wrote in a letter to Jean-Baptiste Le Roy that 'in this world, nothing is certain, except death and taxes'?

Bonus questions:
(a) What name is given to the insect, also known as the cuckoo spit insect, which secretes a frothy substance to protect its larvae from enemies and from drying out?
(b) The titles of which Greek dramatist's plays are often taken from disguises assumed in them by the Chorus, such as Frogs, Wasps and Clouds?
(c) Which rock star, backed by the Frog Chorus, had a number three hit with 'We All Stand Together' in 1984?

Your starter for ten:

13 [The next round was a music round. Trinity identified *Romeo and Juliet* by Prokofiev and went on to identify two musicals and the Shakespeare plays they were based on]

Starter question

14 Which Manchester-born rock star in his early shows often performed with a bunch of gladioli tucked into the seat of his trousers, representing Oscar Wilde, and a hearing aid—?
[The question was successfully interrupted]

Bonus questions:
(a) What is the most commonly used synthetic polymer made by the addition of polymerization and the molecules C_2H_4?
(b) Which German chemist, who shares the 1963 Nobel Prize in Chemistry with Giulio Natta, discovered a way of polymerising ethaline in atmospheric pressure producing a high-density polythene which is more rigid and melts at a higher temperature?

(c) Which term coined by the DuPont company was defined as a generic term for any long-chain polyamide which has recurring amide groups as an integral part of the main polymer chain and which is capable of being formed into a filament in which the structure elements are orienteered in the direction of the axis?

Your starter for ten:

15 *Dropping the Pilot,* John Tenniel's famous political cartoon of 1890 depicts Kaiser Wilhelm II watching which German chancellor—?
[The question was successfully interrupted]

Bonus questions:
(a) Name the town lying approximately 57 degrees west, 52 degrees south, which, after changing its name only once between 1843 and 1982, was renamed at least three times in the space of six weeks during 1982?
(b) For which newspaper was Henry Morton Stanley a correspondent when he was commissioned in 1869 to find Livingstone?
(c) In which African country is Kisangani, known until 1966 as Stanleyville in honour of Sir Henry Morton Stanley?

Your starter for ten:

16 What's the alternative and more common name for the disease African trypanosomiasis?

Bonus questions:
(a) Which Soviet leader surprised the General Assembly in the United Nations in October 1960 by waving his shoe in the air and slamming it on his desk?
(b) Who was elected General Secretary of the Communist Party of the Soviet Union on 11 March 1985?
(c) Whose Liberal Democratic Party – whose programme was neither liberal nor democratic – won the largest percentage of votes in the election—
[Interrupted and successfully answered]

Your starter for ten:

17 What was established in May 1975, being formed from the European Launcher Development Organisation and the European Space Research Organisation?

Your bonuses are on Italian literature:
(a) *'Nel mezzo del cammin di nostra vita'* ('In the middle of the road of our life') is the opening line of which work finished shortly before the poet's death in 1321?

(b) In the *Divine Comedy*, which Roman poet guides Dante on his journey to Hell and Purgatory?

(c) What name did Dante give to the girl that he fell in love with early in his life and who he celebrates in *La Vita Nuova*?

Your starter for ten:

18 Which English author's last novel, *Between the Acts*, was published posthumously in 1941?

[No one answered the starter correctly]

Your starter for ten:

19 Who wrote *Actes and Monuments*, a history of Protestant martyrs published in 1563?

Your bonuses are on art galleries:

(a) In which small West Country town was a new Tate gallery opened in 1983?

(b) Which London artistic institution was founded in 1932 by two great art collectors and houses some very important Impressionist and Post-Impressionist works including Manet's *A Bar at the Folies-Bergère*?

(c) In which English city is the Walker Art Gallery?

Your starter for ten:

20 A splendid example of 13th- and 14th-century Moorish art, what is the name of the famous palace—?

[The question was interrupted correctly]

Your bonuses are on light:

(a) What term is used for light in which the vibrations of electric vector are restricted to one plane?

(b) Which device consisting of a number of largely spaced lines ruled onto a glass surface is used to disperse a beam of light into its constituent wavelengths?

(c) What term is used for a beam of light in which the waves are in phase or have a constant phase relationship?

Your starter for ten:

21 *Concurso interuniversitário.* What does this Portuguese phrase mean in English?

Bonus questions:
[For picture bonuses, New College were shown 'University Challenge' in different languages. They correctly identified two of the three languages]

Your starter for ten:

22　What term is used for elements of the same atomic number which differ in mass number—?
[The question was successfully interrupted]

Bonus questions:
(a) In November 1991, Gretna became the first Scottish club for 104 years to play in the first round proper of which English sporting competition?
(b) Which is the only club in the Scottish Football League to play its home games in England?
(c) Which British football manager has led both an English and a Scottish team to success in the European Cup Winners Cup?

Your starter for ten:

23　From 1984 to 1990, Jonathon Porritt was director of which environmental—?
[The question was successfully interrupted]

Your bonuses are on Shakespeare's clowns:
(a) Which clown who sings 'O mistress mine' is Olivia's servant in *Twelfth Night*?
(b) What is the name of the clown in *The Merchant of Venice* who leaves Shylock's service to join Bassanio?
(c) What was the name of the jester at the court of the King of Denmark whom Hamlet recalls frolicking with as a child?

Your starter for ten:

24　Which former popular entertainment, its name meaning 'empty orchestra' in Japanese, involves singing—?
[The question was successfully interrupted]

Bonus questions:
(a) Which southern Bantu people fought a six-month war against the British in 1879 under their King Cetshwayo?
(b) Which South African political party takes its name from the sacred head ring worn by the Paramount Chief of the Zulus?
(c) What is the name of the Inkatha leader appointed by Nelson Mandela as his minister for home affairs who was a direct descendant of King Cetshwayo?

Your starter for ten:

25 What Joseph Conrad story closely follows the actual advents of his journey up the Congo?

Your bonuses are on dictionaries:

(a) Which multi-volume dictionary excludes living persons and was edited from 1882 to 1891 by Virginia Woolf's father Leslie Stephen?

(b) In 1828, an alternative to Dr Johnson's dictionary of 1755 was offered by which American?

(c) Thomas Eliot's dictionary of 1538 was the first major publication of its kind. What type of dictionary was it?

Your starter for ten:

26 What in degrees, is the value of Pi radiant?

Your bonuses are on royal weddings:

(a) Which English king married Berengaria of Navarre?

(b) Which English king married his cousin, Sophia Dorothea of Celle, divorcing her and imprisoning her twelve years later?

(c) Which English king married Alexandra, the eldest daughter of Christian IX of Denmark?

Your starter for ten:

27 Which member of the royal family was born in 17 Bruton Street in Mayfair on 21 April 1926?

Bonus questions:

(a) The British diplomat Sir Thomas Francis Wade developed a system, later modified by the Cambridge professor Herbert Allen Giles, for writing in Roman script words of which language?

(b) Which British general was given the nickname 'Chinese' because of military exploits in China in 1860–1865?

(c) Which composer's song symphony *Das Lied von der Erde* (*The Song of the Earth*)—?

[The question was successfully interrupted]

Your starter for ten:

28 Which city staged the 1994 European Athletics Championship?

Bonus questions:

(a) Who was apprenticed in 1746 at the age of 18 to John Walker, a Quaker ship owner of Whitby?

(b) In 1768, James Cook was appointed Commander of the Royal Society Expedition to Tahiti to observe which astronomical phenomenon?
(c) As a fellow of the Royal Society, Cook was awarded one its highest honours, the Golden Copley Medal, for his work against which disease?

Your starter for ten:
29 Whose principle states that the apparent loss of weight of a body, totally or partially immersed—?
[The question was successfully interrupted]

Your bonuses are on spa towns:
(a) Which British spa town was known to the Romans as Aquae Sulis?
(b) In which spa town did Marshal Phillippe Pétain set up his collaborationist government after the fall of France in 1940?
(c) The spa town whose Czech name is Mariánské Lázne featured in the title of which cryptic film directed in 1961 by Alain Resnais?

Your starter for ten:
30 Complete this line from Ian Hay's 1936 play *The Housemaster*: 'What do you mean funny? Funny-peculiar or...'?

Bonus questions:
(a) In which novel, published in 1853, is Esther Summerson revealed as the daughter of Lady Dedlock and Captain Hawdon?
(b) Which house west of London was given to the Earl of Northumberland by Elizabeth I?
(c) Which house did Bob Dylan sing about on his first album? It was later a million-selling single by a British group.

The gong interrupts the next question

At the gong, New College had 180 points and Trinity won with 390 points, the highest score of the 1994–1995 series. The presentation of the prize was made by Bamber Gascoigne, who said: 'Wonderful game, a magnificent win. I think they were brilliant. Incredibly quick... Benjamin Franklin here, Romeo and Juliet there, before we'd even had a chord of the music. Wonderful.'

The Answers

1   John Paul Getty Museum
    (a) Oslo
    (b) Pretoria in South Africa
    (c) Santiago in Chile

2   Piltdown Man
    (a) The Fifth Monarchy
    (b) The Battle of Austerlitz
    (c) The Seven Sisters

3   Arthur C. Clarke
    (a) Chile
    (b) Richard Cromwell, the former Lord Protector
    (c) Egypt

4   The Coral Sea
    (a) Daniel Defoe, *A Journal of the Plague Year*
    (b) Charles Pooter, *The Diary of a Nobody*
    (c) William Golding, *Rites of Passage*

5   (Johannes) Brahms

6   Lady Macbeth
    (a) (Henri) Becquerel
    (b) Lead
    (c) Five billion (4.6 is the nearest estimate)

7   [Picture round]

8   Mungo Park
    (a) La Fronde
    (b) Jacobins
    (c) Paris Commune or the Communards

9   Resonance
    (a) Carmel (where he became mayor)
    (b) Elijah
    (c) Felix Mendelssohn

10 Sissy Spacek

11 MCC / Marylebone Cricket Club
    (a) Cantons in Switzerland
    (b) Arrondissements
    (c) Bridges over the Seine

12 Benjamin Franklin
(a) Froghopper
(b) Aristophanes
(c) Paul McCartney

13 [Music round]

14 Morrissey (from The Smiths)
(a) Polythene
(b) Karl Ziegler
(c) Nylon

15 (Otto von) Bismarck
(a) Port Stanley in the Falkland Islands
(b) *The New York Herald*
(c) Zaire (now Democratic Republic of the Congo)

16 African sleeping sickness
(a) Nikita Khrushchev
(b) Mikhail Gorbachev
(c) Vladimir Zhirinovsky

17 European Space Agency
(a) *Divine Comedy* (Dante Alighieri)
(b) Virgil
(c) Beatrice

18 Virginia Woolf

19 John Foxe
(a) St Ives
(b) The Courtauld Gallery
(c) Liverpool

20 Alhambra
(a) Polarized
(b) Diffraction grating
(c) Coherence

21 Inter-university contest (or 'university challenge')

22 Isotopes
(a) FA Cup
(b) Berwick Rangers
(c) Alex Ferguson with Manchester United and Aberdeen

23　Friends of the Earth
　　(a) Feste
　　(b) Launcelot Gobbo
　　(c) Yorick

24　Karaoke
　　(a) Zulus
　　(b) Inkatha
　　(c) Chief Buthelezi

25　*Heart of Darkness*
　　(a) *Dictionary of National Biography*
　　(b) Noah Webster
　　(c) *Latin English Dictionary*

26　180°
　　(a) Richard I
　　(b) George I
　　(c) Edward VII

27　The Queen / Queen Elizabeth II
　　(a) Chinese
　　(b) (Charles George) Gordon
　　(c) Gustav Mahler

28　Helsinki
　　(a) James Cook
　　(b) Transit of Venus
　　(c) Scurvy

29　Archimedes
　　(a) Bath
　　(b) Vichy
　　(c) *Last Year at Marienbad*

30　'Funny ha-ha?'
　　(a) *Bleak House*
　　(b) Syon House
　　(c) 'House of the Rising Sun'

Try Your Luck
Match

Your starter for ten:

1   Often known by a single-word Latin title, what work does the *Oxford Companion to Philosophy* describe as 'a mere 75 pages long, written in sybilline, marmoreal sentences'? It was first published in German in 1921.

Three questions on the solar system:
(a) The Maxwell Montes range includes the highest point on which body of the solar system? The range is about eleven kilometres above mean radius.
(b) At around four kilometres in height, Ahuna Mons is a suspected cryovolcano and the highest peak on which body of the solar system?
(c) About six kilometres high, the central peak of Herschel crater is the tallest mountain on which inner moon of Saturn, whose appearance has been compared to that of the Death Star in the *Star Wars* films?

Your starter for ten:

2   Which French utopian socialist coined the term *féminisme* in 1837, having previously expressed support for women's rights in his work *The Theory of the Four Movements and of the General Destinies*?

Three questions on opera:
(a) Meaning 'compartment' or 'division', what short German term is used for a system of voice classification used to distinguish operatic roles?
(b) What term is used in the Fach system for an elaborate soprano role characterized by trills and cadenzas? A notable example occurs in the so-called 'mad scene' of Donizetti's *Lucia di Lammermoor*.
(c) First played by Mozart's sister-in-law, Josepha Hofer, which coloratura soprano role in *The Magic Flute* sings the aria known as 'The Revenge of Hell'?

Your starter for ten:

3   What plural noun links all of these? Raphael Holinshed's 1577 history
of Britain; a 1950 work by Ray Bradbury set on Mars; books of the King
James Bible between 'Kings' and 'Ezra', and the series of novels that
includes *Prince Caspian*.

Three questions on the irrational number called the 'golden ratio' or 'golden mean':
(a) With a value roughly equal to 1.618, the golden mean can be written as
the ratio of the length of one diagonal to that of one side, for which regular
polygon?
(b) The golden ratio can be expressed as 'one plus root five all divided by two',
or as a continued fraction with all the numerators equal to what value?
(c) In 1948, which designer and architect published *The Modulor*, a system of
human proportions based around the golden ratio?

Your starter for ten:

4   The name of what creature links the following: a common model organism
in plant sciences of the genus antirrhinum; the symbol of the Chinese
zodiac that comes between the rabbit and the snake, and the first in a
series of novels by Thomas Harris that introduced the character Hannibal
Lecter?

Your bonuses are on US politics. In each case, give the state that both of the named
figures have represented in the United States Senate:
(a) Hillary Clinton and Robert F. Kennedy.
(b) Ted Cruz and Lyndon Baines Johnson.
(c) Elizabeth Warren and John F. Kennedy?

Your starter for ten:

5   What academic subject did an Oxford professor describe as an 'analytical
discipline that predates even theology in the study of the humanities'?
The article adds, 'It also requires the study of history, philosophy and
linguistics.'

Your bonuses are on words that contain all five vowels once and once only. Give
each word from the definition:
(a) Discovered in 1974, the chemical element with the atomic number 106?
(b) A vegetable of the species *Brassica oleracea*?
(c) The country that borders both Tanzania and South Africa?

Your starter for ten:

6 Michael Jago, Francis Beckett and John Bew are among recent biographers of which prime minister? He served as postmaster general under Rramsay MacDonald and as deputy prime minister under Winston Churchill.

Three questions on people born in Somerset:
(a) Born near Ilchester, which 13th-century Franciscan friar wrote the work known as the *Opus Majus*, a discussion of topics including grammar, mathematics, optics and moral philosophy?
(b) Born in East Coker in 1651, which explorer completed three circumnavigations of the globe? His published works include the 1703 *Voyage to New Holland*, an account of his expedition to Australia.
(c) Born in Milverton in 1773, which scientist published *A Course of Lectures on Natural Philosophy and the Mechanical Arts*, describing a quantity that now bears his name, relating to the elasticity of a material?

Your starter for ten:

7 Answer with a fraction as soon as your name is called. An unpolarized beam of light is incident on a pair of ideal polarizers whose transmission axes have an angle of sixty degrees between them. What fraction of the original incident intensity is transmitted through the pair?

Three questions on early 20th-century spy fiction:
(a) Give the single word that completes the title of a 1903 work by Erskine Childers, often described as the first spy novel: *The Riddle of the...* what?
(b) Who is the protagonist of John Buchan's novels *Greenmantle*, *Mr Standfast* and *The Island of Sheep*? I need only the surname.
(c) Based on his experiences with British intelligence in the First World War, which literary figure wrote short stories featuring the spy Ashenden? His other works include *Of Human Bondage*.

Your starter for ten:

8 First performed in Vienna not long before the composer's death, which German-language *Singspiel* was Mozart's last opera? Its characters include the lovers Pamina and Tamino, and the bird-catcher Papageno.

Three questions on food:
(a) Its name derived from words meaning 'twice cooked', what foodstuff is the subject of the 2020 work by Lizzie Collingham with the subtitle *The History of a Very British Indulgence*?
(b) What is the single word title of the 1998 book by Mark Kurlansky, subtitled *A Biography of the Fish That Changed the World*?

(c) Used as a collective term for a group of food constituents that are insoluble in water, what word forms the title of Jennifer McLagan's book with the subtitle *An Appreciation of a Misunderstood Ingredient*?

Your starter for ten:

9   What two rivers form the name of the French department whose capital is Melun, in the Île-de-France? The same two rivers appear individually in the names of the three small departments that encircle Paris.

Your bonuses are on books that had a profound effect on the creature in Mary Shelley's *Frankenstein*:
(a) The *Parallel Lives* is a series of fifty biographies of prominent Greeks and Romans by which ancient author?
(b) Which semi-autobiographical novel of 1774 by Goethe concerns a sensitive and passionate young man who falls in love with his friend's fiancée?
(c) An epic poem in blank verse; according to Dr Johnson, it is 'one of the books which the reader admires and lays down, and forgets to take up again'.

Your starter for ten:

10 What single digit appears in front of the decimal point, if the numbers after it are: 1, 4, 1, 5, 9, 2 and so on, in the context of a mathematical constant?

Three questions on fictional nannies:
(a) In the children's books by Christianna Brand, Nurse Matilda is the basis for which title character in film adaptations of 2005 and 2010? Emma Thompson plays the title role.
(b) What is the name of the Australian-born author of the Mary Poppins books, the first of which appeared in 1934?
(c) In J.M. Barrie's stories of Peter Pan, what is the name of the Newfoundland dog that acts as nanny to the children of the Darling family?

Your starter for ten:

11 About 70 miles from John O'Groats, which headland is the extreme northwest point of the British mainland? Its name comes from the Old Norse for a 'turning point', and is unrelated to violent anger or the raging of the sea.

Your bonuses are on UK number one singles of 1969. In each case, name the band or act that released the following:
(a) Which band released 'Bad Moon Rising'?
(b) Which US duo released 'In the Year 2525: Exordium and Terminus'?

(c) Which US artist released 'I Heard It Through the Grapevine'?

Your starter for ten:

12 Answer as soon as your name is called. What number results from adding the Mohs scale value for corundum to the atomic number of lithium, then multiplying the total by the number of faces on an icosahedron?

Three questions on Italy:
(a) What was the function of the building known as the Mamertine in ancient Rome? It is said that at one time it housed St Peter.
(b) Dating from the mid-18th century and based on Roman ruins, the *Carceri* (or *Prisons*) is a series of works by which Italian printmaker and etcher?
(c) Converted from a prison in the 19th century, which art museum in Florence contains bronze statues of David by Verrocchio and Donatello?

Your starter for ten:

13 I need a two-word term here. In the 1970s, the US astronomers Vera Rubin and Kent Ford confirmed the existence of what component of the universe, earlier postulated by Fritz Zwicky?

Your bonuses are on words that differ only in that one of them has an additional second letter 't', for instance 'sand' and 'stand'. In each case, give both words from the definitions:
(a) An expression of dismay that begins Hamlet's Yorick speech; and a Titan of Greek mythology who was the son of Iapetus.
(b) An ancient Athenian legal reformer; and a horizontal plant stem that links clonal individuals to each other.
(c) The scientific study of birds' eggs and of ears, respectively.

Your starter for ten:

14 In marine weather forecasts, what term is used in contrast to 'veering' to describe a wind direction that changes anti-clockwise, for example from west to southwest?

Three questions on the names of vegetables in European languages:
(a) What common vegetable is known in Spanish as *zanahoria*? The French, German and Italian names resemble the English.
(b) *Zwiebel* and *cipolla* are the German and Italian names of what vegetable? The English name is similar to the French one.
(c) Which culinary vegetable is known in Italian as *pomodoro*? The name in most other languages is similar to the English one.

Your starter for ten:

15 What five letters begin the names of all of the following: a Renaissance palace in Copenhagen; a football club in the Norwegian city of Trondheim; the title figure of a comic opera by Richard Strauss; and, in Shakespeare's *Hamlet*, the courtier who accompanies Guildenstern?

Your bonuses are on winners of the Academy Award for Best Original Screenplay. In each case, give the name of the writer from the title of one of his award-winning screenplays and a quotation from another:
(a) *The Apartment*; 'All right, Mr DeMille, I'm ready for my close-up.'
(b) *The Hospital*; 'I'm mad as hell, and I'm not going to take this anymore.'
(c) *Hannah and Her Sisters*; 'Those who can't do, teach; and those who can't teach, teach gym.'

Your starter for ten:

16 In mathematics, what Greek letter links: the first Feigenbaum constant; the Laplace operator and a function in quantum mechanics associated with Paul Dirac?

Three questions on astronomy:
(a) What was the sixth known moon in the solar system, discovered by Christian Huygens in 1655, 45 years after the four Galilean moons of Jupiter?
(b) What was the seventh known moon, discovered in 1671? Saturn's third largest satellite, it shares its name with both a Greek Titan and an ocean formed on Earth in the Neoproterozoic era.
(c) Saturn's second largest satellite, what was the eighth known moon, discovered by Cassini in 1672? It is named after the Titan who also gave her name to a large species of flightless bird.

Your starter for ten:

17 Who was the first Stewart king of Scotland? The grandfather of James I, he had the same regnal name as his maternal grandfather, often known as 'the Bruce'.

Three questions on economics:
(a) Born in 1848, which Italian economist gives his name to an 'optimality' or 'efficiency' in which no one can be made better off without making at least one individual worse off?
(b) A market failure may occur in a situation in which production or consumption of goods and services results in consequences that no one pays for. By what term are such consequences known?

(c) Market failures provide a rationale for government intervention, for example, through taxes, regulation and welfare services. Founded by Carl Menger, which school of economics notably critiques this approach?

Your starter for ten:

18 'The first merit of a painting is to be a feast for the eye.' Those are the words of which leading artist of the French Romantic movement? His works include *Dante and Virgil in Hell* and *Liberty Leading the People*, marking the July Revolution of 1830.

Three questions on representations of Lilith in television:
(a) A version of Lilith is presented as the progenitor of the vampire race in which drama series created by Alan Ball, based on a series of popular novels?
(b) Set in the future city of Tokyo-3, which mecha anime represents Lilith as a 'seed of life', an alien being created to spread life across the universe? The series is known for a dense internal mythology that draws on various religious traditions. I need a three-word title.
(c) Michelle Gomez plays a representation of Lilith in which recent drama series for young adults, based on an *Archie* comicbook series? The name of the title character is enough here.

Your starter for ten:

19 Measured in the SI units of joule-seconds, how much spin angular momentum does a single photon have, to the nearest factor of ten?

Three questions on the ornithologist Peter Davis, who died in 2019:
(a) Davis is perhaps best known for reversing the decline of which large bird of prey, distinguished by its long, forked tail and 'mewing' call? I need a two-word name.
(b) On Lundy Island in 1952, Davis made the first British record of a vagrant American robin, or *Turdus migratorius*. To what family of songbirds does this bird belong?
(c) Davis made several more 'first records' during his six years as warden on which island between Orkney and Shetland?

Your starter for ten:

20 What novel did Dante Gabriel Rossetti describe as 'a fiend of a book – an incredible monster ... the action is laid in Hell – only it seems places and people have English names there'? The novel in question was published under a pseudonym in 1847.

Three questions on a weather phenomenon:

(a) In 2018, what weather-related word gained an additional definition in the Oxford English Dictionary as a term for a person mockingly characterized as over-sensitive?

(b) 'The thing about "snowflakes" is this: they are beautiful and unique, but in large numbers become an unstoppable avalanche that will bury you.' These are the words of which activist and former *Star Trek* actor?

(c) 'You are not a beautiful and unique snowflake. You are the same decaying organic matter as everything else.' These words appear in which novel by Chuck Palahniuk?

Your starter for ten:

21 Produced in the liver, which secretion is released into the small intestine, where it emulsifies fat?

Three questions on particle physics:

(a) Scientists from Kamioka in Japan and Sudbury in Canada shared the 2015 Nobel Prize in Physics for their research into which particles?

(b) Their discovery of neutrino oscillations provided evidence that the particles possess what property, contradicting an idea from the standard model?

(c) In 1930, Wolfgang Pauli postulated the existence of neutrinos to explain the continuous energy spectrum of the products for which nuclear reaction?

Your starter for ten:

22 Born in Lincolnshire in 1877, Janet Lane-Claypon pioneered the use of control studies to make public health decisions. She is seen as a founder of which science, defined as a study of the factors affecting the health of populations, rather than individuals? Its name derives from the Greek meaning 'prevalence of disease'.

Three questions on revolutions of the 21st century:

(a) The Saffron Revolution of 2007 involved anti-government protests led by Buddhist monks wearing saffron-coloured robes. In which country did it occur?

(b) Coloured signs carried by demonstrators gave Kuwait's 2005 Blue Revolution its name. The aim was not to overthrow the government but to achieve what end?

(c) Soldiers were given flowers by protesters demanding the resignation of which president during the 2003 Rose Revolution in the former Soviet state of Georgia?

Your starter for ten:

23 The name of what substance appears in the titles of: the pre-modern Chinese novel sometimes known as *The Outlaws of the Marsh*; the 2019 debut novel of Ta-Nehisi Coates; and a 1989 novel by Laura Esquivel, where it appears before 'Chocolate'?

Three questions on fermented products:

(a) Sauerkraut and the Slavic drink kvass are made anaerobically to produce which acid that gives the fermented products their distinctive tang?

(b) Fermented from black or green tea using a culture of bacteria and yeast, what drink has a name that means 'seaweed tea'?

(c) What traditional lacto-fermented Korean dish is often made using cabbage or radish, and is flavoured with garlic and chilli?

Your starter for ten:

24 What four words in English link the 2019 handbook of Extinction Rebellion with René Magritte's painting *The Treachery of Images*? The words in question precede 'drill' and 'pipe', respectively.

Three questions on a region of Europe:

(a) Formerly the main port of the Austro-Hungarian Empire, what city is now the capital of the Italian region of Friuli Venezia Giulia?

(b) Trieste lies at the head of what large peninsula, bounded by the Gulf of Venice to the west and the Kvarner Gulf to the east?

(c) The majority of the region of Istria, including the town of Pazin and the city of Pula, lies in the territory of what country?

Your starter for ten:

25 Designed by Vlado Milunić and Frank Gehry, the distinctive building known as the Dancing House is in which European capital?

Three questions on 20th-century Nobel Prize nominees:

(a) Nominated numerous times, which US chemist is particularly known for the electron-pair model of the covalent bond, electron dot diagrams and the electron-pair theory of acids and bases?

(b) The US physicians Gladys and George Dick were nominated for their work on which infectious disease, caused by *Streptococcus pyogenes*?

(c) Also nominated numerous times, the French biologist Gaston Ramon in 1923 developed a vaccine against which leading cause of death?

The Answers

1 *Tractatus Logico-Philosophicus* (accept *Tractatus / Logisch-Philosophische Abhandlung*)
 (a) Venus
 (b) Ceres
 (c) Mimas

2 (Charles) Fourier (not Joseph Fourier, the mathematician)
 (a) Fach
 (b) Coloratura (soprano)
 (c) Queen of the Night

3 Chronicles (accept Chronicle, correcting it; *Chronicles of England, Scotland and Ireland, The Martian Chronicles, Chronicles of Narnia*)
 (a) (Regular) pentagon
 (b) One
 (c) Le Corbusier / Charles-Edouard Jeanneret

4 Dragon (snapdragon, dragon, *Red Dragon*)
 (a) New York
 (b) Texas
 (c) Massachusetts

5 Classics (Tom Whitmarsh, Corpus Christi College, Oxford in *The Guardian*, 2012)
 (a) Seaborgium
 (b) Cauliflower
 (c) Mozambique

6 (Clement) Attlee (*The Inevitable Prime Minister, Clem Attlee, Citizen Clem*)
 (a) (Roger) Bacon
 (b) (William) Dampier
 (c) (Thomas) Young

7 One-eighth
 (a) *Sands*
 (b) (Richard) Hannay
 (c) (W. Somerset) Maugham

8 *The Magic Flute / Die Zauberflöte* (premiered on 30 September 1791; Mozart died on 5 December that year)
 (a) Biscuit (Latin: *bis*, 'twice'; *coctus*, 'cooked')
 (b) *Cod*
 (c) Fat

9 Seine and Marne / Seine-et-Marne
 (a) Plutarch
 (b) *The Sorrows of Young Werther*

(c) *Paradise Lost*

10   3 (the first digits of pi, of course)
     (a) Nanny McPhee
     (b) P.L. / Pamela Lyndon Travers
     (c) Nana

11   (Cape) Wrath (ON: *hvarf*)
     (a) Creedence Clearwater Revival
     (b) Zager and Evans
     (c) Marvin Gaye

12   240 ([9+3]*20)
     (a) Prison / jail
     (b) (Giovanni Battista) Piranesi
     (c) (Palazzo del) Bargello / Museo Nazionale del Bargello / or Palazzo del Popolo)

13   Dark matter
     (a) Alas and atlas
     (b) Solon and stolon
     (c) Oology and otology

14   Backing
     (a) Carrot
     (b) Onion
     (c) Tomato

15   R-o-s-e-n (Rosenborg, Rosenborg BK, Rosenkavalier, Rosencrantz)
     (a) Billy Wilder (quotation from *Sunset Boulevard*)
     (b) Paddy Chayefsky (quotation from *Network*)
     (c) Woody Allen (quotation from *Annie Hall*)

16   Delta
     (a) Titan (the largest moon of Saturn)
     (b) Iapetus
     (c) Rhea

17   Robert II (Stewart, later Stuart)
     (a) (Vilfredo) Pareto
     (b) Externalities
     (c) Austrian (school)

18   (Eugène) Delacroix
     (a) *True Blood*
     (b) *Neon Genesis Evangelion*
     (c) (*Chilling Adventures of*) *Sabrina* (accept *Sabrina the Teenage Witch*)

19 10^{-34}
    (a) Red kite / *Milvus milvus*
    (b) Thrush (*Turdidae*)
    (c) Fair isle

20 *Wuthering Heights* (Emily Brontë)
    (a) Snowflake
    (b) George Takei
    (c) *Fight Club*

21 Bile / gall (produced in the liver, stored in the gallbladder)
    (a) Neutrinos (discovery of neutrino oscillations)
    (b) Mass (standard model predicts that neutrinos should have zero rest mass)
    (c) Beta decay (allowed for conservation of energy and momentum)

22 Epidemiology (Greek: *epidemia*, 'prevalence of disease')
    (a) Myanmar / Burma
    (b) Right for women to vote / women's suffrage
    (c) (Eduard) Shevardnadze

23 Water (*Water Margin, The Water Dancer, Like Water for Chocolate*)
    (a) Lactic (acid)
    (b) Kombucha
    (c) Kimchi

24 'This is not a' (Magritte's words were in French, of course)
    (a) Trieste
    (b) Istria
    (c) Croatia

25 Prague
    (a) (Gilbert N.) Lewis
    (b) Scarlet fever / scarlatina (*Streptococcus pyogenes* causes other diseases as well but Gladys and George Dick were nominated specifically for their work on scarlet fever)
    (c) Diphtheria

The Voice

1997 & 2001–present

Roger Tilling

There have been three voiceover announcers on *University Challenge* – Don Murray-Henderson (from 1962 until his death in 1971), then Jim Pope (from 1972 until his death in 2001) and, since 2001, Roger Tilling.

In 1994, during his finals at Queen Mary, University of London, where he was studying Aeronautical Engineering, Tilling remembers the posters going up advertising the fact that *University Challenge* was returning to our television screens. 'Jeremy was going to be hosting and little did I realize that three years later, I would be Mr Voice,' says Roger. He was a temporary announcer in 1997, returning permanently in 2001.

'I didn't plan to be in television or doing voiceovers or anything. I was going to be a pilot, but there were no jobs when I graduated so I went into local radio, doing commercials and all kinds of voiceovers,' he says. 'I just enjoyed doing silly voices. And then, after getting some experience in local radio, one thing just kind of led to another. *University Challenge* takes priority over everything. It's my baby, I suppose.'

From his raised platform on the studio floor – 'I've got my pigeon loft, my scaffolding and a milking stool so I can see just over the tops of the cameras and over Jeremy's head as well' – Roger is an essential, well-recognized and loved part of the programme. As soon as a contestant buzzes, he announces their university or college and their surname.

He admits he's made the odd mistake over names. 'It's usually the really easy ones because I'm concentrating on the complicated ones,' he explains. 'The first thing I do when I turn up for a series is go to the production office and ask if there are any complicated names in the series. If there are, I ask the contestants when we're on the studio floor how to pronounce their names correctly. I don't try to assume how they pronounce them because I'll probably get it completely wrong. I will write it down phonetically. Ironically, it's often the student with the most difficult-to-pronounce name who answers the most questions!'

And it's not just the competitors' names that are sometimes tricky to pronounce quickly; some colleges can present problems. 'Sometimes they're incredibly long, like the School of Oriental and African Studies – SOAS – or whatever. I try to get them to accept an abbreviation, but [the students are] clever; they know the more I have to say gives them extra seconds of thinking.' Roger reckons he's made three mistakes in 25 years. 'That's not too bad. I'll probably make a fourth tomorrow, though!'

He can get very involved in the process. 'You kind of thrive on that little buzz that you get from doing it. I've got to get in quick because they want to answer as quickly as possible. I try to change the intonation as well so it doesn't sound automated. And as the programme speeds up towards the end I have to speed up as well.'

He likes to meet the contestants when they arrive on the studio floor. 'A lot of them are nervous so it's nice to have a joke with them.' During the COVID-19 pandemic, the programme filmed without a studio audience, something Roger regretted. Previously, he would act as warm-up man, explaining to the audience what was about to happen.

Roger's background in science means those are the questions he sometimes knows the answer to. 'I have to stop myself shouting out the answer if there's one I know.'

As well as *University Challenge*, Roger has been the voice of the *Royal Variety Performance*, *Children in Need* and *Comic Relief*, as well as for documentaries on the History Channel and National Geographic (his passion is travel and he has been far and wide including Japan, Asia and even North Korea) and TV commercials. He's in keen demand as a master of corporate ceremonies, too.

Roger says the reason for *University Challenge*'s longevity is that the format doesn't change – 'It's as constant as the Northern Star. You know where you are, it's a tried-and-tested format.' The programme's secret? 'It's one of the toughest shows on television but, because the questions are hard, I think people feel good about themselves if they get one or two questions right. Anything that's difficult is more rewarding in the end.'

Roger is full of admiration for the contestants. 'We cover everything, so they have to have such wide knowledge. It's not just oil paintings and classical music; you have to know about things like grunge music. The whole spectrum is covered these days.'

Try Your Luck
Match

Your starter for ten:

1   Which English cathedral lies roughly midway between Stratford-upon-Avon and Cherbourg? Exemplifying the early English phase of Gothic architecture, it is noted for its fine octagonal spire, the tallest surviving in Britain.

Three questions on missionaries:
(a) Along with Jeannie Lawson, who founded the Inn of the Sixth Happiness in Yang-Cheng during missionary work in China in the 1930s? She was played by Ingrid Bergman in a film of 1958.
(b) Born in Aberdeen in 1848, which Scottish missionary spent many years teaching for the United Presbyterian Church in Calabar, Nigeria, from the 1870s?
(c) Which Scottish missionary wrote the 1857 book *Missionary Travels and Researches in South Africa*, having previously explored Lake Ngami and the Zambezi River?

Your starter for ten:

2   Sacrifice, truth, power, beauty, life, memory, obedience; who used those words within chapter headings in his 1849 extended essay 'The Seven Lamps of Architecture'? Born in 1819, he also published the five-volume work *Modern Painters*.

Three questions on scientific symbols:
(a) In addition to fluorine, which of the six halogen elements has a single-letter symbol?
(b) Symbolized by capital 'I', what physical quantity has the kilogram metre squared as its SI unit?
(c) Finally, what electrical quantity is symbolized with a capital 'I'?

Your starter for ten:

3 Meanings of what four-letter word include: a roll of fabric; to eat food quickly; to run away suddenly; to fasten a door; and a jagged flash of lightning?

Three questions on fruit:

(a) Used in Japanese cuisine, the *yuzu*, *sudachi* and *mikan* are among fruits of what genus?

(b) Taking the second part of its binomial from its Japanese name, *Diospyros kaki* bears orange fruit resembling large tomatoes. What is its common name?

(c) Often known by the Japanese name *nashi*, *Pyrus pyrifolia* bears a crisp-textured, apple-shaped fruit with what generic name?

Your starter for ten:

4 Henry L. Stimson served which US president as secretary of state? Events during his time in office included the London Naval Conference, the Japanese occupation of Manchuria and the start of the Great Depression.

Three questions on physics:

(a) I need a two-word term here. Using commercial aircraft, the 1971 Hafele-Keating experiment was a test of which effect, a consequence of special and general relativity abbreviated as TD?

(b) The Lorentz factor gives the strength of this effect for different relative speeds. What improper fraction does this take for a relative velocity of 60 per cent of light speed?

(c) Created by cosmic rays, which second-generation leptons gave evidence for time dilation when they were detected in large numbers at ground level?

Your starter for ten:

5 The boll weevil is a species of beetle that afflicted what crop in the USA in the early 20th century, with particular devastation in states such as Texas and Alabama?

Three questions on former African countries:

(a) The kingdom of Dahomey flourished in the 18th and 19th centuries in the south of which present-day West African country?

(b) The Upper Volta was a French colony and then an independent republic that adopted what name in 1984?

(c) The Gold Coast was a historical region and later a British colony that gained independence in 1957 as what present-day country?

Your starter for ten:

6   I need a precise, seven-letter term. What form of understatement is
     expressed in the line: 'I am no prophet – and here's no great matter'? The
     term can also be taken as an anagram of the name of the poet who wrote
     those words.

Three questions on long-distance paths designated as Scotland's Great Trails:
(a) The ruined abbeys of Melrose, Jedburgh and Kelso are linked by a long-
distance footpath in which Scottish council area?
(b) A coast-to-coast route from Helensburgh to Dunbar is named after which
pioneering conservationist, a founder of America's national parks?
(c) What geological feature gives its name to a long-distance path from Fort
William to Inverness?

Your starter for ten:

7   Answer as soon as your name is called. What is the length of the body
     diagonal of a cuboid that has side lengths of eight units, nine units and
     twelve units?

Three questions on books:
(a) Give the single word that completes the title of the book by Helen
Macdonald that won the Samuel Johnson Prize for Non-Fiction in 2014: *H Is
for ...*?
(b) Containing the Hugo Award-nominated short story 'How to Talk to
Girls at Parties', the collection *M Is for Magic* is a work by which author of
speculative fiction?
(c) Who created the detective Kinsey Millhone in her *Alphabet Series* of
twenty-five crime novels, beginning with *A Is for Alibi* and ending with *Y Is for
Yesterday*?

Your starter for ten:

8   Used for data ordering in computing and stock control in manufacturing,
     for what does the acronym LIFO stand?

Your bonuses are on terms that begin with the same three letters. Identify each
term from the description:
(a) In economics, a policy in opposition to free trade; it involves the use of
tariffs, subsidies, import quotas or other restrictions on foreign competitors to
stimulate domestic industries.
(b) In mathematics, equality between two ratios; it describes any relationship
that is always in the same ratio, meaning 'a' divided by 'b' is equal to 'c' divided
by 'd'.

(c) In engineering, the technology by which a force is imparted to change the speed and direction of a vehicle. In aeronautics, this force is typically called 'thrust'.

Your starter for ten:

9   Which three vowels follow one another in the original French title of the 1886 novel often known in English as *The Masterpiece*, by Émile Zola? The same vowel combination appears in French words meaning 'heart', 'egg' and 'sister'.

Three questions on cities in Norway:
(a) Located on the Gans fjord in southwest Norway, which city is a major centre of the country's oil and food-processing industries and is the location of the Norwegian Petroleum Museum?
(b) Straddling two principal islands, what is the largest Norwegian city north of the Arctic Circle? It is associated with the shipping and fishing industries.
(c) What port is Norway's second most populous city? Its harbour is characterized by wooden buildings and has UNESCO World Heritage Site status.

Your starter for ten:

10 I need the name and regnal number here. Which royal figure was nominated for the 1901 Nobel Peace Prize for his promotion of the Hague Peace Conference? His troops carried out the Bloody Sunday massacre early in 1905, after which he agreed to demands for a national legislature. In 1918, he was executed with his family.

Your bonuses are on the novels of Charles Dickens. In each case, name the novel in which the following locations appear:
(a) The Blue Dragon alehouse; Mrs Todgers' commercial boarding-house; the packet ship the *Screw*; and the Eden settlement.
(b) The Maypole inn; the Boot tavern; a locksmith's shop called the Golden Key; and Newgate Prison.
(c) Bleeding Heart Yard; the Circumlocution Office; Venice; and the Marshalsea?

Your starter for ten:

11 What four-letter word links: *Orkneyinga* and *Völsunga* in medieval literature; a novel sequence by John Galsworthy; and an investigator with the Malmö police in the crime drama *The Bridge*?

Three questions on Angry Young Men:

(a) Having taken his university degree, Jimmy Porter, the protagonist of John Osborne's 1956 play *Look Back in Anger*, finds himself doing what for a living?

(b) Which Yorkshire-born director established Woodfall Film Productions with Osborne in the late 1950s? Its output included *A Taste of Honey* and *The Loneliness of the Long-Distance Runner*.

(c) Produced by Tony Richardson, which 1960 film has as its protagonist the young factory worker Arthur Seaton, played by Albert Finney?

Your starter for ten:

12 The 16th-century German humanist Hieronymus Wolf is usually credited with the introduction of what two-word term for the Greek-speaking polity of the Middle Ages that centred on Constantinople?

Three questions on collage art:

(a) *Cut with the Kitchen Knife Through the Last Epoch of Weimar Beer-Belly Culture in Germany* is a large-scale collage of 1919 by which Dadaist? She is regarded as a pioneer of photomontage.

(b) Which US artist coined the term 'combines' to refer to his three-dimensional collage works? These include the 1955 *Monogram*, which incorporates half a taxidermied goat and a car tyre.

(c) Which French artist is generally credited with initiating the 'papier collé' or 'pasted paper' technique characteristic of late Cubism in his 1912 work *Fruit Dish and Glass*?

Your starter for ten:

13 Meanings of what seven-letter term include: a building-block of a Chinese character, for example 'fire' or 'tree'; a molecule with an unpaired valence electron; a root in mathematics; and a 19th-century loose political grouping that included Henry Hunt and John Bright?

Three questions on a country:

(a) A 1937 literary collection by Louis MacNeice and W.H. Auden has the title *Letters from...* which island country?

(b) *Independent People* is a major work by which Icelandic writer, who won the Nobel Prize in Literature in 1955?

(c) The medieval Icelandic writer Snorri Sturloson created the 'younger' or 'prose' version of a literary collection known by what short name?

Your starter for ten:

14 Born near Corinth in the early 4th century BCE, Lysippos was a prolific sculptor noted for portrayals of which ruler and his court? These included a monument to companions killed at the Battle of the Granicus River.

Three questions on cocktails recognized by the International Bartenders Association:
(a) Made with vodka, triple sec and lime juice, which cocktail has a Japanese name meaning 'divine wind'?
(b) Similar to a Kamikaze but with cranberry juice instead of lime, the name of which cocktail is also an adjective that denotes a worldwide distribution of a species, as opposed to an endemic distribution?
(c) Which rum and pineapple-based cocktail is named after a Canadian-born actress and co-founder of United Artists, born Gladys Louise Smith in 1892?

Your starter for ten:

15 What surname links: a multiple winner of the Green Jersey in the Tour de France since 2010; the author of the novels *A Certain Smile* and *Bonjour Tristesse*; and the presenter of the 1980 documentary series *Cosmos*?

Your bonuses are on tripoints; that is, places where three countries meet:
(a) In which country is the city of Zāhedān? It is about 50 kilometres south of its country's tripoint with Pakistan and Afghanistan.
(b) The Iguazú Falls is a series of large cataracts close to the tripoint of which three countries?
(c) Situated on a tripoint not far from the centre of Aachen, the Vaalserberg is the highest point in the mainland territories of which country?

Your starter for ten:

16 Answer promptly, naming two of the three animals – a common rodent, a waterfowl and a flightless insect – whose plurals are 'apophonic' or 'mutated'.

Your bonuses are on cinematic adaptations of winners of the Pulitzer Prize for Fiction. In each case, give the novel from the description:
(a) A novel of 1920 by Edith Wharton, adapted for the screen by Martin Scorsese in 1993?
(b) A novel of 1918 by Booth Tarkington, adapted for the screen by Orson Welles in 1942?
(c) A novel of 1994 by E. Annie Proulx, directed in a 2001 film version by Lasse Hallström?

Your starter for ten:

17 What five-letter word of Greek origin can mean: a subsidiary or intermediate theorem; the lower bract of the floret of a grass; the subject or argument of a literary composition; and a headword in a dictionary?

Three questions on physics:
(a) From the Greek for 'stream', what eight-letter term denotes the study of the physics of flow, including fluid and plastic behaviour?
(b) In some fluids, such as a cornstarch-and-water mixture, viscosity increases as velocity gradient increases. What term denotes this behaviour?
(c) In a fluid such as water with constant viscosity, the velocity gradient is simply proportional to shear stress. This type of fluid is named after which foundational figure in classical mechanics?

Your starter for ten:

18 'Describe the tongue of a woodpecker' and 'get the Master of Arithmetic to show you how to square a triangle' are among items on the 'to do' lists in the extensive notebooks of which Renaissance artist? The art historian Kenneth Clark described him as 'the most relentlessly curious man in history'.

Three questions on the tombs of military leaders:
(a) Which ruler's tomb is located at Naqsh-e Rostam near Persepolis? The Athenians defeated his army at the Battle of Marathon.
(b) The tomb of which 19th-century US president is located in Riverside Park in New York, and bears the inscription 'Let us have peace'? It is the largest mausoleum in North America.
(c) Situated on the Left Bank of the Seine, what complex consisting of 17th-century structures and courtyards houses the tomb of Napoleon Bonaparte?

Your starter for ten:

19 To what common British bird do these words from an identification video refer? 'With its deliberate walking action, [it] often looks as if it has had deportment lessons. [Its cry is] a distinctive, ringing, far-carrying *kaaa*, usually repeated three times.'

Three questions on the actor LaKeith Stanfield:
(a) Which 2017 horror film features Stanfield in a supporting role, seemingly the only black friend of the protagonist's in-laws? His strange behaviour leads to the discovery of a disturbing family secret.
(b) Which 2018 absurdist comedy by Boots Riley stars Stanfield as a struggling telemarketer? His co-worker advises him that his sales will

improve if he uses a 'white voice', which he does, with increasingly surreal consequences.

(c) Which 2019 crime thriller stars Stanfield as Demany, the business associate of the jeweller and gambling addict Howard Ratner, played by Adam Sandler?

Your starter for ten:

20 Tirich Mir in Pakistan is the highest peak in what mountain range, a major Asian watershed believed to derive its name from the fact that numerous Indian slaves died of cold while crossing to the west?

Your bonuses are on astronomy. In each case, name the star from the description. All three begin with the same letter:

(a) What name, meaning 'follower' in Arabic, is given to the giant red star that is the brightest of the constellation Taurus? It rises after the Pleiades cluster, hence its name.

(b) The brightest star of the constellation Scorpius has what name, meaning 'rival to Mars', probably because the two objects appear similar when viewed from Earth?

(c) An abbreviation of an Arabic phrase meaning 'the flying eagle', what name is given to the brightest star of Aquila? Together with Deneb and Vega, it forms the Summer Triangle.

Your starter for ten:

21 In zoology, what adaptation is denoted by the adjective 'gressorial'?

Your bonuses are on British popular music. In each case, name the city in which the following acts originated:

(a) Soft Cell, The Sisters Of Mercy and The Kaiser Chiefs.

(b) Engelbert Humperdinck, Showaddywaddy and Kasabian.

(c) Deacon Blue, Primal Scream and Franz Ferdinand.

Your starter for ten:

22 What term can describe a literary work portraying rural life, or the life of shepherds, and the role of a teacher relating to their care or responsibility for a pupil's general wellbeing?

Three questions on the zoologist Dian Fossey:

(a) In 1967, Fossey established the Karisoke Research Centre for the study of gorillas in the Virunga Mountains region of which country?

(b) Born in Kenya in 1903, which anthropologist was an early mentor to Dian Fossey and to the scientists Biruté Galdikas and Jane Goodall, nicknaming them the Trimates?

(c) Following Fossey's murder in 1985, the conservation fund she had founded was renamed in her honour. Which actress became its honorary chair in 1988?

Your starter for ten:

23 What three-word name is shared by a prominent portrait painter born in Antwerp in 1599 and the horse trained by Aidan O'Brien that won the Epsom Derby in June 2019?

Three questions on historic speeches:
(a) Who dissolved Parliament with a pronouncement that included the words: 'Is there a single virtue now remaining amongst you? Ye have no more religion than my horse – in the name of God, go!'
(b) In a 1775 speech on the rights of the colonies, which future governor of Virginia is credited with using the expression, 'Give me liberty or give me death'?
(c) In a speech to troops at Tilbury recorded by the chaplain Lionel Sharp, who said: 'I have the heart and stomach of a king'?

Your starter for ten:

24 What single word is most often used to describe the following theorem? 'Within any axiomatic mathematical system there are propositions that cannot be proved or disproved on the basis of the axioms within that system.' It was formulated by the Austrian-born mathematician Kurt Gödel.

Three questions on abbreviations used in knitting:
(a) Referring to tools commonly used when knitting tubular items such as socks, for what do the letters 'dp' stand in the abbreviation 'dpn', with the 'n' standing for 'needles'?
(b) 'Sl st' means 'slip stitch', the action of slipping a stitch onto the right-hand needle without knitting it. It is often followed by 'psso' – for what do these letters stand?
(c) Found at the beginning of most patterns, and followed by a number of stitches, for what do the letters 'co' stand?

Your starter for ten:

25 In various spellings, what exclamation links all of these: Haydn's Symphony No. 30 in C major; the final part of Mozart's *Exsultate Jubilate*; a well-known chorus from an oratorio by Handel; and a much-covered song by Leonard Cohen?

Three questions on fictional political movements:

(a) Described as a 'big chap with … the sort of eye that can open an oyster at sixty paces', Roderick Spode is the leader of the fascist Black Shorts in the works of which comic writer?

(b) First published in 1928, the novel *Point Counter Point* features the Brotherhood of British Freemen, led by Everard Webley. Who was the author?

(c) In Orwell's *Nineteen Eighty-Four*, Ingsoc is described as the 'prevailing philosophy' of which totalitarian state?

The Answers

1   Salisbury (Lincoln Cathedral had been taller until the storm of 1549)
    (a) (Gladys) Aylward
    (b) (Mary) Slessor
    (c) (David) Livingstone

2   (John) Ruskin ('The Lamp of' in each case)
    (a) Iodine
    (b) Moment of inertia (accept angular mass or rotational inertia)
    (c) Current

3   Bolt
    (a) Citrus
    (b) Persimmon / Sharon fruit / Chinese date plum
    (c) Pear

4   (Herbert) Hoover (in office 1929–1933)
    (a) Time dilation
    (b) Five-fourths / 5 over 4 / 1.25
    (c) Muons (accept mu-mesons or mesotrons, both older names)

5   Cotton
    (a) Benin
    (b) Burkina Faso
    (c) Ghana

6   Litotes (i.e. T.S. Eliot, of course, the line from 'Prufrock')
    (a) (Scottish) Borders (Borders Abbeys Way)
    (b) John Muir (John Muir Way)
    (c) Great Glen (Way; accept but qualify Glen Mor / Glen Albyn)

7   Seventeen (units) (three-dimensional Pythagoras: $8^2 + 9^2 + 12^2 = 17^2$)
    (a) *Hawk*
    (b) (Neil) Gaiman
    (c) (Sue) Grafton

8   Last In, First Out
    (a) Protectionism
    (b) Proportionality / proportional
    (c) Propulsion (accept similar, e.g. 'propelling')

9   'O', 'e' and 'u' (*L'oeuvre*; 'coeur', 'oeuf' and 'soeur')
    (a) Stavanger
    (b) Tromsø
    (c) Bergen

10   (Tsar) Nicholas II
     (a) *Martin Chuzzlewit*
     (b) *Barnaby Rudge*
     (c) *Little Dorritt*

11   Saga (sagas; *The Forsyte Saga*; Saga Norén, played by Sofia Helin)
     (a) Running a (market) sweet stall
     (b) (Tony) Richardson
     (c) *Saturday Night and Sunday Morning*

12   Byzantine Empire (author of *Corpus Scriptorum Historiae Byzantinae*)
     (a) (Hannah) Höch (1889–1978)
     (b) (Robert) Rauschenberg
     (c) (Georges) Braque

13   Radical
     (a) Iceland
     (b) (Halldór) Laxness
     (c) *Edda*

14   Alexander (the Great / III of Macedon)
     (a) Kamikaze
     (b) Cosmopolitan
     (c) Mary Pickford

15   Sagan (Peter, Françoise, Carl)
     (a) Iran
     (b) Brazil, Paraguay, Argentina
     (c) Netherlands (accept Holland, correcting it)

16   Mouse / goose / louse (accept mice, geese and lice, of course)
     (a) *The Age of Innocence*
     (b) *The Magnificent Ambersons*
     (c) *The Shipping News*

17   Lemma
     (a) Rheology (Greek: *rheos*)
     (b) Dilatant / dilatancy
     (c) (Isaac) Newton (i.e. Newtonian)

18   Leonardo (da Vinci)
     (a) Darius I (or the Great; 550–489 BCE)
     (b) (Ulysses S.) Grant (1822–1885)
     (c) Les Invalides / Hôtel national des Invalides

19 (Carrion) crow (*Corvus corone*)
    (a) *Get Out*
    (b) *Sorry to Bother You*
    (c) *Uncut Gems*

20 Hindu Kush ('Killer of Hindus')
    (a) Aldebaran
    (b) Antares
    (c) Altair

21 (Adapted for) walking (Latin: *gressus*, past participle of *gradi*, 'to step' / 'go')
    (a) Leeds
    (b) Leicester
    (c) Glasgow

22 Pastoral
    (a) Rwanda (on the borders of Rwanda, Uganda and DR Congo)
    (b) (Louis) Leakey
    (c) Sigourney Weaver (who portrayed Fossey in the 1988 film *Gorillas in the Mist*)

23 Anthony van Dyck
    (a) (Oliver) Cromwell (1653)
    (b) Patrick Henry
    (c) Elizabeth I (August 1688)

24 (Gödel's first) incompleteness (theorem)
    (a) Double-pointed / double point (needles)
    (b) Pass slipped stitch over
    (c) Cast on

25 Hallelujah / Alleluia
    (a) (P. G.) Wodehouse
    (b) Aldous Huxley
    (c) Oceania

Famous Contestants

Part 3

Actor, comedian and writer **Miles Jupp** had been asked to take part in a celebrity version of *University Challenge* several times, but it was only when his friend and fellow actor Justin Edwards, fresh from his appearance for the University of Manchester in a Christmas alumni special in December 2020 / January 2021 alongside Adrian Edmondson, recommended it that he said yes. And, recalls the former host of BBC Radio 4's *The News Quiz*, when they were at the University of Edinburgh together, where Miles was reading Divinity, his wife Rachel competed in a version of *University Challenge* in India. 'I thought it'd be nice to have some overlap on our CVs.'

The result: Miles, as captain of the University of Edinburgh alumni team, alongside *MasterChef* winner and founder of the Wahaca restaurant chain, Thomasina Miers, triumphed in the 2021 Christmas celebrity series. Their teammates were architecture expert Catherine Slessor and academic Phil Swanson. When the team formed an email group to get to know each other before their appearance, Miles realized he was in formidable company. 'We were discussing our particular strengths and I said I knew a bit about cricket and that was about it, but I realized Phil is a professor and Catherine is an absolute powerhouse. I think she knows everything; she was astonishing. I got messages from friends afterwards saying I contributed basically nothing.'

As well as being a regular fixture on television – from *Balamory* and *Have I Got News for You* to *The Thick of It* and *The Durrells* – Miles had been on *Celebrity Mastermind* twice. 'But this was different,' he says. 'It wasn't ten questions on your specialist subject and ten general knowledge questions; it's so much more wide-ranging. It felt a bit more terrifying the closer it got.'

Miles drew on his *Mastermind* experience. 'When I went on *Mastermind*, one time I won and the other I absolutely went to pieces. So I know what it is to go on these things and not know anything. It's actually completely bearable. I was glad I did it. It was good fun. I was hoping to see Jeremy Paxman being slightly grumpy. I got to hear him say, "Oh, come on," so I loved that.'

Miles's team played Leicester in their first round, beating them 160–125. They then dispatched Bradford 145–125 in the semi-final. 'There were a couple of Latin questions I got right, which was vaguely pleasing because attempting to study Latin sort of ruined my life for about two or three years in my late teens, so there was a degree of "Maybe that wasn't a total waste of time",' recalls Miles. 'And I correctly identified Melton Mowbray from quite a large map despite having very bad geography. I was thrilled with myself for doing that, but then I got the follow-up question wrong.'

Miles's team went on to beat Hertford College, Oxford in the final with a highly respectable score of 235–95. 'We were surprisingly happy. I don't think we were expecting to win; I don't think anyone turns up expecting to win. In between the semi-final and the final [which were recorded on the same day] ,we socialized together for a few hours. So we had a really nice time and we hope to meet up for a reunion dinner.'

Miles likes the 'theatre' of *University Challenge*. 'For my generation it's been under the eye of Paxman, and I love his increasing irascibility. I've always enjoyed watching people get angry – not with me, with other people. I think *The Young Ones* really added to the brand, possibly unintentionally, but it's sort of famous for that episode, as well as being famous in its own right.'

*

Actor, writer and broadcaster **Stephen Fry** was a member of the Queens' College, Cambridge team that reached the finals in 1980, losing to Merton College, Oxford. As well as being part of *The Young Ones*' 'Bambi' cast, he returned to the programme a number of times, for alumni specials and, in 2003, as captain of the 'Gownies' team (Fry, David Baddiel, Frank Skinner and Clive Anderson), failing to beat the 'Townies' (Jeremy Beadle, Gina Yashere, Danny Baker and Johnny Vaughan) with Angus Deayton in the chair in aid of Comic Relief.

Of his 1980 student appearance Stephen says: 'Like everyone else, we were nervous and excited and in awe of Bamber, who was completely charming. We won quite a few games and that took us to a best-of-three final with Merton. We thrashed them in the first game; they pipped us on the very last question of the second, forcing a third, which they won. All in all, we scored more points than them in all three games, but that sounds like sour grapes … It was fun, but I wish I hadn't worn a college tie. It made me look even more like a dick than usual.'

Challenging Tales
Open Season

One headline-making edition featured a team from the Open University. Team member Lance Haward was a retired solicitor and veteran of numerous TV quiz shows. He had always wanted to be on *University Challenge* (and also maintained a love of learning) so he signed up for a course in Classical Greek with the Open University.

After qualifying for the programme, the Open University went on to beat Oriel College, Oxford in the 1999 final by 265 to 210 points. Paxman commented afterwards: 'One of the Open University guys had only signed up for a course at the OU so he could be on the team.'

Lance recalls: '*University Challenge* didn't exist when I was at university, and I never made any secret of the fact I wanted to go on. The one person who was less than enchanted by it was Jeremy Paxman. He thought it was inappropriate.' At 62, Lance is believed to be the oldest member of a winning team.

A BBC spokeswoman said at the time: 'It was well-documented that Lance Haward, from the Open University, had only applied to do a degree with the OU to get on the *University Challenge* team. We are flattered that the programme's popularity and reputation means that students will go to such lengths to be involved. *University Challenge* is, at the end of the day, a quiz show, not an academic qualification.'

Match

Your starter for ten:

1 Isolated and described by Berzelius in 1824, which element has a common dioxide that occurs in minerals such as jasper, opal and quartz?

Three questions on a legendary Greek king:
(a) Danaus, the brother of Aegyptus, was a legendary king of which city of the Peloponnese, a little to the south of Mycenae?
(b) *Danaus plexippus* is a large orange and black butterfly named after the king, and better known by what name, possibly in reference to William III?
(c) Danaë, a descendant of Danaus's daughter Hypermnestra, was the mother of which Greek hero?

Your starter for ten:

2 Used in early transistors and common in infra-red optical systems, which tetravalent element was first isolated from the mineral argyrodite in 1886, and named after its discoverer's homeland? Predicted by Mendeleev, it lies in Group 14, between silicon and tin.

Three questions on kings of England:
(a) Who acceded to the throne aged around nine months, his nominated protector during his minority being his uncle, Humphrey, Duke of Gloucester?
(b) William Marshal acted as regent during the early reign of which king, who acceded to the throne aged nine on the death of his father, King John?
(c) Edward Seymour, later Duke of Somerset, was named Lord Protector during the reign of which king, also aged nine when he acceded to the throne?

Your starter for ten:

3 In which continent are the Allan Hills, the site of the discovery, in 1984, of a meteorite controversially claimed to contain fossils of Martian micro-organisms?

Three questions on astronomy:

(a) With a duration of up to several hours, what transient solar phenomena may be classed as 'C', 'M' or 'X', in increasing intensity of soft X-ray emission?

(b) Another flare classification scheme is based on emission in what specific atomic line, at a wavelength of 656 nanometres?

(c) Which English astronomer observed a white-light solar flare in 1859, during an exceptionally powerful solar storm?

Your starter for ten:

4 Born in 1792, Thomas Jefferson Hogg was the first biographer of which poet, having co-authored with him the controversial pamphlet of 1811 entitled *The Necessity of Atheism*?

Three questions on people with the surname Smith:

(a) What short byname is often applied to the geologist William Smith? It is a term used in the full title of his 1815 *Geologic Map of England and Wales*.

(b) Born in Hull in 1902, Florence Margaret Smith is usually known by what nickname? Her works include *Novel on Yellow Paper* and poetry collections such as *A Good Time Was Had by All*.

(c) Her works including *The Midnight Kittens* and *I Capture the Castle*, Dorothy Gladys Smith is usually known by what five-letter nickname?

Your starter for ten:

5 The name of which British indie band is a former Mac computer keyboard shortcut for the Greek letter 'delta'?

Three questions on artistic depictions of scientific activities:

(a) Which English artist's paintings include a work of 1771 entitled *The Alchemist's Discovery of Phosphorus*, in which the subject's face is illuminated by the contents of a glass vessel?

(b) A work by the Scottish painter Alexander Blaikley shows which prominent scientist speaking to the audience of the Christmas Lectures of 1855?

(c) Depicting the subject carrying out a surgical procedure in front of an amphitheatre of medical students, *The Agnew Clinic* is a work of 1889 by which US Realist artist?

Your starter for ten:

6 Tartu is the second-largest city of which country? It is the site of a university founded in 1632 by Gustavus Adolphus of Sweden, and of the signing of a treaty of 1920 that confirmed the independence of the country in question.

Three questions on the deaths of public figures:
(a) Thought to have drowned while swimming in the Bass Strait in 1967, Harold Holt was the prime minister of which country?
(b) The unsolved murder of Colin Campbell near Appin in the west of Scotland in 1752 served as the inspiration for which novel of 1886 by Robert Louis Stevenson?
(c) Which prime minister of Sweden was assassinated in Stockholm in 1986 while walking home from the cinema?

Your starter for ten:
7 What short given name or byname links all of the following Americans? An outlaw killed in Missouri in 1882; a civil rights leader and politician born in 1941; a professional wrestler who became governor of Minnesota, and an athlete who won four gold medals at the 1936 Summer Olympics.

Three questions on Latin:
(a) What specific eight-letter term denotes a Latin verb that is active in meaning but passive in appearance; that is, one whose principal parts are all passive?
(b) Involving a deponent Latin verb, what common two-word Latin phrase means an abrupt change in topic, or a response that does not follow from the previous statement?
(c) Also involving a deponent Latin verb, what two-word Latin phrase means a reminder of death or mortality?

Your starter for ten:
8 Born in 1802, which English physicist invented the concertina and the Playfair cypher, but is perhaps best known for an eponymous 'bridge' that measures electrical resistance?

Three questions on a novelist:
(a) The crime novels *Police at the Funeral* and *The Tiger in the Smoke* are works by which writer, the creator of the detective Albert Campion?
(b) The plot of Allingham's 1936 Campion novel *Flowers for the Judge* centres on a forged manuscript reputed to have been written by which Restoration dramatist, whose plays include *The Mourning Bride*?
(c) Campion's manservant, Magersfontein Lugg, shares his first name with a battle in which war, during a period of setbacks for the British army that was known as Black Week?

Your starter for ten:

9   Name either of the two people who shared the 2010 Nobel Prize in Physics for 'groundbreaking experiments regarding the two-dimensional material graphene'.

Your bonuses are on creative works. In each case, identify the work from the description. All three titles begin with the same two words:
(a) First published in 1902, a novella by Joseph Conrad that examines the horrors of European colonialism; it inspired Francis Ford Coppola's *Apocalypse Now*.
(b) A mosaic set into the Royal Mile in Edinburgh. It marks the position of a 15th-century Tolbooth and gives its name to a novel by Sir Walter Scott and to a leading Scottish football club.
(c) Set in 18th-century Bavaria, a 1976 film directed by Werner Herzog in which almost all of the actors performed whilst under hypnosis.

Your starter for ten:

10 I need a two-word name here. What industrial region of about 360 square kilometres straddles a major watershed of England, being the source of rivers that flow north and east to the Trent and south and west to the Severn? It comprises most of the boroughs of Sandwell, Dudley and Walsall and the city of Wolverhampton.

Three questions on animation:
(a) Directed by Merian Cooper and Ernest Schoedsack, which film of 1933 is noted for its pioneering stop-motion animation effects developed by Willis O'Brien?
(b) Which animator worked alongside Willis O'Brien on the 1949 gorilla film *Mighty Joe Young*, and went on to lead the special effects teams on films including *The 7th Voyage of Sinbad* and *The Valley of Gwangi*?
(c) Harryhausen's last major cinematic role as a lead animator came in which film of 1981, which featured Harry Hamlin as Perseus and Ursula Andress as Aphrodite?

Your starter for ten:

11 Meaning 'gatekeeper' in Greek, what term denotes the opening between the stomach and the small intestine?

Your bonuses are on terms associated with volcanoes. In each case, give the term from the definition:
(a) What adjective derives from the name of the Roman author who described the violent volcanic eruption that destroyed Pompeii?

(b) What Indonesian word denotes a powerful landslide of ash and water that flows down the sides of a volcano? I need a five-letter, singular word.
(c) 'A kind of volcanic lava with a rough, jagged surface covered with loose clinkers'. I need a short term from the Hawaiian language.

Your starter for ten:

12 Of which artist did J.M.W. Turner say: 'If [he] had lived, I should have starved'? Dying in 1802 at the age of twenty-seven, his works include the panorama *Eidometropolis* and *The White House at Chelsea*.

Three questions on works of the counterculture:
(a) In Jack Kerouac's 1957 novel *On the Road*, the two main characters, Sal Paradise and Dean Moriarty, are based on Kerouac himself and which of his friends?
(b) With sections on how to grow cannabis, how to protest and how to shoplift, what three-word instruction forms the title of the 1971 book by the political activist Abbie Hoffman?
(c) In Ken Kesey's 1962 novel *One Flew Over the Cuckoo's Nest*, set in an Oregon psychiatric hospital, what is the name of the Native American who narrates the story?

Your starter for ten:

13 In astronomy, for what does the second letter stand in the three abbreviations DSN, ESA and HST?

Your bonuses are on concepts in postcolonial theory. In each case, give the term from the definition:
(a) A two-word term coined by W.E.B. Du Bois to refer to an internal conflict experienced by colonized peoples; he described it as 'a sense of measuring one's soul by the tape of a world that looks on in amused contempt and pity'.
(b) A military term meaning a junior officer, used in this context to refer to groups excluded from structures of power; it appears in the title of a major essay by Gayatri Spivak.
(c) A term developed by Edward Saïd in a book of the same name; it refers to reductive and romanticized representations of Asian art and culture.

Your starter for ten:

14 The 22nd parallel north forms the major part of the border between which two countries in Northeast Africa?

Three questions on US journalists:

(a) Born in 1908, which US journalist became noted for his reports broadcast from Europe during the Second World War, including those during the Battle of Britain, which he often opened with the words, 'This is London'?

(b) A protégé of Ed Murrow, which journalist wrote *Berlin Diary*, an account of his experiences in the 1930s, and the major non-fiction work *The Rise and Fall of the Third Reich*?

(c) Once called 'the most trusted man in America', which journalist presented the 1968 television special *Report from Vietnam*, in which he described the Vietnam War as a 'stalemate'?

Your starter for ten:

15 Born in Bologna in 1737, which scientist investigated the effects of what he conceived to be electricity in animal tissue? He gives his name to a process that protects ferrous metals against exposure to the atmosphere by the application of a coating of zinc.

Three questions on the French Republican calendar:

(a) 'The Battle of the 13th of Prairial, Year 2' is the name given in France to the first naval engagement of the revolutionary wars between France and Great Britain. By what date is it usually known in English?

(b) The Thermidorian Reaction saw the fall and execution of Robespierre, ending the Reign of Terror. In which month of the Gregorian calendar did it take place?

(c) Corresponding to 9 November 1799, 'the 18th of Brumaire, Year 8' is the name given to a coup that saw which individual take power as First Consul of France?

Your starter for ten:

16 'Today, 23 years ago, dear Grandma died. I wonder what she would have thought of a Labour government?' Referring to Ramsay MacDonald, those words appear in a diary entry by which British monarch?

Three questions on Chinese poetry:

(a) Li Po, also known as Li Bai, and Du Fu have both been described as 'China's greatest poet'. Both lived during which dynasty?

(b) What number appears in the title of the pre-eminent anthology of Tang poems? It is the triangular number between 276 and 325.

(c) *Three Hundred Tang Poems* was compiled by the Retired Master of Hengtang during which dynasty? The collection appeared about a thousand years after Li Bo was active.

Your starter for ten:

17 Originating from the Greek for 'discover', what term is applied to a technique or aid for learning, discovery or problem-solving, that is based on experiment and especially trial-and-error?

Three questions on double A-sides that were Christmas number ones in the UK singles chart. In each case, you'll hear the year, the artist and one of the A-sides. For five points, name the other:
(a) 1977, Wings, 'Girls' School'.
(b) 1965, The Beatles, 'Day Tripper'.
(c) 1991, Queen, 'These Are the Days of our Lives'.

Your starter for ten:

18 Caused by the growth of a cork-like layer on the skin, what name is given to the rough reddish-brown patches that develop on certain cultivars of apple, pear and potato? In the first scene of *Hamlet*, Horatio uses the same term in reference to the dawn.

Three questions on physics:
(a) In the standard model of particle physics, what is the only fundamental gauge boson to have a symbol that is a Greek letter, rather than a Roman one?
(b) In addition to the W+, W- and Z0 particles, which other fundamental particle is represented by an upper-case letter?
(c) What is the only lepton to have a symbol that is a Roman letter?

Your starter for ten:

19 In January 2020, which director was appointed the first black president of the Cannes Film Festival jury? His films include *She's Gotta Have It, Jungle Fever* and *4 Little Girls*.

Your bonus questions are on Shakespeare's contemporaries. In each case, name the author of the following stage works:
(a) *Tamburlaine the Great* and *Edward II*
(b) *The Battle of Alcazar* and *The Famous Chronicle of King Edward I*
(c) *The Spanish Tragedy* and *Cornelia*?

Your starter for ten:

20 What decade saw the completion of the Rialto Bridge in Venice; the invention of the thermometer by Galileo; the Edict of Nantes that gave French Huguenots equal rights with Catholics; and the death of Christopher Marlowe?

Your bonuses are on videogames released in 2001. Give the title of each game from the description:

(a) The first in an ongoing series by Nintendo, set on an Earth-like planet populated by a species of tiny, plant-animal hybrid aliens. Its creator, Shigeru Miyamoto, reportedly conceived the game while watching ants working together in his garden.

(b) The first in a series of action-adventure games developed by Capcom, praised for its complex combat and gothic art design? The player-character is a demon hunter named Dante.

(c) The first game designed and directed by Fumito Ueda, who went on to create *Shadow of the Colossus* and *The Last Guardian*? Its abandoned castle setting is notably influenced by the paintings of Giorgio de Chirico.

Your starter for ten:

21 I need a two-word term here. Named after a 19th-century French mathematician, Roche lobes are pear-shaped regions surrounding what specific astronomical phenomena?

Three questions on screen versions of books by Daphne du Maurier:

(a) Which Oscar-winning British actress played the eponymous role in the 2017 adaptation of *My Cousin Rachel*?

(b) In which 1944 film, set during the Restoration, did Joan Fontaine play the headstrong aristocrat Dona St Columb, who pursues the philosopher-pirate Jean Aubrey?

(c) Three of Hitchcock's films were adapted from works by Du Maurier. For which of them did he relocate the action from Cornwall to California?

Your starter for ten:

22 In familiar quotations from the Book of Exodus, Coleridge's *Kubla Khan* and Shakespeare's *Macbeth*, the name of what foodstuff precedes 'honey', 'paradise' and 'human kindness'?

Three questions on birds in the song 'The Twelve Days of Christmas':

(a) The traditional version of the song 'The Twelve Days of Christmas' features which bird of the genus *Streptopelia*, whose name is partly onomatopoeic of its song?

(b) Species of which bird in the song include white-fronted, snow, brant, pink-footed and greylag?

(c) Perdrix au choux and Perdrix en Chartreuse are classic recipes incorporating which bird mentioned in the song?

Your starter for ten:

23 In which Commonwealth country does the evergreen tree pōhutukawa feature on festive greeting cards and in poems and stories? Its striking red flowers blossom in December and January.

Three questions on a scientific rivalry:
(a) Starting in the 1870s and also called the Great Dinosaur Rush, how was the rivalry between the US scientists Edward Drinker Cope and Othniel Charles Marsh known?
(b) The feud included a disagreement over the skeleton of an Elasmosaurus, a long-necked aquatic animal of the late cretaceous, belonging to which order?
(c) Cope and Marsh appear as characters in the 2017 novel *Dragon Teeth*, a story set around the Bone Wars by which author, who died in 2008?

Your starter for ten:

24 In the year before Queen Victoria's death, which capital city was looted by troops of the Eight-Nation Alliance, including contingents from Russia, Italy and Japan? The force had ostensibly been sent to protect foreign residents from an uprising known in English as the Boxer Rebellion.

Your bonuses are on pairs of words that are anagrams of each another. In each case, give the two words from the descriptions:
(a) 'Short published reviews of a new film or play'; and 'the cutting of a solid along a plane'.
(b) 'To object to or hesitate over something'; and 'to be shut up in an enclosed space'.
(c) 'Criticized in an angrily insulting manner'; and 'to hand something to a recipient or address'.

Your starter for ten:

25 The heaviest of the actinoids, with the atomic number 103, which element is named after the US scientist who won the 1939 Nobel Prize in Physics for inventing the cyclotron?

Your bonuses are on musicians. In each case, name the orchestral instrument with which each set of people is most associated:
(a) First: Miriam Fried, Tasmin Little and Isaac Stern.
(b) Marisa Robles, Osian Ellis and Sidonie and Marie Goossens.
(c) And finally, Natalia Gutman, Yo-Yo Ma and Steven Isserlis?

The Answers

1   Silicon (not silica, the common name of silicon dioxide)
  (a) Argos
  (b) Monarch (butterfly)
  (c) Perseus

2   Germanium (argyrodite Ag_8GeS_6)
  (a) Henry VI
  (b) Henry III
  (c) Edward VI

3   Antarctica (the meteorite was ALH84001)
  (a) (Solar) flares
  (b) Hydrogen alpha / H-alpha
  (c) (Richard) Carrington

4   (Percy Bysshe) Shelley
  (a) Strata (*A Delineation of the Strata of England and Wales, with Part of Scotland*)
  (b) Stevie
  (c) Dodie

5   Alt-J
  (a) (Joseph) Wright (of Derby)
  (b) (Michael) Faraday
  (c) (Thomas) Eakins

6   Estonia
  (a) Australia
  (b) *Kidnapped*
  (c) Olof Palme

7   Jesse (James, Jackson, Ventura, Owens)
  (a) Deponent (not 'semi-deponent')
  (b) Non sequitur
  (c) Memento mori

8   (Charles) Wheatstone (Wheatstone bridge invented by mathematician Samuel Christie
  and popularized by Wheatstone)
  (a) (Margery) Allingham
  (b) (William) Congreve
  (c) (Second) Boer War / South African War (in 1899)

9   (Andre) Geim and (Konstantin / Kostya) Novoselov
  (a) *Heart of Darkness*
  (b) *Heart of Midlothian*
  (c) *Heart of Glass* (*Herz aus Glas* in the original German)

10   Black Country (not West Midlands, which is much larger)
     (a) *King Kong*
     (b) (Ray) Harryhausen
     (c) *Clash of the Titans*

11   Pylorus / pyloric sphincter
     (a) Plinian (eruption; Pliny the Younger's father was killed in the eruption)
     (b) Lahar
     (c) Aa (pronounced 'ah-ah', similar to 'uh-oh')

12   (Thomas) Girtin
     (a) Neal Cassady
     (b) *Steal This Book*
     (c) 'Chief' Bromden

13   Space (Deep Space Network, European Space Agency, Hubble Space Telescope)
     (a) Double consciousness
     (b) Subaltern (the full title of Spivak's essay is 'Can the Subaltern Speak?')
     (c) Orientalism

14   Egypt and Sudan
     (a) (Ed) Murrow
     (b) (William) Shirer
     (c) (Walter) Cronkite

15   (Luigi) Galvani
     (a) (Glorious) 1 June
     (b) (27–28) July
     (c) Napoleon (I / Bonaparte)

16   George V (in 1924; Queen Victoria had died in 1901, of course)
     (a) Tang (618–907; Li Po, 701–762; Du Fu, 712–770)
     (b) 300
     (c) Ch'ing / Qing (1636–1912; compiled around 1763)

17   Heuristic (Greek: *heuriskein*)
     (a) 'Mull of Kintyre'
     (b) 'We Can Work It Out'
     (c) 'Bohemian Rhapsody' (re-released after Freddie Mercury's death)

18   Russet / russeting ('the morn, in russet mantle clad')
     (a) Photon (symbol is gamma)
     (b) Higgs boson (or Higgs particle; symbol is H0)
     (c) Electron (symbol is e)

19 Spike Lee
    (a) (Christopher) Marlowe (published 1590 and 1594)
    (b) (George) Peele (published 1594 and *c*.1593)
    (c) (Thomas) Kyd (published 1592 and 1594)

20 1590s (1591, 1592, 1598, 1593)
    (a) *Pikmin*
    (b) *Devil May Cry*
    (c) *Ico*

21 Binary stars (Édouard Albert Roche, 1820–1883)
    (a) Rachel Weisz
    (b) *Frenchman's Creek*
    (c) *The Birds*

22 Milk ('land flowing with milk and'; 'drunk the milk of'; 'too full o' the milk of')
    (a) Turtle dove
    (b) Goose / geese
    (c) Partridge

23 New Zealand
    (a) The Bone Wars
    (b) Plesiosauria / plesiosaurs
    (c) Michael Crichton

24 Beijing / Peking
    (a) Notices / section
    (b) Demur / mured
    (c) Reviled / deliver

25 Lawrencium (Ernest Lawrence)
    (a) Violin
    (b) Harp
    (c) Cello

Triple First
Magdalen College, Oxford

Gonville and Caius College, Cambridge
(2004)

Magdalen College, Oxford were the first team to win back-to-back titles, in 1997 and 1998. (They were later joined by Manchester, victors in both 2012 and 2013.) In 2004, Magdalen were in the final again, facing Gonville and Caius College, Cambridge, with a chance to become the first three-time winner.

Magdalen had won their way through by defeating Nottingham University in round one and Sussex University in the second round, before knocking out the Royal Northern College of Music in the quarter-finals and St Andrews in the semi-finals.

Gonville and Caius had stormed through early rounds, knocking out first Reading University and then Strathclyde, despatching St Johns College, Oxford in the quarter-finals and then London Metropolitan in the semis.

For the first time in eight years, it was an Oxford and Cambridge final...

Magdalen College, Oxford
Dave Cox from Ipswich, reading Mathematics
Matt Holdcroft from Bristol, reading Classics
Freya McClements from County Derry, Northern Ireland, reading History
Josh Spero from London, reading Classics

Gonville and Caius College, Cambridge
Lameen Souag, Algerian American, studying Mathematics
Rosemary Warner from Huddersfield, studying Biochemistry

Edward Wallace from London, studying Pure Mathematics
Laura Ashe, originally from Leeds, doing a PhD in medieval literature

Your starter for ten:

1 In a handbook on his life and work, of whom did Iris Murdoch say that he 'stands full in the way of the three post-Hegelian movements of thought: the Marxist, the Existentialist and the phenomenological', describing a French philosopher and member of the French Resistance, who from 1944 dedicated himself entirely to literature but refused the Nobel Prize in 1964.

Your bonuses are on medieval history:
(a) Born in Pavia around 1015, Lanfranc became the Archbishop of Canterbury during the reign of which king?
(b) A noted theologian who was later made a doctor of the church, which pupil of Lanfranc became the Archbishop of Canterbury in 1093?
(c) What name is generally given to the argument by Anselm in his *Proslogion* that goes, 'If God is defined as a being than which no greater can be conceived of, then he must exist in reality since otherwise a being of identical attributes, with the further conceivable attribute of existence in reality, would be greater'?

Your starter for ten:

2 'It is like a piece of drama but has pulled off the trick of dispensing with a script. It's where the entire realist movement in 20th-century art was leading.' To which television series did these words, part of an appreciation for a broadsheet columnist, refer?

Your bonuses are on classical architecture:
(a) In architecture, what name is given to the upper part of a classical building supported by columns or colonnade comprising architrave, frieze and cornice?
(b) In classical architecture, what name from the Greek for 'pillar base' is given to the continuous base supporting a row of columns?
(c) The 'pediment', the upper part of the front of a building in the classical style, typically surmounting a portico of columns, is usually what shape?

Your starter for ten:

3 Published between 1970 and 1981, the novels by Mary Renault, entitled *Fire from Heaven, The Persian Boy*—?
[The question was successfully interrupted]

Your bonuses are on an expression:
(a) Which 16th-century Spanish poet and saint, was an associate of St Teresa

of Ávila and was the author of such mystical works as the *Spiritual Canticle* and the *Dark Night of the Soul*?

(b) In the 1995 autobiographical work *In Search of Stones*, which American psychotherapist and author refers to St John of the Cross in a description of a period of depression which he calls 'the dark night of the senses'?

(c) Which 20th-century American author wrote, 'In a real dark night of the soul, it is always 3 o'clock in the morning'?

Your starter for ten:

4 Which compound has a high rating on the Mohs scale of hardness, has the chemical symbol WC and is often used on the cutting edge of saws and drills to give resistance to wear?

Your bonuses are on plants:

(a) A plant that is the result of a cross between two parent strains, usually with the best features of each, though it doesn't breed true for further generations is given what specific designation?

(b) What name is applied particularly to the primary vertical root of a plant?

(c) What term describes a plant, especially a xerophyte that has thick fleshy leaves or stems adapted to store water?

Your starter for ten:

5 [This was a picture round. Magdalen correctly identified a picture by Cindy Sherman based on a Caravaggio work and went on to identify two others as Michelangelo and Vermeer, but couldn't identify a photographic reproduction of Mantegne's *The Lamentation over the Dead Christ*]

Your starter for ten:

6 Who's being described? 'Born in Pennsylvania in 1928, he became a teacher at MIT in 1955 and two years later published *Syntactic Structures*—?'
[The question was successfully interrupted]

Your bonuses are on severe punishments:

(a) Who, according to Greek mythology, found the cursed flute of the goddess Athena and challenged the god Apollo to a music contest, which he lost, as a result of which Apollo had him flayed alive and his skin nailed to a nearby pine tree?

(b) What punishment was meted out to the French theologian and philosopher Peter Abelard by Canon Fulbert at the Cathedral of Paris, whose niece Abelard he had secretly married?

(c) Born around 288, which saint was a victim of the Diocletian Persecution? He survived being shot with arrows and was nursed back to health, whereupon he presented himself to the emperor, who had him beaten to death and thrown into a sewer?

Your starter for ten:

7 *Fair Em, the Miller's Daughter of Manchester*, *The Merry Devil of Edmonton* and *Arden of Faversham* are among the so-called apocrypha, tenuously or fancifully attributed, wholly or—?
[The question was successfully interrupted]

Your bonuses are on historical events:
To which decade of the 19th century did the following events belong?
(a) The creation of the Austro-Hungarian Empire, the purchase of Alaska from Russia by the USA and the publication of the first volume of Karl Marx's *Das Kapital*.
(b) The ascension to the throne in Sardinia of Victor Emmanuel II, the discovery of Neptune and the publication of Emily Bronte's *Wuthering Heights* all occurred in which decade?
(c) Thirdly, the Decembrist Revolt in Russia, the opening of the Stockton and Darlington railway, and the first performance of Beethoven's Ninth Symphony.

Your starter for ten:

8 GUUAM was formed in 1999 as a counterbalance to the Russia-led Commonwealth of Independent States and is a political economic and strategy alliance between five former Soviet republics whose initial letters make the acronym GUUAM. Name all five.

Your bonuses are on 'welcomes':
(a) Which English composer wrote from 1680 a series of 'Welcome Songs', or ceremonial odes, to Charles II?
(b) What name is given to the garland of flowers traditionally given to visitors in Hawaii as a sign of welcome?
(c) Which Hebrew prophet is commemorated in the Passover ceremony by an unconsumed glass of wine and a door being opened as a sign of welcome. His arrival as an unknown guest is traditionally believed to herald the advent of the Messiah?

Your starter for ten:

9 What two letters link a unit of avoirdupois weight equivalent to 437.5 grains with a magazine indicted in 1971 on charges including 'conspiracy to corrupt the morals of liege subjects and Her Majesty the Queen by raising in their minds inordinate and lustful desires'?
[No one successfully answered the question]

Your starter for ten:

10 Often denoted by z star or z bar, what is the complex conjugate of the complex number z = x + iy?

Your bonuses are on members of the crow family:
(a) Which member of the crow family has adult plumage which is mainly brownish-pink with a distinctive black moustache, is an excellent mimic and habitually collects large quantities of acorns and nuts for its winter food store?
(b) With a glossy black plumage and red bill, which member of the crow family typically performs aerobatic movements around the cliffs and mountains that form its main habitat?
(c) What bird has a smoky grey belly, nape and mantle and is a near relation of the carrion crow, although the two birds tend not to share a habitat?

Your starter for ten:

11 Observing that its 'shape, efficiency, simplicity is really the endpoint of Cartesian perfection', of what vehicle did the broadsheet columnist Zoe Williams write in 2003: 'The perfect clunk-click of symbiosis that people associate with nookie is completely expressed in the relationship [between it and man]'?
[No one successfully answered the question]

Your starter for ten:

12 Which mountains give their name to a French department, a Swiss canton—?
[The question was successfully interrupted]

Bonus questions:
(a) Discovered by Giuseppe Piazzi in 1801 and named after a Roman goddess, which asteroid is the largest known and was the first to be discovered in the belt between Jupiter and Mars where they are most densely concentrated?
(b) Koronis, Eos and Themis are examples of families or groups of asteroids having similar orbits and named after which Japanese-born astronomer, who first noted their existence in 1918?
(c) The name of which Greek god was given to the irregularly shaped asteroid discovered in 1932 and the first to be found whose orbit crosses that of Earth?

Your starter for ten:

13 [This was a music round. The teams were played an excerpt from an opera, which had been distorted with a downward pitch shift undulation. Magdalen correctly identified Verdi's 'Chorus of the Hebrew Slaves' and went on to name two pieces

that had a 'pitch shift' and 'multi echo' applied, but failed to spot a 'pitch-shifted' *Young Person's Guide to the Orchestra*]

Your starter for ten:

14 Gilbert and Sullivan's operetta *Patience* attempted to ridicule which late-19th-century artistic and literary movement whose prominent figures included Walter Pater and Oscar Wilde?

Your bonuses are on a Greek island:

(a) Which island between Crete and the Southern Peloponnese was a major centre for the worship of the goddess Aphrodite, the place of exile for the Spartan king Thyestes and the birthplace of the poet Philoxenus?

(b) *The Embarkation for Cythera*, described as having the lightness and sharpness of a Mozart opera, is a work of 1717 by which French artist also noted for *Gilles* and *Love in the Italian Theatre*?

(c) *The Voyage to Cythera* was the title of a 1989 exhibition by which perennially innovative fashion designer born in Glossop in 1941 and noted early in her career for her influence on the Punk movement?

Your starter for ten:

15 Which four-word phrase completes these words from a speech made by the Queen at London's Guildhall on her 25th wedding anniversary. 'I think everybody really would concede that, on this of all days, I should begin my speech with the words—'?
[The question was successfully interrupted]

Your bonuses are on pairs of words spelled and pronounced alike, but a change of stress marks a change of meaning, for example 'contract' meaning an agreement and 'contract' meaning to shrink. In each case, I want both words:

(a) A verb meaning to confine someone within prescribed limits and a noun meaning 'physician in training', usually in North America.

(b) A verb meaning 'join together' and a noun denoting either a group of commercial interests or a machine that reaps and threshes in one operation.

(c) A verb meaning to make angry and a noun denoting a burnt aromatic?

Your starter for ten:

16 Which mathematician was a joint winner of the 1994 Nobel Prize in Economics for his work on the analysis of the equilibria in the theory—?
[The question was successfully interrupted]

Your bonuses are on an English academic.
(a) Who stated in chapter one of his book first published in 1958 that 'work expands to fill the time available for its completion.'
(b) In Parkinson's Law, what did Parkinson say was the sole cause of men entering local politics?
(c) Finally, in *The Law and the Prophets*, first published in 1960, what did Parkinson say 'rises to meet income'?

Your starter for ten:

17 Which term describes the phenomenon whereby the appearance of the two sexes of an animal species are strikingly different from each other—?
[The question was successfully interrupted]

Your bonuses are on Swiss cantons:
(a) Which canton of Western Switzerland, almost entirely surrounded by French territory, contains the country's third largest city, a focal point of the reformation of 1536?
(b) Which canton takes its name from a tributary of the Po and includes the cities of Bellinzona, Locarno and Lugano?
(c) Divided into half cantons, known as Inner and Outer Rhodes, which canton of Eastern Switzerland gives its name to a straw-coloured cheese whose mature fruity flavour is partly due to the herbal wash it receives during curing?

Your starter for ten:

18 [This was a picture round, with Caius successfully identifying the Iguazu Falls and going on to identify two more]

Your starter for ten:

19 What title did T.S. Eliot give to the fourth and shortest section of *The Wasteland*, in which—?
[The question was successfully interrupted]

Your bonuses are on saints:
(a) Which 1st-century saint is often depicted wearing a sheepskin and bearing a rude wooden cross with a pennon and the words *Ecce Agnus Dei* ('Behold the Lamb of God')?
(b) St John of Beverley, Archbishop of York from 705, numbered among his pupils which historian of early Anglo-Saxon England?
(c) The Archbishop of Constantinople from 398, which St John has a Greek surname which attests to the eloquent quality of his preaching?

Your starter for ten:

20 Taking the theme of a journey that revives memories of an unhappy love affair, *Winterreise* or *Winter Journey* was a song cycle of 1827 by which Austrian—?
[The question was successfully interrupted]

Your bonuses are on flower parts:
(a) What name is given to the two-lobed upper part of a plant stamen, each lobe containing two pollen sacks within which are numerous pollen grains?
(b) What is the name of the sticky surface of the tip of the carpal of the flower which receives the pollen?
(c) The modified leaves that comprise the calyx of a flower are known as what?

Your starter for ten:

21 Which Old English poem is preserved in the 10th-century Vercelli Book, but dates from around 750 or earlier, and records a dream in which the poet sees Christ's cross as both the bloodstained cross of history and an ornately adorned symbol of the passion?
[Neither team answered correctly]

Your starter for ten:

22 What profession, according to the American writer H.L. Mencken, is 'a craft to be mastered in four days and abandoned at the first sign of a better job'?

Your bonuses are on titles:
(a) Firstly, the titles for Jackson Pollock's 1947 work *Full Fathom Five* and Richard Dadd's 1842 painting *Come onto these Yellow Sands* are both taken from which play?
(b) Which Austrian-born artist painted *The Tempest* in 1914, a swirling depiction of his stormy relationship with his lover Alma Mahler, widower of the composer?
(c) Which English composer's incidental music for *The Tempest* in 1862 brought him overnight success, a subsequent work being a cantata entitled *Kenilworth*?

The gong sounds

At the gong, Gonville had 160 points and Magdalen won with 190 points becoming the first institution to win the trophy three times.

The trophy was presented by bestselling author Bill Bryson, who described it as a very exciting match. 'I watched it from the floor and so I had the luxury of seeing all eight contestants at once. You realize that the difference between a successful buzzer and all the rest is a nanosecond,' he said.

Paxman: Honestly, how many could you answer?'

Bryson: I couldn't even get the nookie question! It amazes me how it all drains away with just the tension of being here. It's a stiff challenge for anybody.'

Paxman: What would you say about the accusation that universities are dumbed down? Fair?'

Bryson: There are at least eight who haven't! No, seriously, a whole series of students... I think it's extremely encouraging.'

Challenging Tales
The Win That Wasn't

Watched by 5.3 million viewers, the 2009 final saw Corpus Christi College, Oxford triumph over the University of Manchester. It was a nail-biting final with Manchester leading up to the halfway point, after which Corpus Christi, with their so-called 'human Google' captain Gail Trimble, now a fellow and tutor in Classics at Trinity College, Oxford, surged to a 275–190 victory. Gail had impressed hugely over the previous rounds, answering more questions correctly in the run-up to the final than her teammates combined.

However, following the final it was revealed that teammate Sam Kay was no longer a student at the time of the final's recording, having graduated in June 2008, and was working as a graduate trainee at an accountancy firm. Corpus Christi was stripped of the title, and it was handed to Manchester, giving it its second win of four to date. In a statement the BBC and Granada said: 'The *University Challenge* rules on student eligibility are that students taking part must be registered at their university or college for the duration of the recording of the series. While obviously not intending to, Corpus Christi broke this important rule where other universities and colleges taking part adhered to it. We therefore find ourselves in the regrettable position of having no choice but to disqualify Corpus Christi from the final. This means they forfeit their hard-fought title, which now goes to the Manchester University team.'

The Manchester team captain, Matthew Yeo, said he was saddened to have been given the title at the expense of Corpus Christi.

The Answers

1   John-Paul Sartre
    (a) William the Conqueror.
    (b) St Anselm
    (c) Ontological argument

2   *Big Brother*
    (a) Entablature
    (b) Stylobate
    (c) Triangular

3   Alexander the Great
    (a) St John of the Cross
    (b) M. Scott Peck
    (c) F. Scott Fitzgerald

4   Tungsten carbide
    (a) F1 Hybrid
    (b) Taproot
    (c) Succulent

5   [Picture round]

6   (Avram) Noam Chomsky
    (a) Marsyas
    (b) He was castrated
    (c) St Sebastian the Martyr

7   William Shakespeare
    (a) 1860s
    (b) 1840s
    (c) 1820s

8   Georgia, Ukraine, Uzbekistan, Azerbaijan and Moldova
    (a) Henry Purcell
    (b) Lei
    (c) Elijah

9   OZ

10 $z^* = x - iy$
    (a) Jay
    (b) Chough
    (c) Hooded crow

11 Bicycle

12 Jura
   (a) Ceres
   (b) Kiyotsugu Hirayama
   (c) Apollo

13 [Music round]

14 The Aesthetic Movement
   (a) Cythera
   (b) Jean-Antoine Watteau
   (c) Vivienne Westwood

15 'My husband and I'
   (a) In*tern* and *Intern*
   (b) Com*bine* and *Com*bine
   (c) In*cense* and *In*cense

16 John Ford Nash Jr
   (a) (Cyril Northcote) Parkinson (Parkinson's Law)
   (b) Being unhappily married
   (c) Expenditure

17 (Sexual) dimorphism
   (a) Geneva
   (b) Ticino
   (c) Appenzell

18 [Picture round]

19 *Death by Water*
   (a) John the Baptist
   (b) The Venerable Bede
   (c) St John Chrysostom

20 (Franz) Schubert
   (a) Anther
   (b) Stigma
   (c) Sepals

21 *The Dream of the Rood*

22 Journalism
   (a) *The Tempest*
   (b) Oskar Kokoschka
   (c) Arthur Sullivan

Try Your Luck
Match

16

Your starter for ten:

1   What five-letter word links: the first floor of a Palladian building; the designer of the Shard in London; and a 1993 film written and directed by Jane Campion?

Three questions on caves:

(a) Providing evidence of some of the earliest human habitation in Britain, the site known as Kents Cavern is located in which county of Southern England?
(b) Which village near Dartford in Kent gives its name to a 'skull site' or heritage park? In the 1930s it was the site of the discovery of fossilized fragments of a human skull, dated to around 300,000 years ago.
(c) In 1903, a substantially complete human skeleton, thought to date to at least 9,000 years ago, was discovered in Gough's Cave, part of which limestone gorge in Somerset?

Your starter for ten:

2   Which 19th-century literary figure wrote the poem that begins: 'No coward soul is mine'? After her death, a sibling described her verse as 'wild, melancholy and elevating'.

Three questions on physiology:

(a) The ceruminous glands that produce the substance cerumen are found in what pair of organs of the human body?
(b) Located between the ear and the ascending branch of the lower jaw, what are the largest of the salivary glands?
(c) The sebaceous glands of Zeis, and the modified sweat glands known as the glands of Moll, are found on the edges of which specific parts of the face?

Your starter for ten:

3   In chemistry, the mnemonic 'Have No Fear Of Ice Cold Beer' is used to remember seven chemical elements that tend to occur in what molecular form?

Your bonuses are on given names with festive connotations. Allowing for minor variations of spelling, give the single name that links the following:
(a) The actress who played Claire Underwood in the television series *House of Cards*, and the Barbadian singer better known by her middle name, Rihanna?
(b) The journalist who broke the Cambridge Analytica scandal, and the author of the 1993 novel *The Stone Diaries*?
(c) The actress who played Ada McGrath in *The Piano*, and the co-author of *The Spiderwick Chronicles*?

Your starter for ten:
4   The Carnot cycle in thermodynamics has four phases. Two of them are 'expansion' and 'compression', described as 'adiabatic'; what term precedes these words to describe the other two?

Three questions on astronomy:
(a) What is the two-word name of the NASA spacecraft that made a fly-by of Pluto in 2015?
(b) Indicating a distant place, what two-word Latin nickname has been given to the Kuiper Belt object 2014 MU69, which *New Horizons* flew by in 2019?
(c) Ultima Thule can be termed a TNO, a trans-Neptunian object, or a KBO; for what do the letters 'KB' stand here?

Your starter for ten:
5   The cities of Cody and Laramie, and the greater part of the Yellowstone National Park are all located in which US state, nicknamed the Equality State?

Three questions on wild goats:
(a) Living close to the snow-line, 'Alpine' and 'Spanish' are species of wild goat with what four-letter name?
(b) The walia ibex is an endangered species found only in the Simien Mountains, a UNESCO World Heritage Site in which landlocked African country?
(c) The national animal of Pakistan, the markhor, or *Capra falconeri*, has horns in what distinctive shape?

Your starter for ten:
6   In geometry, what conic section may be expressed by the graph of the equation $y = 1/x$?

Three questions on physics:
(a) 'You cannot win' and 'You cannot break even' are commonly cited summaries of two of the four main laws of which branch of physics?

(b) The 'unattainability statement' of the third law asserts that, using a finite number of thermodynamic cycles, what condition for a system is impossible?
(c) What quantity relating to thermodynamics is often given the symbol 'S'?

Your starter for ten:

7   During the 1930s, in which country did military factions known in English as 'Control' and 'Imperial Way' compete for influence? The latter faction favoured a pre-emptive attack against the Soviet Union, an idea abandoned after a military defeat on the border of Mongolia.

Three questions on Irish sports venues:
(a) Born in 1823, which churchman played a leading role in both the Irish National Land League and the Gaelic League? A major sports stadium in Dublin is named after him.
(b) The major Gaelic sports stadium in Belfast is named after which diplomat who, after exposing human rights abuses in the Congo and Peru, was executed for seeking German military support for the Easter Rising?
(c) What was the former name of the home of the Irish national rugby team? It derived from the name of the marquessate created for the Dublin-born prime minister, the Earl of Shelburne.

Your starter for ten:

8   In 2013, the Children's Laureate Julia Donaldson told the tale of a stolen ring in a published sequel about which pair of fictional characters who, on their wedding night, were dancing by the light of the moon?

Three questions on football clubs and their Latin mottos:
(a) *Nil satis nisi optimum*, meaning 'Nothing but the best is good enough', is the motto of which football club, one of the founding members of the Football League in 1888?
(b) *Arte et labore*, meaning 'By skill and hard work', is the motto of which football club, also a founding member of the Football League?
(c) *Superbia in proelio*, meaning 'Pride in battle', is the motto of what prominent football club?

Your starter for ten:

9   What is the common name of *Artemisia tridentata*, an aromatic shrub found throughout the US southwest? The word appears before 'rebellion' in the name of a loose political movement in which local interests dispute control of public lands with federal agencies.

Three questions on jealousy:

(a) 'Anger and jealousy can no more bear to lose sight of their objects than love.' These words refer to the feelings of Maggie Tulliver in which early novel by George Eliot?

(b) 'Jealousy is no more than feeling alone against smiling enemies.' Which Irish-born author wrote those words in her 1935 novel *The House in Paris*?

(c) Born in 1757, who wrote the poem that begins: 'Cruelty has a human heart / And jealousy a human face'?

Your starter for ten:

10 A church window at Skillington in Lincolnshire depicts which mountain, its highest point being a little below that of Monte Rosa? It is a memorial to the local vicar, Charles Hudson, who died during the first ascent of the mountain in question in 1865, in a party led by Edward Whymper.

Your bonuses are on a shared nickname. Identify each person from the description:

(a) Born Virginia Katherine McMath, an actress and dancer who starred in films such as *Top Hat* and *Monkey Business*. She won an Oscar in 1940 for her leading role in *Kitty Foyle*.

(b) A British rock musician and co-founder of the 1960s group Cream? He collaborated with the Nigerian musician Fela Kuti, and called his memoir *Hellraiser: The Autobiography of the World's Greatest Drummer*.

(c) The trainer of the racehorse Red Rum; he also trained the 2004 Grand National winner Amberleigh House.

Your starter for ten:

11 In October 2018, Dr Donna Strickland became the first woman in 55 years, and only the third ever, to receive what specific acknowledgement of her scientific accomplishments?

Three questions on an English poet:

(a) 'Morning and evening / Maids heard the goblins cry: / "Come buy our orchard fruits, / Come buy, come buy."' These words begin a poem of 1862 by which poet?

(b) What was the short, two-word title of the Pre-Raphaelite journal edited by Rossetti's brother William, to which she contributed seven poems in 1850?

(c) A supporter of the Pre-Raphaelites, which art critic said that 'Goblin Market' was unpublishable because it was 'so full of quaintnesses and offences'?

Your starter for ten:

12 Name either of the Pre-Socratic philosophers, in addition to Thales, who were known as the three thinkers of Miletus, and who flourished during the 6th century BC; both names begin with the same five letters.

Your bonuses are on poisonous plants found in the UK. In each case, give either the common or the scientific name:
(a) A poisonous plant with shiny black berries that can be fatal; its extract was formerly used in beauty rituals, and when applied to the eyes, it causes dilation of the pupils.
(b) A tree with poisonous leaves and seeds; its toxic alkaloid contains chemicals used to make taxol, a drug that slows the rate of cancer.
(c) A tall, upright plant of the parsley family, associated with the death of Socrates.

Your starter for ten:

13 What name links: Thomas, a leading authority on the Peasants' Revolt of 1381; Sir Francis, the statesman and diplomat who thwarted the Ridolfi and Babington plots; and a Christian pilgrimage centre a few miles south of Binham Abbey in North Norfolk?

Three questions on vegetarian literary figures:
(a) 'Now I can look you in the eye with a clear conscience'. Which German-language author reputedly said those words to fish in an aquarium? His works include *The Hunger Artist*, published in 1922, two years before his death.
(b) In a novel of 1818, which vegetarian author has a character state: 'I do not destroy the lamb and the kid to glut my appetite – acorns and berries afford me sufficient nourishment'?
(c) In his introduction to the Russian translation of Harold Williams's 1883 book *The Ethics of Diet*, which novelist wrote of his horror at a visit to a slaughterhouse and the desensitization of its employees?

Your starter for ten:

14 In a two-body orbital system, with masses m1 and m2, what name is given to the quantity equal to the formula m1 times m2, divided by m1 plus m2? This quantity may be used as an effective inertial mass to solve the motion of the system.

Three questions on the year 1963:
(a) In 1963, which US journalist published 'A Bunny's Tale', an exposé of practices at the Playboy club? She went on to co-found *Ms* magazine and the National Women's Political Caucus.

(b) The same year saw the publication of which bestselling non-fiction book by Betty Friedan? It addressed what she called 'the problem that has no name: the quiet desperation of the suburban housewife'.
(c) 'I began to think maybe it was true that when you were married and had children you were brainwashed, and afterward you went about numb.' In which novel of 1963 do those words appear?

Your starter for ten:
15 Concerning the psychological effects of colonialism, *Black Skin, White Masks* and *The Wretched of the Earth* are influential works by which psychiatrist and political philosopher, born in Martinique in 1925?

Three questions on a Nordic country:
(a) Serving from 2000 to 2012, Tarja Halonen was the first female president of which Nordic country?
(b) Finland declared independence in 1917. Ten years earlier, it had elected a parliament using universal suffrage, following reforms in the aftermath of which war?
(c) In 1809, Finland became an autonomous grand duchy under the rule of which Russian tsar?

Your starter for ten:
16 The common name of what genus of tree links: tea rooms designed by Charles Rennie Mackintosh in Glasgow in 1903; the perennial herbaceous plant also known as 'fireweed'; and a 1908 novel by Kenneth Grahame?

Your bonuses are on words defined in the glossary of James Mill's 1818 work *The History of British India*:
(a) Increasingly used in Mill's time to denote Europeans who made their fortune in India, what word is given its original sense of 'a very great deputy vice-regent; the governor of a province under the mogul government'?

(b) Derived from the Sanskrit for 'knowledge', what word does Mill define simply as 'a learned Brahmin'? In modern speech, it denotes an expert on a particular subject who provides their opinion via mass media.
(c) What now-familiar word does Mill define as 'the name used in Bengal for a species of country house erected by Europeans'?

Your starter for ten:
17 Designed by James Maxwell and Charles Tuke, which coastal tourist attraction marked its 125th anniversary in 2019? The tallest structure in Britain at the time of its construction, it is said to have been inspired by a visit of the local mayor to the Paris exhibition of 1889.

Three questions on Chinese historians:

(a) The imperial official Ban Gu is noted for a history of the Former or Western period of which major Chinese dynasty?

(b) Ban Gu's death left the completion of his work to his sister, Ban Zhao, who is sometimes likened to which Byzantine historian, the author of the Alexiad, born in 1083?

(c) Ban Gu's twin brother, Ban Chao, was a general who brought the Tarim Basin under Chinese control. In which present-day 'autonomous region' of China is this basin?

Your starter for ten:

18 Which SI-derived unit is equal to one lumen per square metre? Its symbol may be read as the Roman numerals that represent 60.

Your bonuses are on pairs of titles in which the last word of the first title is the first word of the second, for example: 'Hey Jude' and Jude the Obscure. In each case, give both titles from the description:

(a) An 1888 short story by Rudyard Kipling set in Afghanistan; and a novel of 1885 by Henry Rider Haggard.

(b) The English titles of two works, one a novel first published in Czech in 1985; the other a 1943 work of philosophy by Jean-Paul Sartre.

(c) A 1962 film starring Bette Davis and Joan Crawford; and a novel of 1847 published under the pen name Currer Bell.

Your starter for ten:

19 What precise two words conclude the US writer Michael Pollan's seven-word response to the question of what humans should eat to be 'maximally healthy'? His reply begins 'Eat food. Not too much.'

Three questions on physics:

(a) What pure, common element has the lowest electrical resistivity?

(b) At 300 degrees kelvin, the resistivity of silver is about 1.6 times ten to the minus eight, measured in what SI unit? I need a two-word term.

(c) So, if a silver wire at that temperature has a resistance of 1.6 ohms and a cross-sectional area of one square millimetre, what is its length in metres?

Your starter for ten:

20 Answer as soon as your name is called. One litre of fluid spread evenly over an area of one hectare would have a depth of how many nanometres?

Your bonuses are on 'unpaired words' – that is, words without natural opposites, or with opposites only rarely used – for example 'ruthless' or 'deceitful'. Give each word from the definition:

(a) A word meaning unmoving, motionless or immobile. It is often used to describe elements in Group 18 of the periodic table.

(b) A word describing a violent way of leaving a premises. It has been used specifically in connection with incidents occurring in Prague in 1419, 1483 and 1618.

(c) A word meaning shy, reserved or diffident. The word is the name of a character in a Walt Disney animated film of 1937.

Your starter for ten:

21 What three-letter name links: the title of a novel by the Nobel laureate Mikhail Sholokhov; the manager of Leeds United from 1961 to 1974; and a Terry Gilliam film of 2018?

Three questions on dramas about miscarriages of justice:

(a) Based on a novel of 1974 by James Baldwin, which 2018 film by Barry Jenkins centres on the wrongful imprisonment of Fonny, a young African-American falsely named in a rape case by a racist police officer?

(b) Which 2019 mini-series by Ava Duvernay dramatizes the true story of the Central Park Five, a group of African-American teenagers wrongfully convicted of the rape and assault of a jogger in 1989?

(c) The Mangrove Nine, a group of black British activists charged with inciting a riot during a protest against police racism, were the subject of a 2021 television film by which British director, part of his *Small Axe* anthology?

Your starter for ten:

22 In biochemistry, allosteric control is the inhibition or activation of which macro-molecules? Their names generally end in the suffix '-ase'.

Three questions on French painters:

(a) In 1894, the art critic Gustave Geffroy identified the three grandes dames of Impressionism as Marie Bracquemond, Mary Cassatt and which other artist?

(b) Morisot is said to have persuaded Manet to experiment with paintings executed outside the confines of a studio. What two-word French term denotes this practice?

(c) Morisot is believed to have been related to which painter and print-maker? His works in the rococo style include *The Swing* in the Wallace Collection.

Your starter for ten:

23 Which two consonants begin words meaning: an adversary of the Guelphs and the Pope in medieval Italy; the home country of John Atta Mills and Michael Essien; and, in Shakespeare, a form taken by victims of Richard III and Macbeth?

Three questions on an ancient language:
(a) Pahlavi was the official language of the Parthian and Sassanian empires before the coming of Islam. To what large language family does it belong?
(b) The Pahlavi alphabet developed from which widely used alphabet, an ancestor of the modern Hebrew and Arabic scripts?
(c) Written in a variant of Pahlavi called Avestan, the *Avesta* is a sacred book of what religion?

Your starter for ten:
24 Who was both the sixth prime minister of the French Fifth Republic and its fifth president, serving in the latter post between 1995 and 2007?

Three questions on mathematics and physics:
(a) From an Italian renaissance family, what name is given in topology to a system of three loops connected so that cutting any one loop leaves the other two unlinked?
(b) Similar in idea to a Borromean linkage, a system of subatomic particles in which a group of three is stable, but a pair is not, is named after which Soviet theoretician?
(c) Observed in red giant stars, the triple-alpha process features what specific isotope as a short-lived intermediary state?

Your starter for ten:
25 Stevens the butler and Miss Kenton the housekeeper are characters in which Booker Prize-winning novel? The prologue is titled, 'July 1956, Darlington Hall'.

Three questions on a mythical animal:
(a) In *Through the Looking-Glass*, which mythical animal says to Alice: 'Well, now that we have seen each other, if you'll believe in me, I'll believe in you'?
(b) The name of what political philosophy appears in the full title of George Orwell's 1941 essay *The Lion and the Unicorn*?
(c) The lion and the unicorn appear on the arms of which Commonwealth country, along with the motto *A mari usque ad mare* ('From sea to sea')?

The Answers

1   Piano (*piano nobile*, Renzo Piano, *The Piano*)
    (a) Devon (near Torquay)
    (b) Swanscombe
    (c) Cheddar (Gorge)

2   Emily Brontë (Charlotte Brontë's description)
    (a) Ears (specifically, in the outer ear canals)
    (b) Parotid (glands)
    (c) Eyelids

3   Diatomic (elements) (i.e. composed of only two atoms)
    (a) Robin (Wright) / Robyn (Rihanna Fenty)
    (b) Carole (Cadwalladr) / Carol (Shields)
    (c) Holly (Hunter) / Holly (Black)

4   Isothermal (accept hyperbolic, correcting it; not isentropic)
    (a) New Horizons
    (b) Ultima Thule (aka 486958 Arrokoth)
    (c) Kuiper Belt (object)

5   Wyoming
    (a) Ibex
    (b) Ethiopia
    (c) Corkscrew / screw / spiral

6   Hyperbola (not parabola, ellipse or circle)
    (a) Thermodynamics
    (b) (Reaching a temperature of) absolute zero
    (c) Entropy

7   Japan
    (a) (Archbishop Thomas) Croke (Croke Park)
    (b) (Roger) Casement (Casement Park)
    (c) Lansdowne Road (Stadium, demolished in 2007)

8   The Owl and the Pussycat
    (a) Everton
    (b) Blackburn Rovers
    (c) Manchester City

9   Sagebrush
    (a) *The Mill on the Floss*
    (b) (Elizabeth) Bowen
    (c) (William) Blake ('A Divine Image')

10 Matterhorn (four of the party died during the descent)
    (a) Ginger Rogers
    (b) (Peter Edward) 'Ginger' Baker
    (c) (Donald) 'Ginger' McCain

11 The Nobel Prize in Physics
    (a) Christina Rossetti ('Goblin Market', of course)
    (b) *The Germ*
    (c) (John) Ruskin

12 Anaximander / Anaximenes (not Anaxagoras, a contemporary)
    (a) Deadly nightshade / *Atropa belladona*
    (b) (English / common) yew / *Taxus baccata*
    (c) Hemlock / *Conium maculatum*

13 Walsingham
    (a) (Franz) Kafka
    (b) (Mary) Shelley
    (c) (Leo) Tolstoy

14 Reduced mass
    (a) (Gloria) Steinem
    (b) *The Feminine Mystique*
    (c) *The Bell Jar* (Sylvia Plath)

15 (Frantz) Fanon (*Les damnés de la terre*)
    (a) Finland
    (b) Russo-Japanese (War) (1904–1905)
    (c) Alexander I (reigned 1801–1825)

16 Willow (Willow Tea Rooms, Rosebay willowherb, *The Wind in the Willows*)
    (a) Nabob / nawab
    (b) Pundit (Sanskrit: *pandita*, 'learned man')
    (c) Bungalow

17 Blackpool Tower
    (a) Han (c.32–92 CE)
    (b) Anna Comnena (both have been described as the 'first' female historian)
    (c) Xinjiang (accept the former name Sinkiang, correcting it)

18 Lux (i.e. LX)
    (a) 'The Man Who Would Be King' and *King Solomon's Mines*
    (b) *The Unbearable Lightness of Being* and *Being and Nothingness*
    (c) *What Ever Happened to Baby Jane?* and *Jane Eyre*

19 'Mostly plants'
    (a) Silver

(b) Ohm metres
(c) 100 (metres)

20 100
(a) Inert
(b) Defenestrate / defenestration
(c) Bashful

21 Don (*And Quiet Flows the Don*, Don Revie, *The Man Who Killed Don Quixote*)
(a) *If Beale Street Could Talk*
(b) *When They See Us*
(c) Steve McQueen

22 Enzymes
(a) (Berthe) Morisot
(b) Plein air
(c) (Jean Honoré) Fragonard

23 Gh- (Ghibellines, Ghana, ghosts)
(a) Indo-European (accept Indo-Iranian, Western Iranian, Northwestern Iranian)
(b) Aramaic
(c) Zoroastrian(ism)

24 (Jacques) Chirac
(a) Borromean (rings / links)
(b) (Vitaly) Efimov
(c) Beryllium-8

25 (*The*) *Remains of the Day* (Kazuo Ishiguro, of course)
(a) Unicorn
(b) Socialism (*The Lion and the Unicorn: Socialism and the English Genius*)
(c) Canada

Infamy

St John's College, Oxford

vs

Emmanuel College, Cambridge
(2010)

This is perhaps the first final that featured a contestant who was a real media star. The press loved American-born Alex Guttenplan. In an earlier round he had countered Jeremy's retort of 'Good guess' with 'It wasn't a guess' and that firmly cemented him in the role of viewers' favourite.

St John's had had an impressive road to the final with victories over Durham, Loughborough, Girton College, Cambridge, Manchester University and then Imperial College London in the semi-finals. Emmanuel's path hadn't been so easy, having survived an early round only thanks to being one of the highest-scoring losers.

St John's College, Oxford
Oliver Chen from Houston, Texas, studying History and Economics
Lauren Parry from Colchester in Essex, studying Chemistry
George Woudhuysen (captain) from London, reading History
David Townsend from Sydney, Australia, studying Law

Emmanuel College, Cambridge
Andy Hastings from Nottingham, reading Medicine
Jenny Harris from Salwarpe, Worcestershire, reading French and Latin
Alex Guttenplan (captain) from London, reading Natural Sciences
Josh Scott originally from Aberystwyth, studying Medicine

Your starter for ten:

1   *Time Out of Joint* by Philip K Dick, *Infinite Jest* by David Foster Wallace—?
[The question was successfully interrupted]

Your bonuses are on pre-Revolutionary French provinces:
(a) Which medieval duchy merged with Guyenne after the Hundred Years' War to create one of the largest provinces in pre-revolutionary France and has a name derived from *Vasco*, the Spanish word for Basque?
(b) Which American state was the site of a French colony established in 1604 and is thought by some to be named after a province that lay between Bretagne and Orléanais?
(c) Centred on Paris, the name of which province is thought by some to refer to its position surrounded by the river Seine, Marne and Oise?

Your starter for ten:

2   The Steel Yard in London, a self-governing enclave close to the present-day Cannon Street station, was, during the medieval ages, the trading base of which Northern European league?

Your bonuses are on British film documentaries:
(a) The winner of two awards at the 2009 Sundance Film Festival, Havana Marking's documentary followed contestants in an *X Factor*-type singing competition in which Asian country?
(b) *Of Time and the City* is director Terence Davies's 2008 film about which city in which he was born in 1945?
(c) Depicting Philippe Petit's 1974 wire walk between the twin towers of the World Trade Center, which film won the 2009 Oscar for Best Documentary Feature?

Your starter for ten:

3   Which decade saw the painting of the *Mona Lisa*, the birth of John Calvin, the marriage of James IV of Scotland to Margaret Tudor and the accession of King Henry VIII?

Your bonuses are on Gilbert and Sullivan's Modern Major-General:
(a) In *The Pirates of Penzance*, the Major-General says he can 'quote the fight historical from marathon to waterloo, in order categorical'. How many years lie between those two battles? You can have a hundred years either way.
(b) He also claims that he can quote 'in elegiacs all the crimes of Heliogabalus'. One of this Roman emperor's most notorious crimes, although probably invented, was his attempt to smother his guests at a dinner party by what unusual means?

(c) He also claims that he can 'write a washing bill in Babylonic cuneiform' a type of inscription in what precise shape?

Your starter for ten:

4   What astronomic phenomenon was observed in 1611 by the German Jesuit Christoph Scheiner? His conclusion, disputed by Galileo and later proved to be mistaken, was that they were hitherto discovered planets orbiting the sun.
[Neither team answered correctly]

Your starter for ten:

5   Hartfield, Longbourn House, Norland Park, Kellynch Hall, the Parsonage in Fullerton and an unidentified house in Portsmouth are the family homes of the central characters in the novels of—?
[The question was successfully interrupted]

Your bonuses are on bioluminescence – the emission by living organisms of light without heat:
(a) In bioluminescence, light is emitted when luciferin is oxidized to oxyluciferin. There are several distinct types of luciferin. What enzyme catalyses their oxidation?
(b) What name is given to the specialized light-emitting glands or organs, which are a common feature of bioluminescent deep water fish and cephalopods?
(c) The rare *Phosphaenus hemipterus* and the common *Lampyris noctiluca* are both native to Britain and, regardless of their common name of 'glow worms', are not worms, but belong to which group of insects?

Your starter for ten:

6   [This was a picture round, the teams being shown a road sign for a city] Baile Átha Cliath – how is this city known in English?

Your bonuses are road signs in their Celtic language. In each case, I want you to tell me their names in English and identify the Celtic language which they are written:
(a) Aberdaugleddau
(b) Tewynn Pleustri
(c) Dùn Èideann

Your starter for ten:

7   What name has been shared by thirteen popes including: the First, or the Great, who defied the Doctrine of the Incarnation; the Third, who crowned Charlemagne 'Emperor of the West'; and the Tenth, who

permitted the sale of indulgences to raise funds for the rebuilding of St Peter's Basilica in Rome?

Your bonuses are on a Greek historian:
(a) Born around 200 BC and detained in Rome from 168, which statesman's histories, not all extant, chronicle the rise of Rome from 220 BC to the destruction of Carthage in 146 BC?
(b) Polybius's work on government was an influence on which French philosopher, whose 1748 work *The Spirit of the Laws* advocates the separation of powers?
(c) Polybius is also thought to have been an influence on the *Discorsi*, a 1518 work by which Florentine political philosopher?

Your starter for ten:

8   Who is this? The son of a Lancashire cotton merchant, he served as a Tory MP from 1809 to 1850. In 1822, he became home secretary and created the Metropolitan Police in—?
[The question was successfully interrupted]

Your bonuses are on Mexican history:
(a) In 1911, the liberal Francisco Madero ousted which dictator, who had become president in 1876 and whose rule was known as the *Porfiriato*?
(b) After Madero's death in a counter-revolutionary coup, which commander of the popular army known as the Division of the North fought the military regime and raided the USA in 1916?
(c) Which agrarian leader joined forces with Villa against the Carranza government? Killed in an ambush in 1919, he gives his name to a guerrilla movement formed in 1994?

Your starter for ten:

9   'Some dogs are Great Danes, all Great Danes are large, therefore some dogs are large.' This is an example of what type of logical deductive argument?

Your bonuses are on books published in the 1620s:
(a) *On the Movement of the Heart and Blood in Animals* was published in Latin in 1628 by which English physician?
(b) Published in 1629, the first English translation of Thucydides' *History of the Peloponnesian War* was an early work by which political philosopher?
(c) Detailing a new system of logic, the 1620 *Novum Organum* is a work by which philosopher and statesman?

Your starter for ten:

10 Words meaning 'tropical hardwood', 'small freshwater duck' and 'animals in harness' are formed by adding what three consecutive letters of the alphabet to the word 'tea'?
[Neither team successfully answered the question]

Your starter for ten:

11 *The Ship of Death* and *Bavarian Gentians* are among the last poetical works of which literary figure who died of tuberculous in Southern France in 1930, his final—?
[The question was successfully interrupted]

Your bonuses are on linguistics. In each case, give the term from its definition, and the answer in each case contains the Greek-derived component 'gloss' or 'glot':
(a) The geographical boundary or delineation of a certain linguistic feature.
(b) The use of two or more varieties of language for different purposes in the same community, for example, Classical Arabic and Local Colloquial Arabic in North Africa.
(c) Finally, represented in the International Phonetic Alphabet by a dotless question mark, the consonant sound which is made by bringing the vocal cord tightly together and releasing them suddenly.

Your starter for ten:

12 [The teams were played a piece of music that was an early recording of classical music. It was a work by two composers and they were asked to name either of them; neither team identified Johann Sebastian Bach and Charles Gounod so another starter question was asked]

Your starter for ten:

13 Born around 340 BC, which Greek philosopher posited a materialist universe unregulated by divine providence? He advocated mental wellbeing based on freedom from anxiety and from the fear of death, although he is popularly associated with hedonism—
[The question was successfully interrupted]

[The bonuses were on music, and Emmanuel were played three more pieces written for the castrato, this time sung by female modern-day sopranos; they managed to identify all three composers – Handel, Purcell and Bluck]

Your starter for ten:

14 What initial three letters link a variety of hops associated with Pilsner beer, the largest island of Estonia, a the small German state on the French

border, the man who became president of Georgia during 2008 and a Swedish—?

[The question was successfully interrupted]

Your bonuses are on terms coined by the Swedish chemist Jöns Jacob Berzelius:
(a) What term for the existence of a chemical element in two or more forms in one state of matter was coined by Berzelius in 1841?
(b) What general one-word term for the existence of molecules that have the same number of the same kind of atoms and therefore the same chemical formula, but different chemical and physical properties was defined by Berzelius in 1830?
(c) The decomposition of bodies and the formation of new compounds into the composition of which they do not enter was given what name by Berzelius in 1836?

Your starter for ten:

15 If a clerihew and a limerick add up to a Spenserian stanza, which verse form is the sum of a couplet, a rubaiyat and a triolet?

Your bonuses are on 21 September:
(a) As well as being the date on which in 1962 this programme was first broadcast, it also saw the birth in 1934 of which Canadian poet, singer and songwriter, who performed on the Pyramid Stage at Glastonbury in 2008 at the age of 73?
(b) *Africa Must Unite* is among the works of which statesman, the first prime minster of Ghana, born on 21 September 1909?
(c) *Love and Mr Lewisham, When the Sleeper Wakes* and *The Shape of Things to Come* are works by which prolific writer and thinker, born 21 September 1866?

Your starter for ten:

16 What two-word term denotes the principle of molecular biology proposed by Francis Crick in 1958 that information can only pass from genetic material to protein and not vice versa?

[Neither team proffered an answer]

Your starter for ten:

17 'As if we were villains on necessity, fools by heavenly compulsion, knaves, thieves, and treachers by spherical predominance.' These words of Edmund in *King Lear* refer to what pseudoscience?

Your bonuses are on a contemporary artist and his models:
(a) Kathleen or Kitty Garman was the daughter of the sculptor Jacob Epstein

and the first wife of which British artist. She sat for his portrait of her, *Girl with a White Dog*, in 1951?

(b) According to the title of Lucian Freud's painting of her, which sold for over £17 million in 2008, Sue Tilley has what specific job title?

(c) Which Australian-born performance artist was the subject of many paintings by Lucian Freud in the early 1990s?

Your starter for ten:

18 Including those squares consisting of more than one unit square, how many squares in total are visible on a three-by-three squared grid?

Your bonuses are on an Italian thinker:

(a) Author of *The Prison Notebooks*, which political philosopher led the Communist Party in the Italian parliament until his arrest in 1926?

(b) From the Greek for 'deed' what term did Gramsci use for 'that which needs to be combined with theory to bring about change in the world'?

(c) What term did Gramsci use for the ideological means by which the dominant class gains the spontaneous and consensual adherence of other classes to its rule?

Your starter for ten:

19 [The teams were shown a picture of Henry VIII, and Emmanuel correctly identified the artist as Hans Holbein; they were shown three more paintings by Holbein and correctly identified Edward VI and Sir Thomas More, but didn't get Sir Thomas Cromwell]

Your starter for ten:

20 *The Loom of Youth, The Foxglove Saga, Last Seen Wearing, The Desperate Diary of a Country Housewife, The Mennyms* and *Vile Bodies* are novels by different authors who share what surname?

Your bonuses are on geology:

(a) Which rock, formed by the solidification of thin layers of molten lava, comprises much of the surfaces of Mercury, Venus, Mars and the moon?

(b) Basalt is usually composed primarily of crystals of augite or hornblende, olivine and which other mineral that occurs in various forms of including Labradorite and makes up more than half the Earth's crust?

(c) Basalt forms the distinctive columnous strata of the Giant's Causeway in Ireland and the similar structures found on which island in the Inner Hebrides, the location of Fingal's Cave?

Your starter for ten:

21 R, L, Z, S, P and T are the initial letters of the capitals of the only six European countries that have coastlines on which body of water?
[Neither team got the correct answer]

Your starter for ten:

22 Jim Bolger, Jenny Shipley, Helen Clark—?
[The question was successfully interrupted]

Your bonuses are on Oliver Cromwell:
(a) Which city in Lancashire gives its name to a battle of August 1648 in which Cromwell defeated a Scots force under Hamilton?
(b) Which borough in East Lothian gives its name to Cromwell's decisive victory over David Leslie's Scots army with its surprise dawn attack on 3 September 1650?
(c) On 3 September 1651, at which city in the Severn Valley did Cromwell defeat Charles II's Scots army after which Charles fled abroad?

Your starter for ten:

23 What word means between 1919 and 1930 when applied to cars, and then, in this millennium, 2000, 2003 and 2007 when applied to port?

Your bonuses are on an African country:
(a) Bamako on the Niger river is the capital of which large, landlocked country of Western Africa?
(b) Shortly before it became an independent state in 1960, Mali, then called the French Sudan, merged with which of its neighbours to form the Mali Federation?
(c) The name of which town in central Mali, at the end of a Trans-Saharan caravan route, is sometimes used figuratively to imply a distance and exotic destination?

Your starter for ten:

24 If the difference between two positive numbers is 5 and the difference between their squares is 55, what is the sum of the two numbers?

Your bonuses are on US national historic landmarks; in each case, name the state in which the following are located:
(a) The Bunker Hill Monument and the Lexington Green.
(b) The Martin Luther King historic district and the Dixie Coco-Cola Bottling Company plant.
(c) The Lowell Observatory and the Navaho National Council Chamber.

Your starter for ten:

25 Which market town in North Shropshire has a three-letter name derived from a Saxon term meaning 'marsh'? It was the childhood home of the essayist William Hazlitt from 1787 and formed part of the state of 'Hanging Judge' Jeffreys in the 17th century?

Your bonuses are on royalty:

(a) In England, the period from 1199 to 1307 saw only three monarchs on the throne of England. The first was King John; who were the other two?

(b) In the 122 years from 1867 to 1989, Japan had three emperors. Who was the first of these, whose restoration in 1868 marked the beginning of Japan's modernization?

(c) From 1643 to 1792, three kings occupied the throne of France. Name all three.

Your starter for ten:

26 Unnamed in the text of the poem, by what term does Coleridge refer to the man who hears the Ancient Mariner's tale?

Your bonuses are on bionomic numeral classification. In each case, give the common names of the following plants and animals, each of which is a homophone of a name of a letter of the alphabet:

(a) *Pisum sativum*

(b) *Garrulus glandarius*

(c) *Camellia sinensis*

Your starter for ten:

27 Disenchantment Bay, Glacier Bay and Pavlof Bay are among the numerous bays on the coastline of which US state?

Your bonuses are on Michelangelo's sculptures:

(a) One of Michelangelo's first major sculptures, now in the Bargello in Florence, is of which Roman god?

(b) There are three attributable sculptures by Michelangelo in Milan, Florence and most notably in St Peter's in Rome of which popular religious subject?

(c) In the UK, the Michelangelo sculpture called the *Taddei Tondo* is on public display in which institution?

Your starter for ten:

28 In computing, Ubuntu, SUSE and Red Hat are among—?

[The question was successfully interrupted]

Your bonuses are on spices:

(a) Which leguminous plant has a name meaning 'Greek hay' and produces yellowish seeds that are often used in the making of curries?

The gong sounds before the last question can be answered

At the gong, St John's College had 100 points
but Emmanuel College had amassed a massive 315 points.

The trophy was presented by Britain's first female Poet Laureate, Carol Ann Duffy. She said, 'Amazing. They really got into the zone, I think. Quite an extraordinary victory. I've been watching it since I have been about 9, we used to play at home with my brothers, and I've never seen such a comprehensive championship win. Fantastic!'

The Answers

1   Titles taken from lines in *Hamlet*
    (a) Gascony
    (b) Maine
    (c) Île-de-France

2   Hanseatic League
    (a) Afghanistan
    (b) Liverpool
    (c) *Man on Wire*

3   1500s
    (a) 2,305
    (b) He was going to drown them in rose petals
    (c) Wedge

4   Sun spots

5   Jane Austen
    (a) Luciferase
    (b) Photophores
    (c) Beetles

6   Dublin (in Irish)
    (a) Milford Haven in Welsh
    (b) Newquay in Cornish
    (c) Edinburgh in Scots Gaelic

7   Leo
    (a) Polybius
    (b) (Charles Louis de Secondat, Baron) Montesquieu
    (c) Niccolo Machiavelli

8   Sir Robert Peel
    (a) Profinio Díaz
    (b) Pancho Villa
    (c) Emiliano Zapata

9   Categorical syllogism
    (a) William Harvey
    (b) Thomas Hobbes
    (c) Sir Francis Bacon

10 K, L and M (teak, teal and team)

11   D.H. Lawrence
     (a) Isogloss
     (b) Diglossia
     (c) Glottal Stop

12   [Music starter]

13   Epicurus
     [Music bonuses]

14   SAA
     (a) Allotropy
     (b) Isomerism
     (c) Catalysis

15   A sonnet
     (a) Leonard Cohen
     (b) Kwame Nkrumah
     (c) H.G. Wells

16   Central Dogma

17   Astrology
     (a) Lucian Freud
     (b) Benefits Supervisor
     (c) Leigh Bowery

18   14
     (a) Antonio Gramsci
     (b) Praxis
     (c) Hegemony

19   [Picture round]

20   Waugh
     (a) Basalt
     (b) Feldspar
     (c) Staffa

21   Adriatic

22   Prime Ministers of New Zealand
     (a) Preston
     (b) Dunbar
     (c) Worcester

23   Vintage
     (a) Mali
     (b) Senegal
     (c) Timbuktu

24   11
     (a) Massachusetts
     (b) Georgia
     (c) Arizona

25   Wem
     (a) Henry III and Edward I
     (b) Meiji
     (c) Louis XIV, Louis XV and Louis XVI

26   The Wedding Guest
     (a) Pea
     (b) Jay
     (c) Tea

27   Alaska
     (a) Bacchus
     (b) The Pietà
     (c) The Royal Academy

28   Linux
     (a) Fenugreek

Try Your Luck

Match

Your starter for ten:

1 Which Mediterranean city became the capital of a newly independent country in 1956? It was the location of the Jasmine Revolution of 2011, and its suburbs encompass the ancient city of Carthage.

Three questions on a Scottish island:
(a) The 5,000-year-old Callanish Standing Stones are located on which large Hebridean island?
(b) Near to the Callanish Stones is Dun Carloway, a prehistoric circular stone tower of a type known in Scotland by what five-letter name?
(c) In 1831, a stone case was discovered buried in the dunes of Uig Bay on Lewis's west coast. It contained what carved items?

Your starter for ten:

2 Which 20th-century poet said: 'Deprivation is for me what daffodils were for Wordsworth'?

Three questions on the thirteen North American colonies that signed the Declaration of Independence in 1776:
(a) Which of the colonies was the second to be founded by the Pilgrim Fathers; its name comes from the Algonquian for 'Land on the long tidal river'?
(b) Founded in 1634 for the settlement of English Catholics, which colony was the first to be governed by a lord-proprietor holding a royal charter?
(c) Which of the colonies was founded in 1733 by the English philanthropist James Oglethorpe as a colony for the industrious poor, and was the last to be chartered?

Your starter for ten:

3 The French word for 'high' is an anagram of the name of which US state?

Your bonuses are on US state capitals but, in each case, I need the name of the state, not the capital:

(a) The name of the capital of which state is also a word meaning 'agreement or harmony between people or groups'?

(b) The capital of which state has a name meaning 'the protective care of God, or of nature, as a spiritual power'?

(c) Possibly originating in a Greek word for 'red', a name now given to a mythical bird is also the name of the capital of which state?

Your starter for ten:

4   Samara and Tolyatti are cities on which major river? It flows more than 3,500 kilometres through a single country from its source in the Valdai Hills to a delta situated largely in the Astrakhan Oblast.

Three questions on an artist:

(a) Born in Barcelona in 1893, which artist did the poet André Breton describe as 'the most surrealist of us all'? His works include *The Farm* and *Dog Barking at the Moon*.

(b) What English title is given to Miró's work of 1925 containing images that may be a bird, a kite and a balloon, and which was described by him as depicting 'a sort of genesis'? It is on permanent display in New York's museum of Modern Art.

(c) Which Spanish island is the location of a museum and art gallery dedicated to Miró? He lived and worked there from 1956 until his death in 1983.

Your starter for ten:

5   I need a two-word term here. The distance between the centres of charge of two atoms, multiplied by the magnitude of that charge, defines what quantity, measured in debye units?

Three questions on astronomy:

(a) What is the nearest white dwarf star to our solar system, being about 8.6 light years away? I need its name and single-letter designation.

(b) What is the nearest red dwarf that is a single star, rather than part of a multiple system? It is about six light years away.

(c) With a mass only slightly higher than that of the sun but a radius about 25 times as great, what name is usually given to the red giant star alpha Boötis, the brightest member of its constellation?

Your starter for ten:

6   Jérome Coignard's book *A Woman Disappears* concerns which crime,

committed in Paris in 1911? The title and subtitle refer to both the object in question, and the Louvre Museum.

Three questions on diarists:
(a) Mary Drew is noted for diaries written from the 1870s as unofficial private secretary to her father, that is, which Liberal prime minister?
(b) Regarded as a 'feminist icon' for her posthumously published diary, what was the surname of Alice, who died in 1892, overshadowed in her lifetime by her brothers William and Henry?
(c) *Growing Up with the Impressionists* is a title given to the diary of Julie Manet, the daughter of which leading painter, who died in 1895?

Your starter for ten:
7   Answer promptly, naming two of the three Irish counties, in addition to Leitrim and Louth, that border Northern Ireland.

Three questions on a marine organism:
(a) Found in shallower waters around the British coast, the cephalopod *Sepia officinalis* has what common name?
(b) Charles Darwin noted that cuttlefish have the ability to change colour. This is due to pigment-containing sacs or cells in their skin, with what collective name?
(c) Cuttlefish bone is often given to pets as a dietary supplement because it is rich in what chemical element?

Your starter for ten:
8   What surname is concatenated with 'random' to give an alternative title for Chess960, a game variant invented by the eleventh World Chess Champion?

Three questions on institutions of the European Union:
(a) The European Parliament sits in Brussels and in the Louise Weiss building in which French city?
(b) The Court of Justice of the European Union sits in the district of Kirchberg in which country?
(c) The European Central Bank has its headquarters in which German city?

Your starter for ten:
9   Attributed to Paul Dirac, what form of notation in quantum mechanics uses operators represented by a vertical line alongside either a forwards- or backwards-pointing chevron?

Three questions on legendary or fictional islands:
(a) First appearing in Plato's *Timaeus*, which legendary island was said to have been swallowed up by the sea following an earthquake?
(b) In Jonathan Swift's *Gulliver's Travels*, what was the name of the flying island visited by Gulliver in his third voyage? Its inhabitants are mainly interested in mathematics, music and philosophy.
(c) Supposedly located in the Irish Sea between Barrow-in-Furness and the Isle of Man, what island is the setting for the *Thomas the Tank Engine* books by the Reverend W. Awdry?

Your starter for ten:
10 Used, for example, to demonstrate the motions of the planets around the sun, what mechanical model of the solar system is thought to have been invented by George Graham in the early 1700s and named after the noble title of his patron, Charles Boyle?

Your bonuses are on music. All answers are people who share the same given name:
(a) Nicknamed Flash Harry, who was the chief conductor of the London Promenade Concerts between 1948 and his death in 1967?
(b) As Master of the Queen's Music, which Australian composer wrote the pageant *The Valley and the Hill* for the Silver Jubilee of 1977, and the later 'Ode for Queen Elizabeth'?
(c) Born in 1921, which composer and trumpeter wrote the scores for the films *Whistle Down the Wind* and *The Bridge on the River Kwai*?

Your starter for ten:
11 'Muddy hill' and 'pig-sty hill' are alternative derivations of the name of which metropolitan borough? The location of the National Motorcycle Museum and the National Exhibition Centre, it is situated between the cities of Coventry and Birmingham.

Your bonuses are on winners of the Royal Society's Copley Medal, awarded for outstanding achievements in scientific research:
(a) The 1936 recipient, Arthur Evans, was recognized for uncovering evidence of the Bronze Age Minoan civilization on which Greek island? It is the fifth-largest in the Mediterranean.
(b) In 1976, Dorothy Hodgkin was the first female recipient of the medal, in recognition of her work on the structures of complex molecules. These included which hormone, secreted when blood glucose levels rise?
(c) In 2021, Jocelyn Bell Burnell became the second woman to receive the medal, recognising her work on the discovery of which rapidly spinning neutron stars? They give off regular bursts of radio waves or other radiation.

Your starter for ten:

12 A plaque in Gower Street in Bloomsbury marks the foundation, in 1848, of which 'brotherhood' or movement, inspired by Italian art of the fourteenth and fifteenth centuries?

Three questions on polysyllabic words:
(a) Containing two double-Ps, and referring to an implement used for driving horses, what polysyllabic word does the OED define as a sprightly or impertinent young fellow?
(b) Containing three double-Ss, what word means an excessive desire to own or dominate or to show jealous tendencies towards another person?
(c) Concerning the maintenance of accounts, what word contains three consecutive sets of double letters?

Your starter for ten:

13 Of the six wives of Henry VIII, name the two who appear as characters in the play usually attributed to both Shakespeare and John Fletcher?

Your bonuses are on the artist Sonia Delaunay:
(a) What term did the art critic Guillaume Apollinaire apply to the Cubist-influenced style of painting developed by Delaunay and her husband Robert in around 1912? The term comes from the name of a musician in Greek myth.
(b) In 1917, Delaunay was commissioned to design costumes for *Cléopâtra*, a ballet production performed by which dance company, founded by Diaghilev?
(c) Delaunay also designed clothes for which film actress? Born in 1897, she was a star of the silent era, and made a noted comeback in the 1950 film *Sunset Boulevard*.

Your starter for ten:

14 To the nearest whole number, the weight of how many metric tonnes per square metre is equal to standard atmospheric pressure on Earth at sea level?

Three questions on artists in legal entanglements:
(a) Born in Thuringia in 1891, which Expressionist artist was jailed in 1939 on a charge of plotting to kill Adolf Hitler? He was later released due to lack of evidence.
(b) When Leonardo's *Mona Lisa* was stolen from the Louvre in 1911, which noted artist, born in Málaga in 1881, was questioned by police as a suspect?
(c) Depicting a female nude in red, what is the title of the painting which resulted in the renowned Indian artist M.F. Husain being issued with a warrant for his arrest in 2006?

Your starter for ten:

15 Listen carefully. The year 2020 is comprised of two digits, each of which appears exactly twice. What is the next year that has this property?

Three questions on fictional plagues:
(a) Regarded as a key precursor of post-apocalyptic fiction, *The Last Man* is an 1826 novel by which author? It is presented as a 'found narrative' of the only survivor of a worldwide plague.
(b) Which 1954 novel by Richard Matheson concerns Robert Neville, the apparent sole survivor of a pandemic, whose symptoms resemble conventional representations of vampirism?
(c) Which Portuguese Nobel laureate wrote the 1995 novel *Blindness*? It depicts the social breakdown that results from an epidemic causing loss of sight.

Your starter for ten:

16 Possibly named after a figure of Norse mythology, the Aegir, or Eagre, is a tidal bore on the lower reaches of which major English river? It occurs when a high spring tide from the Humber Estuary meets the river's downstream flow.

Three questions on island peaks:
(a) More than 4,800 metres in height, the highest island peak in the world is Puncak Jaya, on which large island? Its territory is shared by two countries.
(b) Almost 4,000 metres high, Jade Mountain is on which island? Until 1945, it was the highest peak in the Japanese empire.
(c) At a little over 3,300 metres, which volcano is the highest peak on a Mediterranean island?

Your starter for ten:

17 First performed in 1920, which piece of music was named in first position in the Classic FM Hall of Fame in 2019, three places above its composer's next highest entry, *Fantasia on a Theme by Thomas Tallis*?

Your bonuses are on etymologically unrelated words that begin with the same three letters. In each case, give the word from the definition:
(a) A modern-day country of the Americas whose territory was the target of the ill-fated 17th-century colonization project known as the Darien scheme.
(b) A term coined in 1791 by the Irish-born artist Robert Barker to describe his large landscape paintings intended to be exhibited in 360 degrees on a cylindrical wall.
(c) Derived from the Malay language, a group of nocturnal armoured mammals of the order *Pholidota*, sometimes called the 'scaly anteaters'.

Your starter for ten:

18 What is the closest US state capital to the Canadian capital, Ottawa? A major French city with a similar name is situated about 100 kilometres southwest of Avignon.

Your bonuses are on the Barnes Foundation, an art collection in Philadelphia:
(a) Born in 1872, the chemist Albert C. Barnes made a fortune by developing the antiseptic argyrol, a form of MSP, the letter 'S' in this context representing which metallic element?
(b) The collection includes a portrait of Barnes by which Italian artist? With Carlo Carrà, he coined the term 'metaphysical painting' in 1917.
(c) The Barnes Foundation houses a notable collection of paintings by which French artist? Born in 1869, he was a leading member of the Fauvists.

Your starter for ten:

19 Historically known as Propontis, which small inland sea partly separates the Asiatic and European parts of Turkey? Enclosed by the Bosphorus and the Dardanelles, it connects the Black Sea with the Mediterranean.

Your bonuses are on prime ministers during the reign of Queen Victoria, as described in Sellars and Yeatman's *1066 and All That*. In each case, name the person from the description:
(a) '[It was his] memorable political rule that it did not matter what the Cabinet said, so long as they all answered at once. This he called the collective responsibility of the Cabinet.'
(b) 'He spent his time taking special trains in all directions and galloping to Harrow on a cream-coloured pony, thus … becoming an object of terror and admiration to all foreign governments.'
(c) 'He spent his declining years trying to guess the answer to the Irish question; unfortunately, whenever he was getting warm, the Irish secretly changed the question.'

Your starter for ten:

20 Expressed in square kilometres, adding the surface areas of Earth and Venus gives a value close to what power of ten?

Three questions on semiconductors:
(a) What process involves the intentional introduction of minute amounts of impurities into semiconductor material to increase conductivity?
(b) What term is applied to the interface, or 'junction', between two types of semiconductor materials within a single crystal structure? One side has an excess of electrons and the other, an excess of missing electrons.

(c) During the early 1950s, which Group 14 metalloid element was the major semiconductor material? Mendeleyev predicted its existence, calling it 'eka-silicon'.

Your starter for ten:

21 The grandson of Sundiata Keita, which ruler is noted for his pilgrimage to Mecca in 1324 and his construction of the Grand Mosque at Timbuktu? Adjusted for inflation, he is thought to have been the wealthiest individual in history.

Three questions on the digestive process:
(a) What name derives from the Greek for 'to digest', and is given to an enzyme in the digestive process that breaks down proteins into smaller amino acids?
(b) Which organ of the human body is primarily responsible for the production and release of protease, amylase and lipase?
(c) During digestion, starch is broken down into what sugar, composed of two molecules of glucose bonded together?

Your starter for ten:

22 With a name derived from the Greek for 'glue', which widespread protein has unusually high tensile strength and is associated with connective tissue such as cartilage and tendons?

Three questions on parallel worlds in fiction:
(a) Which Studio Ghibli film begins with 10-year-old Chihiro and her family crossing into the world of Kami, or spirits? When they fail to leave by sunset, her parents are turned into pigs, and she must work to break the curse.
(b) The Fog World and the Otherworld are common names for alternate planes of reality in which series of psychological horror games, set in an eponymous fictional town? I need the two-word series title only.
(c) In which ongoing TV series are the residents of Hawkins, Indiana plagued by creatures from an alternate dimension referred to as the Upside Down?

Your starter for ten:

23 Denoting a popular Christmas decoration, what word can also mean a showy trinket that would appeal to a child, and a jester's baton surmounted by a head with asses' ears? Oliver Cromwell alluded to the latter sense when he used the word to describe the Mace of the House of Commons.

Three questions on Ireland:
(a) Situated on the Wild Atlantic Way on Ireland's west coast, which cliffs rise to over 200 metres at O'Brien's tower?

(b) Rising to more than 500 metres above the Irish Midlands, the Slieve Bloom Mountains straddle the border of County Offaly and which county to the east?
(c) Which river rises in the Sperrin Mountains and flows for about 120 kilometres, meeting the sea near Derry?

Your starter for ten:

24 What weapon is associated with the Hindu god Shiva; the flag of Barbados; the emblem of the car manufacturer Maserati; and the personification Britannia?

Three questions linked by a name:
(a) A UNESCO World Heritage Site, the Maya Devi temple at Lumbini is dedicated to the mother of which religious founder?
(b) Born in 1959, the designer Maya Lin is perhaps best known for which black granite memorial in Washington, DC?
(c) Maya Fey is a companion of Phoenix Wright in which videogame series by Capcom?

Your starter for ten:

25 What year appears in the title of the poem by Wordsworth that begins: 'Milton! Thou shoulds't be living at this hour'? The same year saw the arrival of the Rosetta Stone in Britain, the signing of the Treaty of Amiens and Napoleon's appointment as First Consul.

Your bonuses are on Southeast Asia. In each case, give the predominant cardinal direction in which one would travel in the shortest straight line from the first city to the second. For example, Bangkok to Manila is east:
(a) Yangon to Mandalay, both in Burma or Myanmar?
(b) Kuala Lumpur in Malaysia to Medan in Indonesia?
(c) Hanoi to Ho Chi Minh City, both in Vietnam?

The Answers

1   Tunis (Tunisia, of course)
    (a) Lewis (accept Harris and Lewis)
    (b) Broch
    (c) (Lewis) chessmen / chess pieces / gaming pieces

2   (Philip) Larkin
    (a) Connecticut (the first being Massachusetts)
    (b) Maryland
    (c) Georgia

3   Utah (*haut*)
    (a) New Hampshire (capital Concord)
    (b) Rhode island (capital Providence)
    (c) Arizona (capital Phoenix)

4   Volga
    (a) (Joan) Miró
    (b) *The Birth of the World*
    (c) Mallorca

5   Dipole moment (specifically, the electric dipole moment)
    (a) Sirius B (must hear 'B'; not Sirius A, which is not a white dwarf)
    (b) Barnard's Star (Proxima Centauri is closer, but is part of the Alpha Centauri system)
    (c) Arcturus

6   The theft of the *Mona Lisa / La Gioconda* (*Une femme disparait: le vol de la Joconde au Louvre en 1911*)
    (a) (W.E.) Gladstone
    (b) James (*The Diary of Alice James*; sister of William James and Henry James, of course)
    (c) (Berthe) Morisot (Morisot married Édouard Manet's brother Eugène; he was not a major painter and died earlier, 1892)

7   Donegal, Cavan and Monaghan
    (a) (European / common) cuttlefish
    (b) Chromatophores (term used for colour-producing cells in various organisms)
    (c) Calcium

8   Fischer ('Fischerandom', after Bobby Fischer; back row of pieces are shuffled to give a total of 960 different starting positions)
    (a) Strasbourg
    (b) Luxembourg
    (c) Frankfurt

9   Bra-ket or bra and ket (notation)
    (a) Atlantis
    (b) Laputa
    (c) Sodor

10 Orrery (named after the 4th Earl of Orrery; not astrolabe, which was used in antiquity)
    (a) (Sir Malcolm) Sargent
    (b) (Malcolm) Williamson
    (c) (Sir Malcolm) Arnold

11 Solihull
    (a) Crete
    (b) Insulin
    (c) Pulsars

12 Pre-Raphaelite
    (a) Whippersnapper
    (b) Possessiveness
    (c) Bookkeeper / bookkeeping

13 Catherine of Aragon and Anne Boleyn
    (a) Orphism (accept Orphic Cubism)
    (b) Ballets Russes
    (c) Gloria Swanson

14 10
    (a) Otto Dix
    (b) (Pablo) Picasso
    (c) *Mother India* (or *Bharat Mata*)

15 2112
    (a) Mary Shelley
    (b) *I Am Legend*
    (c) (José) Saramago

16 (River) Trent
    (a) New Guinea
    (b) Taiwan
    (c) (Mount) Etna (on Sicily)

17 *The Lark Ascending* (by Ralph Vaughan Williams)
    (a) Panama
    (b) Panorama
    (c) Pangolins

18 Montpelier (Vermont; French: Montpellier, double 'l')
   (a) Silver (Mild Silver Protein)
   (b) (Giorgio) de Chirico
   (c) (Henri) Matisse

19 (Sea of) Marmara
   (a) (Lord) Melbourne
   (b) (Lord) Palmerston
   (c) (William) Gladstone

20 10^9 (accept one billion)
   (a) Doping
   (b) PN (accept but qualify 'Grown junction'; PN standing for positive and negative)
   (c) Germanium

21 (Mansa) Musa (I of Mali)
   (a) Peptidase (accept pepsin; Greek: *peptós*; not trypsin or protease – different etymology)
   (b) Pancreas
   (c) Maltose

22 Collagen (Greek: *kolla*, 'glue')
   (a) *Spirited Away*
   (b) *Silent Hill*
   (c) *Stranger Things*

23 Bauble
   (a) (Cliffs of) Moher
   (b) Laois
   (c) (River) Foyle

24 Trident
   (a) (Gautama / Siddhartha) Buddha / Shakyamuni
   (b) Vietnam (Veterans Memorial)
   (c) *Ace Attorney*

25 1802 ('London, 1802')
   (a) North
   (b) West
   (c) South

Where Are They Now?

Part 3

Lucy Clarke's team Jesus College, Oxford were 2020 quarter-finalists. She completed her BA in History and English at Regent's Park College, Oxford, and her master's in Shakespeare Studies at King's College London and Shakespeare's Globe, before returning to Oxford to begin her DPhil in History at Jesus College. Dr Lucy Clarke now lectures in English and History and is a researcher in residence at the University of Oxford History Faculty.

'When I was about seven years old,' she says, 'one of my early memories was watching *University Challenge* with my dad. From that point onwards, I knew I wanted to be on the show. It was like the one desperate thing I really, really wanted to do. At my college we had quite an intense selection process where we had a quiz which a load of people did and then there was a bunch of questions that we all had to write answers to and then we had a buzzer round. It felt quite intense at the time. We got quite a nicely balanced team, having some art students and also a scientist.'

In 2020, Lucy was one of many competitors today who had to contend with something contestants from early series of the show didn't – social media trolls. Following her appearance, Lucy was surprised to see on Twitter that some viewers commented negatively on her appearance – she had dyed pink hair and a nose ring. Although she looked like half the students in the country and was cleverer than most, she was obliged to deal with a wave of vulgar and misogynistic online comments.

'It was baffling to me that there were so many people who just decided that they absolutely hated me from appearing on a TV quiz show. It was just utterly infuriating. So much of it had to do with the fact that they just didn't see female contestants as being as worth as much as male contestants. I never felt particularly unsafe or anything like that. I just felt completely righteous anger.' She later wrote in *The Guardian*: 'Female contestants walk an impossible tightrope. Answer more than a couple of questions, or smile after you get an answer right, and you are arrogant: I became a "show-off" and "Ol' bighead". In 2009 Gail Trimble was "smug" and "cocky" because she answered more questions correctly than anyone on the show ever. Quieter female contestants are "useless". Quiet male contestants rarely face this.'

Despite her online experience, Lucy says students today should not hesitate to enter the process. 'Go for it,' she says. 'Absolutely go for it. No matter what else happened, it was some of the most fun I had that year and I'm really proud of having gone on.'

*

David Stainer was the captain of Oriel College, Oxford, who were runners-up in 1999 to the Open University. He read Philosophy, Politics and Economics and had appeared on *Fifteen to One* before *University Challenge*. Since leaving university and qualifying as a solicitor, he has become something of a stalwart in the world of quizzing, appearing on a number of other high-profile quiz shows, even scooping £64,000 on *Who Wants to Be a Millionaire?* Less of a prolific TV quizzer these days, David keeps his hand in setting specialist subject questions for *Mastermind* and he is the reigning BBC *Brain of Brains* champion.

As for a number of students, the 1998–1999 academic year was the second time David's team had attempted to get on the programme – Oriel wasn't selected the previous year. 'The selection process at Oriel then was extremely informal,' David remembers. In fact, he was largely in charge of organizing the team as his friend, who was the president of the Junior Common Room (JCR) knew he liked quizzes and asked him if he would 'sort it out'.

'I said, well, yes. I didn't even, I must admit, organize any official trial or whatever. I had already done a pretty tough weekly quiz at the Oxford Union with three friends from college and we were pretty competitive, and I'm afraid we simply filled in the form with our names on it. And I was prepared to say to anyone who moaned about that, go off and find your own team! I think it was known that we were the most quiz-obsessed people in the college.

'I had been interested in factual books, non-fiction, and quizzes since quite a young age. I think as soon as I could read I had a marked preference for factual books. And then I remember being involved in Cub Scout quizzes. By the time I was in sixth form, I was doing a few local pub quizzes. And then I think university was the trigger for getting more seriously involved in it because I met some other people who were very keen and we started doing regular quizzes in Oxford and I'd been on *Fifteen to One* before *University Challenge*.

'I think I'd be lying if I said my enjoyment of quizzing was purely the noble pursuit of knowledge. I do like the competitive element. I wasn't someone who was ever any good physical sports at school; I was quite bad at them. So things

331

like quizzing have always been a good opportunity for me to kind of slake my competitive nature in a way. I made a lot of great friends in quizzing over the years – it's a very nice community – and most notably, I met my wife while quizzing. It's a hobby I've never regretted.'

David remembers he found the process of filming the programme 'tremendously enjoyable. I've done a lot of quiz shows over the years, and the two I've enjoyed most are *University Challenge* and *Only Connect*. Both are team things which involve going away as a team, staying in a hotel, filming a match or matches and being able to kind of enjoy each other's company in the sights of Manchester or Cardiff [where *Only Connect* is filmed].

'I have never really suffered from nerves, and I guess I've always felt reasonably confident of my own abilities, and yes, luck won't always go your way but I was confident of being able to do my best, so I wasn't nervous. It was just a very enjoyable, very positive experience that I still look back on with a great deal of fondness.'

David's Oriel team of 1999 were famously beaten in the final by the Open University 265–210. Following the screening, Jeremy Paxman was reported on the BBC website to have criticized the older OU team (average age 46) as having 'two professional quiz players' including one who 'had only signed up for a course at the OU so he could be on the team'. The OU team members denied they were professionals, but the press jumped on the controversy.

'At the end of the day, the Open University is a university like any other,' says David, 'and in many ways it is a much more impressive university than the many others because it's got people who haven't had early advantages in life and have to fit in their studies on top of their often full-time occupations.'

David says there's quite a lot of what he calls serious quizzing going on nowadays. 'I play in the Quiz League of London and have done for about 20 years. Gosh, is it really that long? But there are equivalent leagues around the country. In the online era there's something called the Online Quiz League, which has just got up and running, which is all played via Zoom. And there's also a circuit called the Quizzing Circuit where people gather monthly to do Grand Prix, which is individual quiz papers, a little bit like doing an exam.

'There's quite a thriving and flourishing serious quiz circuit, and I guess *University Challenge* is one of the one of the ways that keen young players come into the game. It's not the only way, but equally there's a lot of people for whom that was their first experience of quizzing, and I think that's probably a really crucial role that the series has.

'When it came back on TV when I was about 16 years old, quite an impressionable age, as someone who was interested in general knowledge I was fascinated by this very hard show asking questions much harder than I was used to from other quiz shows I was watching. It serves a very useful role of bringing people in who are interested in *University Challenge* or, more generally, in their university quiz societies, after which they start hearing about other aspects of the quiz world and can carry on that interest if they want to. Some drift away from it after they've done *University Challenge*, but many end up doing a lot of quizzing activity over the years.'

Away from quizzing, David says appearing on *University Challenge* 'probably was not an unhelpful thing' when it came to applying for jobs after graduating. 'I do recall it definitely came up in most of the interviews I had. It's just something a bit different, isn't it?'

He adds: 'I think one of the nice things about quizzing is that, if you ask four or five top quiz players what methods they use, you'd probably get four or five different answers. I've read an awful lot of books, but there are some very eminent quizzers who almost never read books and do all their learning and research off the internet. Also, you learn quiz-related stuff by doing quizzes. Stuff does come up again, and you learn through doing.'

*

Sarah Healey (née Fitzpatrick) appeared as captain of the winning Magdalen College, Oxford team in 1998. She has been Permanent Secretary of the Department for Digital, Culture, Media and Sport since April 2019, having joined the Civil Service in 2001 as part of the Prime Minister's Strategy Unit and also worked in the Education, Work and Pensions and Exiting the European Union departments. She was appointed a Companion of the Order of the Bath (CB) in the Queen's Birthday Honours in 2019.

Sarah recalls: 'The team that entered and won *University Challenge* the year before were friends of mine, so I was very involved in their victory and impressed, as I have always loved quizzes and watched *University Challenge* when it came back with Jeremy Paxman. The team from the year before ran the selection process by setting lots of quiz questions in a big room and then basically appointing the top four people to the team. I have to say, I am fairly sure they made me captain because I was their friend and they didn't really know the others.'

She remembers the filming experience as 'kind of surreal. I remember that we had a few close shaves, but then were looking at being in the semi-finals, which I could hardly believe. Also, I hadn't taken enough clothes with me – as you needed a different top every time but I had only brought two or three and I needed four or five in the end. I went shopping in Manchester for one, and then the wardrobe department lent me the silver shirt I wore in the final.

'I remember also feeling a sense of responsibility for my team, keeping people together and spirits up. We had a lot of fun hanging around during filming. We hadn't known each other very well beforehand so needed to build up a bit of a rapport in order to work together well during the contests.'

Sarah says the gender balance in *University Challenge* teams and the social backgrounds of many participants is worthy of mention. 'As someone who was a female captain of a winning team, I think it's a shame there are not more women on the show. And of the eight contestants between the team from the year above and my team, seven of us went to state schools – that was really important to me especially coming from a very old and august institution like Magdalen College, Oxford. I hope we encouraged some people to apply who might not have done otherwise.'

Following their victory Sarah remembers the press attention was intense. 'That was all a bit strange, managing calls from newspapers and requests for interviews and things while still trying to do my university work. When it really went a bit out of control, the TV company kindly rang and asked if they could help, but it was all thankfully dying down by then.

'It is funny just how many people still remember us winning, recognize me from that and want to chat about it. I enjoyed chatting to David Lidington once when I was working in the Cabinet Office and he was Chancellor of the Duchy of Lancaster about both being *University Challenge* winners. Lots of ministers and civil servants are fans. It can be a good talking point.'

*

One of the very earliest series of *University Challenge*, in 1964, saw **Professor Norman Hammond** compete for Peterhouse, Cambridge. A renowned archaeologist who has held academic posts at some of the world's top universities including Cambridge and Boston, a research post at Harvard and visiting professorships at institutions including the University of California at Berkeley, Jilin University in China and the Sorbonne in Paris, he is a Fellow of the British Academy and the archaeology correspondent for *The Times*.

He remembers: 'We were competing over the 1963–1964 academic year, and my wife was on the Newnham College team a year later. We started out with beating St Anne's, Oxford by the record score of 410–80, which stood I think for the best part of a decade. These days the questions are often longer, particularly the mathematical and scientific ones. Ours would have been short answers, even on matters of science. And I don't think we were having to do mathematical formulae at all.

'I came up in October 1963 and Peterhouse were having auditions for *University Challenge* and, having been on *Brain of Britain* before I came up to Cambridge, I thought, "Oh, this is fun," so I tried out and was put on the team.' Professor Hammond was 18 when he was on *Brain of Britain*. 'I think I was the youngest person they'd ever had.'

Quizzes weren't really around in the early 1960s, he remembers. 'There weren't quiz nights at pubs or anything like that. *Round Britain Quiz*, which was the intellectual one, and *Brain of Britain*, which was the fact-based one, were almost the only ones around.'

Professor Hammond was reading Archaeology and Anthropology. He went to Cambridge on a Trevelyan Scholarship, which was based in part on having written an independent research thesis about pre-Reformation chapels in Sussex. He is a leading expert on archaeology and has written a number of books about the ancient Maya civilization and one on the archaeology of Afghanistan.

Recalling his time on *University Challenge*, he says: 'They got us to Manchester. Sometimes it was on the train, but I remember that there were a couple of times when they sent a hire car. And the four of us piled into this fancy vehicle, something like a Rover 2000, and we were driven up across the Peak District in gorgeous winter weather, and then put into a hotel in Deansgate, near the studio [on Quay Street in Manchester city centre, the original filming location]. We didn't have a reserve member in those days; neither did we have a cadre of support going up to Manchester. If there was a studio audience, it was not one drawn from the two colleges. I guess local Mancunians were possibly invited in from the university to sort of provide background noise, but definitely no people coming up from Cambridge.'

Professor Hammond remembers Bamber Gascoigne as 'very nice. He was incredibly young looking. I mean, he was incredibly young in those days anyway, but he looked the same age as a student and we socialized with him just as though he was one of us. Jeremy Paxman is, I think, to a very large extent, the voice and the man wielding the whip, whereas Bamber Gascoigne was somebody who knew as much as we did about a lot of the things we knew about. We admired him. That Paxman thing about "Come on" and the raised eyebrow when a really egregious wrong answer is given is not something that Bamber did. It was a much more sort of informal, cuddly event, even though it was also daggers drawn.'

Peterhouse's second match was against University College London. 'And that one we lost very narrowly, but Bamber Gascoigne rejected two correct answers. We went back to Cambridge and reported this to the relevant dons who said, "No, you were right." So Richard Molyneux, the captain, wrote to *University Challenge* and said, "This is what Professor Kenney, Fellow of the British Academy, says about the answer that Mr Hammond gave to the question about Roman gods – it wasn't that the answer we gave was wrong, but both answers were right." And then there was a history of maths question as well. And we came back in. We were up against Leeds and they beat us.

So it was possible for a team to appeal on the grounds that correct answers were rejected and to be reinstated.'

And the key to being a successful *University Challenge* player? 'What you needed was somebody who was really quick on the buzzer. And Dick Jones had the most incredible reflexes, as well as a very broad general knowledge. He would hit the buzzer, and give what was more often than not the right answer, and that would then give the rest of us the chance to chew over the additional questions.'

Professor Hammond points out that people have their own universities and colleges that they follow. 'So it's a bit like football, you're backing a team. It's partly the amazement when sitting there watching it on the telly. You actually know the answer to something and it's amazing with how bright the students are, particularly the ones who can solve the mathematical and scientific problems. It's the entertainment of the hitting of the buzzer, people getting it right, getting it wrong. It's active, it's not the ruminative performance you get on *Round Britain Quiz* on the radio.

'It was a whole lot of fun. And we gained a washing machine. We were collectively paid, I think, £50 and that provided Peterhouse with its first washing machine for undergraduates, instead of us having to send stuff out to the Swiss Laundry. So the *University Challenge* Memorial Washing Machine, which was a combined washer and dryer, was duly installed in the college's communal bathhouse.'

*

Some notable team members have gone on to make their names in the worlds of media or entertainment, and some of their recollections are included elsewhere in this book. Other recent competitors may not be household names but have gone down in the annals of *University Challenge* for other reasons. **Daniel Lawson**, captain of the Magdalene College, Cambridge team who were runners-up in 2021, has run the Cambridge University Quiz Society for many years; American **Brandon Blackwell**, who appeared for the winning Imperial College London team the previous year, has been a successful competitor on the famous US quiz show *Jeopardy!*; **Max Fitz-James**, captain of Edinburgh's winning team in 2019, is now one of the programme's question-setters; writer **Michael Taylor**, a member of the 2015 winning team, Gonville and Caius, also became a question-setter; and **Dorjana Sirola**, from 2002's winning Somerville College, Oxford team, is the only person to have won both as a student and as a member of a Professionals team, playing for the Bodleian Library team in 2006. The linguist and software expert has also regularly been highly placed in the World Quizzing Championships.

Try Your Luck
Match

Your starter for ten:

1   At the age of 16, Amy Tinkler, Team GB's youngest competitor in the Rio Olympics, won a bronze medal in which sport?

Three questions on a mathematical simulation:
(a) Which Turing-complete simulation was devised by the British mathematician John Horton Conway in 1970?
(b) Conway was inspired by the 1948 paper 'The General and Logical Theory of Automata' by which Budapest-born mathematician?
(c) What six-letter name is used for the smallest moving pattern in the game? It repeats in a four-cycle and contains five cells.

Your starter for ten:

2   What seven-letter word is a generic term for a thin, moist layer of bacteria and other micro-organisms that forms on a nutrient-rich surface, an example being tooth plaque?

Three questions on recent sporting records:
(a) In 2020, Ben Mertens, a 15-year-old Belgian, became the youngest player to win a qualifying match in the world championship of what sport? He traced his success to having once won a miniature table at a fairground.
(b) In tennis, the unseeded teenager Iga Swiatek won the 2020 French Open to become the first player from which country to win a grand slam singles title?
(c) In 2020, which 21-year-old became the first Slovenian, and the youngest man in 116 years, to win the Tour de France?

Your starter for ten:

3   'Circumvallate' and 'foliate' are among types of the small bumpy projections known as 'papillae', found on what muscle of the human body?

Three questions on styles of beer:
(a) What name is given to the unblended Belgian beer made via spontaneous fermentation, and often flavoured with cherry or raspberry?
(b) Often described as salty, the style of German sour beer known as *Gose* is associated with which major city, 100 kilometres northwest of Dresden?
(c) The top-fermented copper-coloured beer known as *Altbier* is associated with which city, the capital of North Rhine Westphalia?

Your starter for ten:
4 Meaning 'naked gills', what name is given to an order of marine gastropods that are typically shell-less and brightly coloured, and also known as sea slugs?

Three questions on US states and Canadian provinces:
(a) What is the only US state that borders the Canadian province of Alberta?
(b) What is the only US state that borders New Brunswick?
(c) Finally, what is the only US state that borders the Yukon territory?

Your starter for ten:
5 In ballet, what term denotes both a dancer's leap or jump and the point attained in such a leap? More generally, it means a particular height or altitude above a given level.

Your bonuses are on the fashion designer Elsa Schiaparelli:
(a) Schiaparelli is often associated with which adjective, using it both in the title of her autobiography, and in the name of a shade she introduced in 1937?
(b) In which comic novel of 1949 does the narrator, Fanny, say that she longed to put the label of her Schiaparelli jacket on the outside, so that 'people would know where it came from'?
(c) The allure of a Schiaparelli evening dress forms a crucial part of the narrative of *The Girls of Slender Means*, a short novel of 1963 by which writer?

Your starter for ten:
6 Born in Manchester in 1970, which singer-songwriter's surname may be obtained by mixing the colours in the titles of Taylor Swift's fourth album and a 2000 single by Coldplay?

Three questions on astronomy:
(a) If the diameter of the Earth is 12,000, the unit is 'kilometres'. What unit is being used if the diameter of the sun is 4.64?
(b) What planet of the solar system is roughly four light hours from the sun?
(c) What astronomical body is about 1.282 light-seconds from Earth?

Your starter for ten:

7 Based on a paper published in 1794, the Scottish chemist Elizabeth Fulhame has been credited with the invention of what concept, later named by Berzelius? It is the process of speeding a reaction by the addition of another substance that provides an alternative reaction pathway.

Three questions on obscurity:
(a) 'They do not easily rise out of obscurity whose talents straitened circumstances obstruct at home.' Born in about AD 60, which poet wrote this in his *Satires*?
(b) In *The Curse of Minerva*, which Romantic poet described the setting sun over the Peloponnese as 'not, as in northern climes, obscurely bright'?
(c) 'I strive to be brief, and I become obscure.' Which Roman poet wrote this in his *Ars Poetica*?

Your starter for ten:

8 What bird links all of the following? Huginn and Muninn, the companions of Odin in Norse mythology; Grip, the pet of the title character in Dickens' *Barnaby Rudge*; and Moses, the spy and tale-bearer in *Animal Farm*.

Three questions on shorter words that can be made using the letters of the word 'Hogmanay'. Give the word from the definition:
(a) Sometimes called the Tree Alphabet, an old Celtic system of writing that uses lines and notches to represent letters?
(b) A variety of grape associated with the production of Beaujolais Nouveau, chiefly by the process of carbonic maceration?
(c) A genre of cartoons and comicbooks; its name can be translated as 'impromptu drawings'?

Your starter for ten:

9 What, specifically, is the subject of the 2019 work of non-fiction by Cecelia Watson, the subtitle claiming that it can 'improve your writing, enrich your reading and even change your life', having described it as 'a misunderstood punctuation mark'?

Your bonuses are on pairs of countries. In each case, the last three letters of the first country are the same as the first three letters of the second. Name both countries from the descriptions:
(a) The location of the thirteen-kilometre Great Seto Bridge; and the Latin American country that, in 1906, was the site of the first overseas visit by a serving US president.

(b) The official UN name of an African country that borders Liberia and Ghana; and a European country that left the Commonwealth in 1949.
(c) The birthplace of the novelist Bao Ninh; and a country that declared independence from South Africa in 1990.

Your starter for ten:

10 'The War of the Eight Saints' from 1375 to 1378 led to the end of the Papacy's 70-year residence in which city of southern France?

Three questions on grammar in English and Latin:
(a) What name is given to a form of verb functioning as a noun, ending with the suffix '-ing' in English? The equivalent form in Latin ends with the suffix '-ndum'.
(b) Having a gerund in its title, which play by Shakespeare includes the characters Gremio, Lucentio and Christopher Sly?
(c) Which of Shakespeare's female characters has a name that derives from the Latin gerundive for 'worthy of admiration' or 'admirable'?

Your starter for ten:

11 Carraig Aonair, meaning 'Lonely Rock', is the Irish name of which landmark situated about eight miles off the coast of County Cork? Between Lundy and Irish Sea in the BBC Shipping Forecast, it gives its name to a biennial yachting race first held in 1925.

Three questions on kinetic art:
(a) What name was adopted by the Russian sculptor who settled in St Ives in Cornwall in the 1930s and whose works include *Kinetic Construction* and the *Linear Construction* series?
(b) Which French artist experimented with ideas of kinetic art in his *Rotoreliefs* series, extending his use of so-called readymade objects?
(c) Said to have been coined by Duchamp, what name is given to the kinetic sculptures consisting of flat metal parts attached to wires? They are associated with the work of the 1930s by the US sculptor Alexander Calder.

Your starter for ten:

12 Which poet mocked the scholar Lewis Theobald, calling him Tibbald, the son of the goddess of dullness, in a work first published anonymously in 1728 and entitled *The Dunciad*?

Your bonuses are on official symbols of US states. Identify each state from the description:

(a) A state that borders Alabama and South Carolina; its state crop is the peanut, the state fruit is the peach, and the state-prepared food is grits.

(b) The largest of the six New England states, in which blueberry pie is the state dessert and maple syrup is the state sweetener.

(c) The state that Britain gained in exchange for Havana in 1763; orange is the state fruit, and key lime pie is the state pie.

Your starter for ten:

13 What seven-letter word may follow 'xiphoid' in human anatomy; 'stochastic' in probability theory; and 'Haber-Bosch' in industrial chemistry?

Three questions on the numbers on a standard dartboard:

(a) The numbers on a standard dartboard are arranged to reduce the chance of hitting a high number by accident. What two low numbers are on either side of the 20?

(b) The numbers at the top, bottom and sides, where 12, 3, 6 and 9 would be on a clock, add up to 40. The numbers at the top and bottom are 20 and 3; what are the other two?

(c) After the 20 at the top, what is the next even number clockwise round the board? It is equal to the sum of the number between it and the 20 and the first two numbers anti-clockwise from the 20.

Your starter for ten:

14 The birthplace of Samuel Johnson in 1709, which city has a Gothic cathedral with three spires known as the Ladies of the Vale, the Vale being the Trent Valley northeast of Birmingham?

Three questions on leguminous plants:

(a) The 'sensitive' or 'humble' plant, commonly cultivated for its rapid leaf movements in response to touch, is a member of which genus of plants in the pea family?

(b) Distinguished by their often blue, white or pink upright flower spikes, which herbaceous plants in the pea family derive their name from the Latin for 'wolf'?

(c) *Glycine max* is a legume with what common name? It is the source of fermented foods such as tempeh, miso and stinky tofu.

Your starter for ten:

15 Which organ of the human body contains Broca's area and Wernicke's area, both associated with speech production?

Your bonuses are on the TV series *Sex and the City*. I need the given name and birth surname of each character:

(a) Which character in *Sex and the City* shares a surname with the Stockport-born jurist who presided at the trial of King Charles I in 1649?

(b) Which character shares a surname with the closest city to the 1644 Battle of Marston Moor?

(c) Finally, which leading character shares a surname with a political philosopher born in Wiltshire in 1588?

Your starter for ten:

16 With a single throw of two dice, and excluding movements mandated by cards, in a standard UK game of Monopoly, if one starts at 'Go', what is the probability of landing on a railway station?

Three questions on political campaigners:

(a) The Abeokuta women's revolt was a successful mass protest against oppressive taxation in which country in the 1940s? It took place in a city about 70 kilometres north of what was then the county's capital, one of West Africa's largest cities.

(b) In which country did Wangari Maathai found the Green Belt Movement in 1977, an attempt to tackle rural poverty through the direct action of tree planting?

(c) In May 1988, four women stormed the studio of the BBC *Six O'Clock News* to protest against which new clause of the Local Government Act, usually referred to by its number?

Your starter for ten:

17 Which English king defeated the Danish leader Guthrum at the Battle of Edington, in Wiltshire? Guthrum was later baptized, took the new name of Athelstan and retired to East Anglia.

Your bonuses are on terms in critical theory. Each answer is a four-letter word:

(a) In his 1974 work, what short word does Raymond Williams call 'the defining characteristic of broadcasting'? He contrasts this with what he describes as 'discrete' forms of communication, such as film.

(b) What English word is typically used to translate Jacques Lacan's concept of *manque*? In his psychoanalytic framework, it is defined as the cause of desire.

(c) In a 1936 essay, what word did the German cultural critic Walter Benjamin use to refer to the quality that is lost when a work of art is reproduced? He defines it as the sense of 'its unique existence at the place where it happens to be'.

Your starter for ten:

18 A novel of 1983 by D.M. Thomas and a film of 2002 directed by Atom Egoyan share what six-letter name? It also appears in the Book of Genesis as the name of mountains that served as the resting-place of Noah's ark.

Three questions on an island:
(a) The Palace of Phaistos, in the Messara valley, and Zakros, on the eastern coast, are among the archaeological sites of which Mediterranean island?
(b) Which ancient city near Phaistos is noted for its mural inscription of the most complete Greek legal code before the Hellenistic age?
(c) Beginning in 1900, which British archaeologist began excavation of the Cretan palace of Knossos, resulting in his naming of the Minoan civilization?

Your starter for ten:

19 Answer in German or English, but not Latin. The name of what former German state appears in the names of two leading football clubs, based in Dortmund and Mönchengladbach?

For your bonuses, imagine a straight line from the Vatican to the city of Mecca. Name each of the following places that lie on, or close to, that line:
(a) An island just off the coast of the Peloponnese; in antiquity, it was sacred to Aphrodite, and its name appears in the title of a painting by Watteau.
(b) With its own international airport, a tourist resort on the Red Sea coast of Egypt, southwest of Sharm el-Sheikh, and noted for scuba diving.
(c) And finally, a major city on the site of the ancient Greek colony of Parthenope; its football team is often a leading contender in Serie A.

Your starter for ten:

20 On the basis of mitochondrial DNA studies, 'Masai', 'reticulated', 'Northern' and 'Southern' have been proposed as separate species of which large African mammal, traditionally seen as a single species showing subtle variations in coat pattern?

Your bonuses are on popular songs inspired by literature. In each case, give the name of the song from the description:
(a) A song inspired by Heathcliff's mourning of Catherine in *Wuthering Heights*; it was written by Jim Steinman and performed by Celine Dion, among others.
(b) A song indirectly inspired by the protagonist of Steinbeck's *The Grapes of Wrath*; it was written and performed by Bruce Springsteen.
(c) Finally, a 1967 song inspired by the works of Lewis Carroll; it was written by Grace Slick and performed by Jefferson Airplane.

Your starter for ten:

21 'Nothing happens in the world that doesn't happen in the East End.' These words are associated with which artistic partnership? They have been based in Spitalfields since the late 1960s, having met at St Martin's School of Art.

Three questions on a language and a people:
(a) Which Indo-European language has varieties known as Kurmanji and Sorani? Lacking a homeland, its speakers are estimated at more than 15 million.
(b) Which pact between the Allied powers and Ottoman Turkey provided for an autonomous Kurdistan after the First World War? It was later replaced by the Treaty of Lausanne, which failed to mention a Kurdish nation.
(c) In addition to Iraq, which other country officially recognizes an internal entity by the name of Kurdistan?

Your starter for ten:

22 Assuming a somewhat circuitous route, what is the minimum number of international border crossings that would be required in a land journey between Oslo and Hong Kong?

Three questions on the inspiration for works by Shakespeare:
(a) A major source for Shakespeare's *All's Well That Ends Well*, what name is given to the collection of novels by Boccaccio, published around 250 years earlier?
(b) First performed in 1582, the play entitled *Rare Triumphs of Love and Fortune*, whose author is unknown, was one of the supposed influences for which of Shakespeare's later plays?
(c) Co-written with John Fletcher, and often thought to be Shakespeare's final play, the plot of *The Two Noble Kinsmen* is based on which of Chaucer's *Canterbury Tales*?

Your starter for ten:

23 The daughter of the sun god Helios and a nymph, which figure in Greek mythology is the title character of a novel by Madeline Miller? She changed the companions of Odysseus into swine.

Your bonuses are on recent television dramas co-produced by the BBC and HBO; give the title of each series from the description:
(a) A 12-part series created by and starring Michaela Coel, which explores the aftermath of a sexual assault. I need a precise four-word title here.

(b) A short series following a group of young graduates competing for jobs at the fictional investment bank Pierpoint. Myha'la Herrold plays the main character, Harper.

(c) Finally, an ongoing adaptation of a trilogy of fantasy novels. Dafne Keen and Amir Wilson play the two young protagonists, with Ruth Wilson and Lin-Manuel Miranda also among the main cast.

Your starter for ten:

24 Born in 1678, which composer was, for most of his career, associated with the Ospedale della Pietà, a home for orphans in Venice? His best-known work is a group of four violin concertos named after a natural cycle.

Three questions on planetary transits:

(a) Which astronomer was the first to correctly predict the transits of Mercury and Venus, although he never witnessed either event, having died the year before the 1631 transit of Mercury?

(b) Denoted with a double quotation mark, what unit is often used to show the degree of separation between the sun's centre and that of the transitory planet?

(c) The second and last transit of Venus in the 21st century was in 2012. When was the first? The same year saw NASA's *Spirit* and *Opportunity* craft land on Mars, and Cassini-Huygens enter the orbit of Saturn.

Your starter for ten:

25 Divided into two parts entitled 'Poverty' and 'Riches', which novel by Charles Dickens begins: 'Thirty years ago, Marseilles lay burning in the sun, one day'? Its title character is Amy, the daughter of William.

Your bonuses are on alkaline earth metals, as represented by the illustrations of Murray Robertson on the website of the Royal Society of Chemistry:

(a) Which alkaline earth metal has an image inspired by chlorophyll, the molecule that enables green plants to photosynthesize?

(b) The image for what element is 'a highly abstracted metallic mushroom cloud', alluding to the presence of this element in nuclear fallout?

(c) What element is illustrated by an image representing its former, highly toxic, use in luminous paint on clock and watch dials?

The Answers

1   Gymnastics (accept women's floor [exercise])
    (a) (The) Game of Life
    (b) (John) von Neumann
    (c) Glider

2   Biofilm
    (a) Snooker
    (b) Poland
    (c) (Tadej) Pogacar

3   Tongue
    (a) Lambic
    (b) Leipzig
    (c) Düsseldorf

4   Nudibranch / nudibranchia
    (a) Montana
    (b) Maine
    (c) Alaska

5   Elevation
    (a) Shocking (*Shocking Life* and Shocking pink)
    (b) *Love in a Cold Climate* (Nancy Mitford, of course)
    (c) Muriel Spark

6   Jason Orange (*Red* and 'Yellow')
    (a) Light-seconds
    (b) Neptune
    (c) The moon

7   Catalysis (accept catalyst, correcting it)
    (a) Juvenal
    (b) (Lord) Byron
    (c) Horace

8   Raven (*Corvus corax*)
    (a) Ogham
    (b) Gamay
    (c) Manga

9   Semicolon
    (a) Japan and Panama
    (b) Côte d'Ivoire and Ireland
    (c) Vietnam and Namibia

10　Avignon (after a popular name of the Florentine Council of War)
　　(a) Gerund
　　(b) *The Taming of the Shrew*
　　(c) Miranda (Latin: *mirandum*)

11　Fastnet (Rock)
　　(a) Naum Gabo
　　(b) (Marcel) Duchamp
　　(c) Mobiles

12　(Alexander) Pope (1688–1744)
　　(a) Georgia
　　(b) Maine
　　(c) Florida

13　Process
　　(a) 1 and 5
　　(b) 6 and 11 (at 3pm and 9pm respectively)
　　(c) 18 (i.e. 1 + 5 + 12)

14　Lichfield
　　(a) Mimosa
　　(b) Lupin (Latin: *lupus*)
　　(c) Soy / soya bean

15　The brain
　　(a) Carrie Bradshaw (John Bradshaw, 1602–1659)
　　(b) Charlotte York
　　(c) Miranda Hobbes (Thomas Hobbes)

16　One in nine (accept four in thirty-six ; also accept 11.11%, 0.11111; a throw of 5 leads to King's Cross Station)
　　(a) Nigeria (Abeokuta is north of Lagos, of course)
　　(b) Kenya
　　(c) (Clause or Section) 28 (prohibiting the 'promotion' of homosexuality by local authorities, particularly in an educational context)

17　Alfred (the Great)
　　(a) Flow
　　(b) Lack
　　(c) Aura

18　Ararat
　　(a) Crete (Minoan palaces)
　　(b) Gortyn / Gortyna
　　(c) (Arthur) Evans

19 Preussen / Prussia (not Borussia, the Latin name that appears in the two club names)
   (a) Kíthira / Cythera
   (b) Hurghada
   (c) Naples

20 Giraffe
   (a) 'It's All Coming Back to Me Now'
   (b) 'The Ghost of Tom Joad'
   (c) 'White Rabbit'

21 Gilbert and George (Gilbert Proesch and George Passmore)
   (a) Kurdish
   (b) (Treaty of) Sèvres
   (c) Iran

22 Two (Norway to Russia, then Russia to China)
   (a) *The Decameron*
   (b) *Cymbeline*
   (c) 'The Knight's Tale'

23 Circe
   (a) *I May Destroy You*
   (b) *Industry*
   (c) *His Dark Materials*

24 (Antonio) Vivaldi
   (a) (Johannes) Kepler
   (b) Arcsecond / arcsec
   (c) 2004

25 *Little Dorrit*
   (a) Magnesium (chlorophyll contains a single atom of magnesium at its centre)
   (b) Strontium
   (c) Radium

Behind

the Scenes

'Fingers on buzzers, this is your starter for ten.'

For eight competitors, host Jeremy Paxman's calm tone signals the start of one of the most intense half-hours of their lives, in front of a television audience of millions. Their knowledge, intelligence and powers of recall are about to be tested to the most intense degree. Two four-strong teams of predominantly young people are about to subject themselves to one of the toughest TV quiz shows of all time, *University Challenge*, and I have the chance to see behind the scenes for this quarter-final during the 2021–2022 series between Royal Holloway and Robert Gordon University, the latter making an appearance for the first time in 28 years.

For the most part, they are supremely prepared. These students have spent months participating in practice quizzes, honing their buzzer skills and working on their specialisms. And now they're here in a TV studio, ready to put their knowledge to the ultimate test. But how did they get to be here in these eight hot seats? How do you become part of a *University Challenge* team? And how do you cope with the weight of representing your university?

*

University Challenge has been part of the UK TV landscape for 60 years, moving from a highbrow, intelligent and relatively niche-audience programme to televisual national treasure status, and the universities and colleges that offer up the teams have developed practical systems by which to select their five representatives. (Each team has a reserve member who attends all the rounds and watches from the green room in case of illness or unavailability, when they will be drafted in at the last minute.)

Around 120 teams apply each year, and 28 are selected to appear in a series. With so many applying each year, the show's producers and researchers have a tough job to decide which teams will make the cut for each series. There are always going to be plenty of disappointed students. Persistence is often rewarded, however, and going through the process two or three times can be beneficial. The same can be said for those reserve members each team has. Occasionally, the reserve may return the following year, leading their team as captain. Their previous experience as a non-competing contestant can be invaluable to teammates.

The producers are looking for more than brainy students, though. They are making a television show, after all and, while the tried-and-trusted formula is one that keeps on working, a great deal of thought is given to selecting teams with interesting and engaging team members. The gender balance is increasingly important. One of the few criticisms levelled at the programme over the years has been the balance being weighted more heavily towards male competitors. Often, two opposing teams would be entirely male. The reasons for this have been considered widely, and the programme, while not exercising positive discrimination towards would-be teams, is happy to see that a gender balance is emerging naturally from the universities.

Generally, a call goes out early in the academic year asking for potential participants to come forward. Then follow variations of whittling down the hopefuls. These may comprise mass quizzes with or without interviews, discussions among the university quiz society or, in the case of universities that are not regular names to grace the *University Challenge* studios, a smaller group of hopefuls applying to the programme. Once the university team is selected, it faces a second selection process, this time administered by the programme's producers and researchers.

Executive producer Peter Gwyn explains the start of each year's selection process: 'We would hope to get the application forms completed by the universities well before Christmas. We will then conduct our interview audition talks and test papers.' In a typical year the production team panel will conduct auditions in person, travelling to locations around the country. The audition process is in two parts – a 40-question general knowledge test, conducted under exam conditions, and then interviews.

The questions section is designed to be hard, and covers a wide range of subjects. The aim is to identify teams with a good selection of degree courses and interests. The individual test papers are marked, and then the four main team members' answers are aggregated, with a team receiving one mark for each question that at least one member has answered correctly.

The five-strong teams (including the reserves) will already have completed their individual application forms, and the subsequent informal interviews, which last around twenty minutes, serve to assess the dynamics between team members, the captain's leadership, familiarity with the programme, quizzing experience and preparation plans. Photographs of the would-be contestants are taken, as well as a short video of each team in which the members introduce themselves as they would do on the programme.

As the production team gathers to decide on the 28 teams for a series, the final decision takes into account all aspects of the audition process. The programme is looking for exceptional general knowledge, an engaging screen presence and teams who represent a good cross-section of the country's higher education establishments.

Among the decision-makers are some of the people who actually set the questions. Several former competitors now work on the programme, and one of these is Richard Gilbert. He writes many of the show's questions, and has been on both sides of the fence. As a Linguistics student at the University of Manchester, he was captain of the winning team of 2013. This became only the second team in the history of the show to retain the winners' trophy, and their victory over University College London allowed Manchester to claim its fourth victory in eight years. It equals Magdalen College, Oxford, and, as of April 2022, Imperial College London, which has also won the competition four times. (The first ever series champions were the University of Leicester which beat Balliol, Oxford, over three matches. Leicester's team was Oliver Andrew, studying for a PGCE; Madalane Hall, English; Geoffrey Ford, Geology; and John Hewitt, History. The prize for the university was a first-edition copy of Samuel Johnson's *Dictionary*.) Richard began as a researcher before moving up to senior researcher, then assistant producer and now questions producer, his current job. He says: 'I'm very lucky that I get to spend my day reading about things that I find personally interesting.'

*

When the programme's producers have selected the 28 teams, it's time for the recordings. These days the teams travel from all over the country to the studios at Dock 10 at MediaCity UK in Salford, Greater Manchester. MediaCity is where the North West's television industry is now centred. Previously, Granada and the BBC had their studios in Manchester city centre a few miles away, but now many of our favourite programmes are researched, written, edited and produced at the 200-acre development on the Manchester Ship Canal, home to BBC North, BBC Sport and Children's Entertainment and, over the river, *Coronation Street*.

The team members arrive in Salford with a couple of friends or family for the first few rounds. This is where the highest-scoring teams and the highest-scoring losers in the first round are whittled down to face the next knockout rounds before the quarter- and semi-finals and then the final. The students might compete in more than one round a day in the knockout rounds. The pressure is intense, and the production team understands this, looking after the contestants, making sure everything runs smoothly, so the team members can concentrate on the task ahead. Teams are put up in a hotel on the MediaCity site adjacent to the studios.

'We currently record in three blocks at the end of February, the end of March and the end of April,' says Peter, 'so the final will be recorded roughly at the end of April.' The logistics involved in organizing the blocks of recordings are impressive. It's a finely tuned operation to get the teams to Salford and ready for their respective appearances. Of course, the production team is used to this and everything runs like clockwork, albeit hampered at the time of writing by ongoing COVID restrictions, but only slightly.

During the pandemic, preparations for *University Challenge* didn't stop. Under lockdown, universities had to work out different ways of selecting the best teams At most colleges and universities, the selection of successful teams went online. The programme's production changed, too. After an enforced hiatus, the decision was made to record without an audience. As of writing, the no-audience approach continues. And to this there's a mixed response from today's teams. Previously, each contestant was allowed to bring three companions to the filming; these may have been parents, friends or partners. For some, seeing a friendly face out there in the audience, or in the hotel at MediaCity in Salford was helpful. For others, with no audience and only the crew in the studio, there is less pressure to perform. The participants can still see their friends and relatives before or after filming. Owing to the blocks of recordings, the contestants will be in Salford for a number of days depending on the stage of the competition. They may then return for another few days as the later rounds are recorded.

*

The teams walk over from the nearby hotel and are greeted and settled into the green room to prepare for the filming. This is a large office-like space with comfy sofas and huge windows overlooking the Manchester Ship Canal. There's a kitchen area where the competitors can grab a cold drink or make a cup of tea or coffee. And there's a basket of crisps and chocolate to provide a little sustenance. The two opposing teams scheduled for a screening share the green room. And what's immediately obvious is the camaraderie and support that exists between these opponents. They chat among themselves and to production staff and wish each other good luck.

Then it's time to go. The assistant producers and researchers walk the two teams down the corridors to the studio, checking who's going to be on the right or the left. 'Do we have the same seats as the last round?' they ask. There's a stop for the toilets, and it's on to the studio floor.

The floor manager Lynn Wright takes control now. She knows what she's doing; she's worked on many other popular programmes including *Coronation Street* and is technically retired, but she's happy to come back to work on *University Challenge*. Lynn's earpiece connects her to the gallery, and as she listens to the technical preparations, she's busy making sure the team members have a glass of water and checking that nothing is going to appear on screen that shouldn't, such as a logo on the competitors' clothing.

The five camera operators are in position and, while the make-up team checks the contestants for shiny faces, the production team take their places where, before the COVID environment, the audience used to sit.

Roger Tilling, the voice of *University Challenge*, is on set chatting to the production team before he takes his place on a raised platform. It's raised so he can clearly see above the cameras which team member has buzzed first. That's essential. He needs to be quick before host Jeremy Paxman demands an answer. The contestants are told to speak their answer almost immediately they press their buzzer, so Roger has to name the college and the contestant before this happens.

Once the competitors are settled in and the names are checked, there's a practice round essentially to calm the nerves and get them into the zone for answering questions. Questions editor Tom Benson takes the host's chair for a few minutes and runs through a few fairly easy practice questions. The buzzers are tested, and everyone is now more relaxed, ready for the main event.

Host Jeremy Paxman appears on set and is mic'd up. He takes his chair, and now it's getting serious. Paxman checks the cards in front of him on which the questions are printed. He chats briefly to the competitors while listening in his earpiece to instructions from the gallery. The camera operators check their pictures. It's time to record.

Floor manager Lynn tells the teams, 'Have fun everyone – it's only a game. OK, everybody, stand by…' and then that famous theme tune – 'College Boy' by Derek New, the current version of which was recorded by the Balanescu Quartet – echoes around the studio.

As the music and the crew's applause (later enhanced to sound like a full studio audience) fades away, Paxman looks into camera and introduces the two teams.

At this stage in the competition these two teams have competed a number of times, and Paxman takes the opportunity to remind viewers of their performances so far, who they have beaten and by how much. He also asks the teams to introduce themselves and mentions the average age of the teams.

Then it's down to business. 'This is your starter for ten…'

*

The set has remained reassuringly recognizable over the years, with the quizmaster to the right of the two teams as the viewer sees them. The captain of each team sits second from the right. On screen, of course, the two teams appear one on top of the other, a split-screen production device to enable viewers to see easily which player has buzzed first.

Most teams have a fluffy mascot that sits in the centre of their desk (although Manchester's disruptive 1975 team had a clog). In the middle of the floor is a globe, a nod to a scientific instrument. During the Christmas specials this is often decorated with tinsel or twinkly lights.

The format of every show is the same. It all adds to the familiarity that viewers love. There are the starters for ten points which are answered by the fastest on the buzzer. Then there are three bonus questions for five points on each of which the team can confer. The captain can answer after considering or can nominate a team member to answer.

There are the music and picture rounds. They appear in roughly the same part of the quiz each time, and Peter Gwyn explains that this is a timing issue. 'The PA [production assistant] in the gallery times the show as we're doing the recording. After a number of minutes of gameplay has elapsed, we'll then go to a picture and questions, the music round and the second picture round.'

Half an hour slips by and the famous gong sounds to signify the end of the round. The show's recording takes slightly longer than the length of the programme that's eventually broadcast a few months later, owing to the requirement for the production team to quickly check through the recording and identify any questions the quizmaster may need to repeat.

The teams remain in their seats as Jeremy Paxman re-records whatever is deemed necessary – there may have been a point of order on an answer. The teams may be asked to repeat their introductions or their farewells and, as the handful of re-records are filmed, the electronic scores on the front of Jeremy Paxman's desk are altered to ensure continuity.

The losing team congratulates the winners and the contestants are escorted back to the green room, relieved and chatting to each other as they commiserate on wrong answers. There's a sense of true camaraderie among the teams and a genuine mutual respect.

The team members head off, either back home or to their university digs, or, if they're the victors, they may have another round to play the next day so it's back to the hotel. The production team prepares for the next two teams. There may be as many as three recordings on a day, so there may be six teams to accommodate. The minimum number of matches a series-winning team could play would be six, explains Peter. 'It would be possible for that to go up to eight, if a team was among the four highest-scoring losers or they needed to play all three of their quarter-final matches. So it's either six, seven or eight matches to complete the series.'

Speaking after today's round, George Harvey, the captain of the Royal Holloway team, who is studying for a master's in Physics, considers what makes a *University Challenge* contestant: 'You have to be the type of person who enjoys learning, finding things out. You can't "become" the right type of contestant just for *University Challenge*.'

And teammate Joanna Brown, who is studying for a PhD in Creative Writing, adds: 'We didn't know each other before this – now we'll be friends for a long time.'

What is the secret of the programme's long-running success? Executive producer Peter cites the 'absolute simplicity of the format' in large part. 'We have the least complicated rules of any quiz programme in television; anyone can play along at home. I think the play-along value is very important to viewers. One thing we hear from viewers all the time is they feel that if they watch the programme and can answer two questions correctly then there's hope. I think there's something endlessly appealing about a young generation of extremely bright people performing extremely well. And I think, in the main, almost universally, our contestants are very charming, likeable, agreeable people who are taking part because it's the title it is. There's no prize on offer other than the trophy so they take part for the love of competing and the honour of the university.'

Match

Your starter for ten:

1 One of the five adjectives used to describe the life of man in Hobbes' *Leviathan*, what word is also the last adjective in Milton's *Paradise Lost*?

Three questions on language families:
(a) Formerly known as Malayo-Polynesian, what widespread language family includes Bahasa Indonesia, Filipino, Maori and Hawaiian?
(b) The Austroasiatic family includes two national languages of mainland Southeast Asia. One is Khmer, or Cambodian; what is the other?
(c) Which Afroasiatic language is one of the six official languages of the United Nations?

Your starter for ten:

2 What initial letter links the names of: a coastal city of Morocco to the southwest of Rabat; the largest city of Benin, and the capital of the Republic of Guinea?

Three questions on magnetic effects:
(a) Named after the US physicist who discovered it in 1879, what effect causes a voltage across a conductor when a magnetic field is applied at right angles to a flow of current?
(b) Causing splitting of atomic energy levels, what is the strong magnetic field version of the Zeeman effect? It is named after two German physicists.
(c) Born in 1857, which Irish scientist gives his name to the precession of a magnetic moment about an external magnetic field?

Your starter for ten:

3 Which prominent novel did Martin Amis describe as 'an indefinite visit from your most impossible senior relative, with all his pranks, dirty habits, unstoppable reminiscences and terrible cronies'? The work in question was originally published in two parts, in the domains of King Philip III.

Three questions on fabrics:

(a) With a name derived from the Persian for 'milk and sugar', what fabric has a surface of puckered and flat sections, typically in a striped pattern?

(b) What thick, hard-wearing twilled cloth with a short nap has a name that can also mean pompous or pretentious language?

(c) Poplin, a strong fabric in a plain weave, is believed to have been named in reference to the 14th-century popes in exile in which French city?

Your starter for ten:

4   'The internal actions and reactions of a system of rigid bodies in motion are in equilibrium.' This principle is attributed to which 18th-century French mathematician, in his *Treatise on Dynamics*?

Three questions on D.H. Lawrence:

(a) Paul Morel is the male protagonist of which semi-autobiographical novel by D.H. Lawrence, first published in 1913?

(b) In his 1915 novel *The Rainbow*, what is the surname of the Midlands family that Lawrence follows over three generations from 1840 to 1905?

(c) *Lady Chatterley's Lover* was first published privately in Florence in 1928. In which year was it finally published in London in an unexpurgated form, after a landmark obscenity trial?

Your starter for ten:

5   In sport, what surname links all of these: Charlotte, a former captain of the England women's cricket team; the champion triple-jumper Jonathan; and the ski-jumper Michael, known as Eddie the Eagle?

Three questions on technology:

(a) In the early 20th century, Philo Farnsworth, Herbert Ives and Isaac Shoenberg were among those who developed technology in early forms of what domestic appliance?

(b) Developed by the American George Carey, an earlier form of picture transmission used cells that relied on the photoelectric properties of which metalloid element in the oxygen group of the periodic table?

(c) In the 1960s, the PAL system was one of two principal television systems that gained widespread adoption in Europe. What was the other, used in France?

Your starter for ten:

6   Which English novelist's creations include the master embalmer Mr Joyboy; the hairdresser Trimmer; Viscount 'Boy' Mulcaster; and the headmaster Augustus Fagan?

Your bonuses are on exhibitions at the Tate galleries in 2019. In each case, name the artist from the description:
(a) Which British photojournalist was the subject of a retrospective at Tate Britain that featured images of conflict in Vietnam, Northern Ireland and Syria, as well as urban and rural scenes of life in Britain?
(b) Focusing on his work from 1912 until his death in 1947, which French artist's work appeared in Tate Modern's exhibition *The Colour of Memory*? His paintings include *Nude in the Bath* and *Stairs in the Artist's Garden*.
(c) Tate Liverpool held the first UK retrospective of which US artist and activist's work? Part of the 1980s New York art scene, he was known for his colourful images and motifs, including a barking dog and a radiant baby.

Your starter for ten:
7   Which abbey was the second Cistercian foundation in Britain and the first in Wales? Situated north of Chepstow on the River Wye, its name appears in the title of a poem by Wordsworth.

Three questions on physics:
(a) As an SI base unit, the metre is defined in terms of the second and what fundamental constant?
(b) The kelvin is defined in terms of the second, metre, kilogram and what constant, now set to exactly 1.380649×10^{-23} in SI units?
(c) As of 20 May 2019, the kilogram is defined in terms of the second, metre and what physical constant, named after a German physicist?

Your starter for ten:
8   What six-letter word appears in all of the following titles? A 1951 novella by Carson McCullers; a novel by Muriel Spark set in South London; and the 17th-century poem by Michael Drayton that begins 'Fair stood the wind for France'?

Your bonuses are on Russian history. In each case, give the name or term from the description. All three answers begin with the same letter:
(a) A warship whose crew mutinied at Odessa in 1905, an event dramatized in a 1925 film by Sergei Eisenstein?
(b) A Cossack who led a major rebellion against Catherine the Great from 1773 to 1775?
(c) A term meaning 'restructuring'; along with *glasnost*, this was one of Mikhail Gorbachev's pillars of reform in the Soviet Union in the 1980s.

Your starter for ten:

9   At standard temperature and pressure, the air in a room of 78 cubic metres has a mass that approximates to what round number in kilograms?

Three questions on 20th-century discoveries in astrophysics:
(a) In 1912, Henrietta Swan Leavitt of the Harvard Observatory published research on the period-luminosity relationship of what class of variable stars?
(b) A graduate of Vassar College, Vera Rubin used data on the rotation of stars in spiral galaxies as evidence for the existence of what material, predicted in the 1930s?
(c) In 1967, Jocelyn Bell detected bursts of radio waves at a frequency of 0.75 hertz from the constellation Vulpecula, the first observation of what type of star?

Your starter for ten:

10 Name the predecessor of either of the two US presidents who share a surname with the person who, in 2019, became the UK's prime minister

Your bonuses are on names or titles. In each case, the last word of the first answer gives the first word of the second, for example, 'Hey Jude' and *Jude the Obscure*. So in each case, give two answers from the descriptions:
(a) A tragedy by Shakespeare set during the Trojan war; and the first female commissioner of the Metropolitan Police?
(b) The only history play by Shakespeare to be set during the 13th century; and the leader of the British Labour Party between 1992 and 1994?
(c) A Shakespeare comedy also known as *What You Will*; and a 1968 horror film by George A. Romero that features reanimating corpses?

Your starter for ten:

11 From the French for 'to ice', what adjective is used of cloth or leather that has a smooth surface with a high lustre? It is more commonly known as a descriptor of glazed or candied fruit, and in the name of a type of smooth, thin icing?

Your bonuses are on transuranic elements. In each case, identify the element from its anagram:
(a) 'Nine tenses' is an anagram of the name of which transuranic element, the heaviest of the halogens?
(b) 'Umber-like' is an anagram of the name of which transuranic element, named after a city in California?
(c) Finally, 'minute pun' is an anagram of the name of which actinide metal, with the atomic number 93?

Your starter for ten:

12 In 1883, in an attempt to undermine the rise of social democracy, which European politician introduced the world's first national health insurance scheme?

Three questions on ducks:
(a) What name is given to a coloured patch of wing feathers that is a distinguishing feature of many species of dabbling duck? The same word denotes a device used in medicine for examining an internal body cavity.
(b) Having a green speculum and a blue forewing, *Anas clypeata* has what common name, referring to its distinctive spoon-shaped bill, used to strain animals and plants from water?
(c) Also having a green speculum, of a similar colour to a stripe on the head of the male, what is the smallest species of duck that is native to Britain?

Your starter for ten:

13 What given name was shared by daughters of John Frederick, Margrave of Brandenburg-Ansbach, and Charles II, Duke of Brunswick? Both of them became the queen consort of a Hanoverian king of England.

Three questions on the African leader Kenneth Kaunda, who died in 2021:
(a) Kaunda led which landlocked country in south-central Africa to independence from British rule in 1964, remaining its president until 1991?
(b) Kaunda was a leading figure in which international organization, founded in 1961 as a response to decolonization and the Cold War? It is known by the initials NAM.
(c) Kaunda allowed which political party and black nationalist organization to set up a base in Lusaka when it was banned in South Africa?

Your starter for ten:

14 Javelin, gladiator and palace are varieties of which vegetable of the parsley family? Cultivated for its tapering root, it has a sweet, nutty flavour that intensifies after exposure to the first frosts of winter.

Three questions on European queens:
(a) Which Mediterranean island was ruled by queens called Charlotte and Catherine Cornaro in the 15th century and by Queen Elizabeth II from 1952 to 1960?
(b) During the 14th and 15th centuries, Joans I and II were queens of which Italian kingdom, named after a city? It was ruled by Joan the Mad, Queen of Castile, after the death of her father, Ferdinand II in 1516.
(c) Queens of which country have included Christina, the daughter of

Gustavus Adolphus, and Ulrica Eleanor, who succeeded her brother Charles XII in 1718?

Your starter for ten:

15 From the Greek for 'narrow passage' or 'neck of land', what word was originally used to describe Corinth, but has since been associated with Seattle, Gibraltar and Panama?

Your bonuses are on the second millennium of the Common Era. All answers are years that contain at least three consecutive numbers, for example '1456' or '1239':
(a) Which year saw the completion of the official history of the Chinese Song dynasty? Work on this history had begun several decades earlier during the reign of Kublai Khan.
(b) Which year saw the completion of Murillo's *The Immaculate Conception* and of Bernini's *The Tomb of Pope Alexander VII*?
(c) Which year saw the premiere of Olympe de Gouges's abolitionist play *Zamore and Mirza* and the publication of William Blake's *Songs of Innocence*?

Your starter for ten:

16 From the Latin for 'nest', what five-letter term in ecology denotes the functional role of an organism in an ecosystem, including its interactions with other organisms and its environment?

Three questions on US presidental assassinations:
(a) Abraham Lincoln was shot by John Wilkes Booth at Ford's Theatre in Washington in what year?
(b) Which president died 80 days after being shot at a railway station in Washington? He was succeeded by his vice-president, Chester A. Arthur.
(c) The secret service assumed official responsibility for protecting US presidents after whose assassination in 1901?

Your starter for ten:

17 Developed from the 1960s by the French mathematician René Thom, what theory shows how the growth of an organism proceeds by a series of gradual changes that are triggered by, and in turn trigger, large-scale changes or jumps? It has also been applied to engineering, economic and political events.

Three questions on Afrofuturism:
(a) The term Afrofuturism was coined by the critic Mark Dery in conversation with which US science fiction writer? His works include *Babel-17* and *Nova*.
(b) Featuring the characters Starchild and Dr Funkenstein, the P-Funk

universe is an Afrofuturist mythology created by which US musician, the leader of the Parliament-Funkadelic Collective?

(c) Which Marvel superhero is the king of the fictional African nation of Wakanda, a technologically advanced society fuelled by a fictional rare metal called vibranium?

Your starter for ten:

18 Since the late 19th century, successive flags of what country have included those known as Yellow Dragon, Five Races Under One Union, Blue Sky, White Sun and a Wholly Red Earth and the current Five-Star Red Flag?

Three questions on events of 1971:

(a) Held at the Melbourne Cricket Ground in place of an abandoned Test between England and Australia, a match in early January 1971 is regarded as the first of what now-common format?

(b) 1971 saw the birth of which series of books for children, later turned into a BBC programme narrated by Arthur Lowe? The author is said to have been inspired when his 8-year-old son asked: 'What does a tickle look like?'

(c) Which BBC Two music show was broadcast for the first time in 1971? Its presenters have included Richard Williams and Annie Nightingale.

Your starter for ten:

19 Of the three contiguous historic English counties that begin with the letter 'B', which extends furthest north?

Three questions on a shape:

(a) In solid geometry, what common word is used to denote a polyhedron with two triangular and three trapezoidal faces? The triangular prism is a special case of this.

(b) Meaning 'wedge-tooth', the genus *Sphenodon* is a group of reptiles native to New Zealand and given what common name, from the Maori for 'peaks on the back'?

(c) Meaning 'wedge-shaped', cuneiform script is an early writing system originally devised to transcribe what language? It was later adapted to Akkadian.

Your starter for ten:

20 Meanings of what five-letter word include, in nutrition, the edible seeds of leguminous plants cultivated for food; in physics, a short burst of radiated energy; and in medicine, a term that may follow 'femoral', 'carotid' or 'radial'?

Your bonuses are on places that lie on or close to a straight line connecting the Spanish resorts of Torremolinos and Magaluf. In each case, name the place from the description:

(a) The mountain range that is the location of Mulhacén, the highest point on the Iberian peninsula.

(b) A major city on the River Segura, about 80 kilometres southwest of Alicante.

(c) A coastal resort northeast of Alicante; the screenwriter Derren Litton used it as the setting of a television series first broadcast in 2007.

Your starter for ten:

21 *Adult Orgasm Escaped from the Zoo* and *The Devil with Boobs* are among the English titles of works by which avant-garde actor and playwright? Born in Northern Italy, he won the Nobel Prize in Literature 1997.

Your bonuses are on aspects of culture that have been given Intangible Cultural Heritage status by UNESCO. In each case, name the country that is home to each practice:

(a) Classical horsemanship and the high school of the Spanish Riding School?

(b) The Winegrowers' Festival of Vevey?

(c) 'A festive combination of music and dances and all the practices associated with rumba'?

Your starter for ten:

22 What five-letter word connects: a cultural institution on London's Bow Street; a golf course at Hoylake on Merseyside; an oil and gas company headquartered at The Hague; and a military force whose first marshal was Lord Trenchard?

Three questions on the scientist and Nobel laureate Elizabeth Blackburn, born in 1948:

(a) During postdoctoral research at the University of Yale, Blackburn sequenced the ends of the chromosomes of the protozoan tetrahymena, identifying which repetitive DNA segments?

(b) With her PhD student Carol Greider, Blackburn discovered telomerase. This enzyme possesses what activity, allowing DNA to be generated from an RNA template?

(c) Blackburn's work with the psychologist Elissa Epel has shown that chronic stress has what effect on telomere length?

Your starter for ten:

23 Described as a tragicomedy and set in Rome, which film won Paolo Sorrentino the 2014 Academy Award for Best Foreign Language Film?

Three questions on arguments:

(a) Officially known as 'Promoter of the Faith', what two-word English expression is used in the Roman Catholic church for one appointed to posit arguments against a proposed beatification or canonization?

(b) Born in New York in 1918, which Nobel laureate is associated with a thought experiment relating to gravitational waves in general relativity, referred to as the 'sticky bead argument'?

(c) The argument that it is prudent to 'play it safe' and to believe in God's existence, rather than to risk the possibility of regret, is referred to as the 'wager' of which French thinker?

Your starter for ten:

24 Which figure of Greek mythology served as inspiration for: the 1959 winner of the Palme d'Or, set in Brazil; a cycle of sonnets by Rainer Maria Rilke; a 2004 album by Nick Cave and the Bad Seeds; and a comic opera by Offenbach?

Three questions on silence in television:

(a) Which ongoing British anthology series includes the episode 'A Quiet Night In', an almost-silent farce concerning a pair of inept burglars?

(b) Which recent animated comedy series featured the largely silent episode 'A Fish Out of Water', in which the main character attends an underwater film festival wearing a breathing apparatus that prevents him from speaking?

(c) Which US series featured the 1999 episode 'Hush', in which demons called the Gentlemen steal the main characters' voices? It was written by the showrunner Joss Whedon in response to critical praise of the show's dialogue.

Your starter for ten:

25 Taking its name from the distinctive blue line in its spectrum, which element is used in manufacturing germanium transistors and appears in the periodic table between gallium and thallium?

Three questions on annual music festivals:

(a) Montpellier Gardens in Cheltenham is the main venue for an annual festival featuring which genre of music?

(b) Founded near Oxford in 1989 by Leonard and Rosalind Ingrams, which annual seven-week opera festival is now held at the Wormsley estate in Buckinghamshire?

(c) Staged each August at Daresbury in Cheshire, what is the name of the UK's biggest dance music festival?

The Answers

1   Solitary ('poor, nasty, brutish and short'; 'through Eden took their solitary way')
    (a) Austronesian
    (b) Vietnamese
    (c) Arabic (the others are Chinese, English, French, Russian and Spanish)

2   C (Casablanca, Cotonou, Conakry)
    (a) Hall (effect, after Edwin Hall, 1855–1938)
    (b) Paschen-Back (effect, after Friedrich Paschen, 1865–1947, and Ernst Back, 1881–1959)
    (c) (Joseph) Larmor

3   *Don Quixote* (Cervantes, of course)
    (a) Seersucker
    (b) Fustian
    (c) Avignon

4   (Jean-Baptiste le Rond) d'Alembert
    (a) *Sons and Lovers*
    (b) Brangwen
    (c) 1960

5   Edwards
    (a) Television
    (b) Selenium
    (c) SECAM (Système Electronique Couleur Avec Mémoire)

6   Evelyn Waugh (in *The Loved One*, the *Sword of Honour* trilogy, *Brideshead Revisited* and *Decline and Fall*)
    (a) (Sir) Don McCullin
    (b) (Pierre) Bonnard
    (c) Keith Haring

7   Tintern (Abbey) ('Lines Written a Few Miles above Tintern Abbey')
    (a) Speed of light (in vacuum)
    (b) Boltzmann's (constant)
    (c) Planck's (constant)

8   Ballad (*The Ballad of the Sad Café*; *The Ballad of Peckham Rye*; 'The Ballad of Agincourt'. NB Drayton also wrote an historical poem in ottava rima on Agincourt.)
    (a) *Potemkin*
    (b) (Yemelyan) Pugachev
    (c) *Perestroika*

9   100 (density of air at STP is 1.229 kg/m3; 1.229*78 = 95.784)
    (a) Cepheid

(b) Dark matter

(c) Pulsar (accept neutron star)

10 (Abraham) Lincoln (who preceded Andrew Johnson/ (J.F.) Kennedy (who preceded Lyndon Johnson)

(a) *Troilus and Cressida* and Cressida Dick

(b) *King John* and John Smith

(c) *Twelfth Night* and *Night of the Living Dead*

11 Glacé

(a) Tennessine

(b) Berkelium

(c) Neptunium

12 (Otto von) Bismarck (1815–1898; the Health Insurance Act of 1883)

(a) Speculum

(b) Shoveler

(c) Teal

13 Caroline (consorts of Georges II and IV)

(a) Zambia

(b) Non-aligned movement

(c) African National Congress (ANC)

14 Parsnip

(a) Cyprus

(b) Naples (not Sicily)

(c) Sweden

15 Isthmus (Greek: *isthmós*; do not accept 'strait')

(a) 1345

(b) 1678

(c) 1789

16 Niche (Latin: *nidus*)

(a) 1865

(b) (James A.) Garfield

(c) (William) McKinley

17 Catastrophe (theory)

(a) (Samuel R. / Chip) Delany

(b) George Clinton

(c) Black Panther / T'Challa

18 China (Qing Dynasty, early republic, later republic / present-day Taiwan / People's Republic)

(a) One Day International (ODI / accept 'limited overs' or similar)
(b) *Mr Men* (and *Little Miss*)
(c) *The Old Grey Whistle Test*

19 Bedfordshire (contiguous with Buckinghamshire and Berkshire)
(a) Wedge
(b) Tuatara
(c) Sumerian

20 Pulse
(a) Sierra Nevada (accept Cordillera Penibética)
(b) Murcia
(c) Benidorm

21 Dario Fo
(a) Austria
(b) Switzerland
(c) Cuba

22 Royal (Royal Opera House; Royal Liverpool Golf Club; Royal Dutch Shell; Royal Air Force)
(a) Telomeres
(b) Reverse transcriptase / reverse transcription
(c) They shorten

23 *The Great Beauty*
(a) Devil's advocate
(b) (Richard) Feynman
(c) (Blaise) Pascal

24 Orpheus (*Black Orpheus, Sonnets to Orpheus, The Lyre of Orpheus, Orpheus and the Underworld*)
(a) *Inside No. 9*
(b) *Bojack Horseman*
(c) *Buffy the Vampire Slayer*

25 Indium
(a) Jazz
(b) Garsington (Opera Festival)
(c) Creamfields

And Finally... Monkman
Wolfson College, Cambridge

VS

Balliol College, Oxford
(2017)

The 2016–2017 series was the one that probably garnered the most media interest in recent years with two contestants, Eric Monkman and Bobby Seagull, managing to get their own BBC Two series, *Monkman & Seagull's Genius Adventures*. Eric made the final, which was contested by Wolfson College, Cambridge and Balliol College, Oxford.

Wolfson College, Cambridge
Justin Yang from Vancouver, Canada,
studying for a PhD in Public Health and Primary Care
Ben Chaudri from near Cockermouth in Cumbria, studying Natural Sciences
Eric Monkman (captain) from Oakville, Canada, studying Economics
Paul Cosgrove from Cookstown in Northern Ireland,
studying for an MPhil in Nuclear Energy

Balliol College, Oxford
Freddy Potts from Newcastle, reading History
Jacob Lloyd from London, reading for a DPhil in English
Joey Goldman (captain) from London, reading Philosophy and Theology
Ben Pope from Sydney, doing a DPhil in Astrophysics

Your starter for ten:

1   In Thomas Hardy's *The Return of the Native*, which city does Eustacia's grandfather describe as 'that rookery of pomp and vanity'? In an eponymous work of 1933, George Orwell called it 'the land of the bistro and the sweatshop'?

Your bonuses are on the ancient mathematician and philosopher Hypatia:
(a) In which city of the Eastern Roman Empire did Hypatia teach philosophy? She died there in AD 415 at the hands of a Christian mob soon after Saint Cyril became the city's bishop.
(b) Hypatia was the daughter of Theon of Alexandria, himself a mathematician and astronomer. He's credited with preserving which of Euclid's works?
(c) Associated with the philosopher Plotinus and the supreme principle known as 'the One', which late school of Greek philosophy did Hypatia espouse?

Your starter for ten:

2   First Man in Armour, Speaker of the Temple and Three Child Spirits are among the characters in which opera?

Your bonuses are on reptiles:
(a) Which country has the highest number of recorded species of reptile with more than 850? These include the freshwater crocodile and the desert death adder.
(b) With more than 800 species, which country's reptiles include the Cozumel Spiny Lizard and the Sonoran spotted whiptail?
(c) With about 750 species, which country's reptiles include the Amboina sailfin lizard and the Lesser Sundas cat snake?

Your starter for ten:

3   'I had the sound first, without the spelling. Then in one of my occasional perusals of *Finnegans Wake* by James Joyce I came across the word—'
[The question was successfully interrupted]

Your bonuses are on medieval earls of Orkney:
(a) Firstly, an early earl of Orkney, Sigurd the Stout, was killed at which battle of 1014, fought near Dublin? The Irish High King, Brian Boru, was also killed.
(b) Secondly, Sigurd's son, Thorfinn the Mighty, extended his rule over Caithness and which area? It's named after its relation to Norse settlements in Orkney rather than its position on the island of Great Britain.
(c) And finally, Kirkwall Cathedral in Orkney is dedicated to which earl, later

a saint? Known as the Martyr he was later murdered on the island of Egilsay in about 1117.

Your starter for ten:

4　Who was the UK prime minister when the short-lived French Second Republic was established? His minority Whig administration held power because the Conservatives were split between Protectionists and Peelites.

Your bonuses are on chloroform:
(a) In an 1847 paper based on his findings from self-experimentation, which Scottish physician first described the use of chloroform as an anaesthetic?
(b) Used as a chemical weapon during the First World War, which poisonous gas is generated on the oxidation of chloroform in the presence of UV light?
(c) Apart from amylene, what solvent is typically added to stabilize chloroform and prevent oxidation if long-term storage is required?

Your starter for ten:

5　[This was a picture round]

Your starter for ten:

6　Which lower-case Greek letter represents in statistics the standard deviation of a—
[The question was successfully interrupted]

Your bonuses are on duelling:
(a) In 1598 which literary figure killed the actor Gabriel Spenser in a duel fought with swords? He avoided the gallows but was branded on the thumb as a convicted felon.
(b) In Hamburg in 1704, which composer fought a duel with his friend Johann Mattheson in a quarrel during the performance of the latter's opera *Cleopatra*? A large coat button is said to have deflected Mattheson's sword.
(c) Considered the founder of modern algebra, in particular of group theory, which French mathematician died—
[The question was interrupted]

Your starter for ten:

7　What two-word term appears in the title of a work of 2005 by Joan Didion and denotes a cognitive disorder involving the belief that one event happens as a result of another without a plausible link of causation?
[Neither team got the correct answer]

Your starter for ten:

8   Traditionally regarded as a holy relic, the Iron Crown of Lombardy is housed in the cathedral of which city? Situated about 15km northeast of Milan, it is a regular venue of the Italian Formula One Grand Prix.

Your bonuses are on cosmology in the 18th century:
(a) Born in Stockholm in 1688, which thinker was an early proponent of the nebular hypothesis, the idea that the solar system formed from a cloud of rotating gas?
(b) Which German philosopher applied Newtonian principles to the nebular hypothesis in his 1755 work *Universal Natural History and Theory of the Heavens*?
(c) Which French scientist independently advanced the nebular hypothesis in a work of 1796? Noted for his works on celestial—
[The question was interrupted]

Your starter for ten:

9   Born in 1854, which Frenchman gives his name to a sphere used in optics, a symmetry group associated with the special theory of relativity and the conjecture about the topology—?
[The question was interrupted]

Your bonuses are on prose authors cited in the Oxford English Dictionary:
(a) The OED cites which Scottish author as the first user of the term 'freelance'? In this case, he's referring to a mercenary knight in a historical novel of 1819.
(b) Which 19th-century English novelist is cited in the OED as the first user of the noun 'rampage', the verb 'flummox' and the word 'doormat' when applied to a person?
(c) The OED states that which US author may have coined the word 'nerd' in the 1950 children's book *If I Ran the Zoo*?

Your starter for ten:

10 The contestants were played part of a recording of a lecture by a major 20th-century figure and were asked to identify him. This is what they heard: 'But liberty is not merely a cultural matter—'

[The recording was successfully interrupted at this point]
Bonus questions: Recorded in 1948, that lecture was one of the inaugural Reith Lectures, the BBC series of annual lectures by significant thinkers. The bonuses are excerpts from three recent Reith lectures. Identify the lecturer:
(a) [A female voice] 'The freedom to make contact with other human beings

with whom you may wish to share thoughts your hopes, your laughter and at times even your anger and indignation is a right that should never be violated.'
(b) [A male voice] 'But the bedrock nature of space and time and the structure of our entire universe are surely among science's great open frontiers.'
(c) [A male voice] 'But the thing is, I think there are boundaries still about what can and cannot be art, but the limits are softened.'

Your starter for ten:

11 Said to be based on Truman Capote, which character in *To Kill a Mockingbird*—?
[The question was interrupted]

Your bonuses are on Tudor executions. In each case, there is a list of three names of people executed in successive years of the 16th century. Name one of those three years and the name of the reigning monarch.
(a) The Nun of Kent, Sir Thomas More and Anne Boleyn.
(b) Lady Jane Grey, Nicholas Ridley and Thomas Cranmer.
(c) The Roman Catholic priest Thomas Aufield, the conspirator Anthony Babington and Mary Queen of Scots.

Your starter for ten:

12 The atomic number of sulphur is 16. What is the sum of the atomic numbers of the four elements whose symbols spell the word 'snob'?
[Neither team got the correct answer]

Your starter for ten:

13 What given name links the 17th-century Queen of Sweden known as the Minerva of the North—?
[The question was interrupted]

Your bonuses are on languages and the two-letter ISO codes used to denote them in Wikipedia addresses. English, for example, is EN:
(a) The two-letter ISO code for which major African language is the same as the internet top-level domain of the country between Turkey, Georgia and Azerbaijan?
(b) The element between potassium and scandium in the periodic table has a symbol that corresponds to the ISO code for which Romance language?
(c) Which Turkic language has a two-letter ISO code that is also the postal abbreviation for the US state between Indiana and Tennessee?

Your starter for ten:

14 In Earth science, what four-letter term denotes the zone that separates the

Earth's crust from the mantle? It is a shortened form of the surname of a Croatian seismologist.

Your bonuses are on flowering plants. In each case, give the common or the scientific name of the family described:
(a) Which family includes the clematis, anemone and marsh marigold? It's usually named after a distinctive meadow flower avoided by cattle.
(b) Which family includes the cranberry, the azalea and the rhododendron? It's often named after the low evergreen shrub that is the main food of the red grouse.
(c) Apples, almonds, cherries and strawberries belong to which family named after a common garden flower?

Your starter for ten:
15 [This was a picture round]

Your starter for ten:
16 For what does the letter 'J' stand in the abbreviation JTB, used in the modern interpretation of the philosophy of Plato to define—
[The question was interrupted]

Your bonuses are on physics:
(a) Named after an Indian physicist born in 1894, what broad class of particles in the standard model of particle physics have integer spin?
(b) What type of massless boson with zero electrical charge is involved in transmitting the strong force between quarks?
(c) Which three heavy bosons carry the weak nuclear force?

Your starter for ten:
17 Who was the first Scottish king to make a pilgrimage to Rome? He came to the throne after defeating Duncan I in battle and was himself—
[The question was interrupted]

Your bonuses are on the academic and translator David Bellos:
(a) In 1994, Bellos won the Prix Goncourt for his biography of which French author who died in 1982? His novels, some translated by Bellos, include *Life: A User's Manual* and *Things: A Story of the Sixties*.
(b) Bellos has translated several novels by Ismail Kadare from French into English. In what language were they originally written?
(c) In 1989, Bellos published a biography of which French actor and film-maker? His works include *Monsieur Hulot's Holiday*.

Your starter for ten:

18 What final letter links the English names of the four countries whose cities include Pokhara, Ziguinchor, Braga and Porto Alegre?

Your bonuses are on cities in South America:
(a) Founded by Pedro de Valdivia in 1541, which South American capital shares its name in part with a major site of pilgrimage in northwestern Spain?
(b) Home to its country's busiest airport, Santa Cruz de la Sierra is a major city in which landlocked country?
(c) Which major South American city is dedicated to St Sebastien? It was the capital of its country from independence in 1822 until 1960.

Your starter for ten:

19 In stage works, which two letters begin the names of an ancient British ruler and a flamboyant soldier in love with Roxanne? They're the title characters of the works by Shakespeare and Edmond Rostand.

Your bonuses are on geology. In each case, the contestants have to give both four-letter terms defined. The two terms in each question differ only by a single letter.
(a) Firstly, the site of excavation of minerals, and consisting of small particles, the opposite of coarse.
(b) Secondly, the unsorted sediment laid down by a glacier, for example, boulder clay, and tabular intrusive igneous rock.
(c) And finally, fine-grained sediment deposited by rivers, and a simple compound whose mineral form is halite.

Your starter for ten:

20 What three-letter word often precedes the names of plants to indicate that they are considered inferior, worthless or unfit for human consumption? Examples include fennel, violet and rose.
[Neither team got the correct answer]

Your starter for ten:

21 The timespan of which Chinese dynasty encompassed the lives of the literary figures Gavin Douglas, Thomas Mallory and Edmund Spenser?

Your bonuses are on German cities as they've appeared over the years in references on this programme:
(a) The birthplace of Brahms and Mendelssohn, which city links early European coffeehouses with the mouth of the River Elbe?
(b) The birthplace of Albrecht Durer, which city links the 16th-century pocket watch with Wagner's Meistersingers?

(c) The birthplace of Lucien Freud, which city links the limestone bust of Nefertiti with a 1973 album by Lou Reed?

Your starter for ten:

22 Which element did the German physicist Friedrich Ernst Dorn discover in 1900—

The gong sounds

At the gong, Wolfson College, Cambridge had 140 points and Balliol College, Oxford won with 190 points.

The presentation of the prize was done at Gonville and Caius College, Cambridge by Professor Stephen Hawking: 'I have said in the past that it's not clear whether intelligence has any long-term survival value. Bacteria multiply and flourish without it. But it has one of the most admirable qualities, especially when displayed by such young minds. Many congratulations to both teams and especially to Balliol College, Oxford on becoming series champions on University Challenge, a programme I have long enjoyed.'

Challenging Tales
Derailment

Bobby Seagull, 2017's Emmanuel College, Cambridge team captain, recalls a near upset before one of his team's rounds: 'Three of the team went up to Manchester early from Cambridge,' he says. 'The others left later, but their train got delayed and then the train was cancelled. They had to get on a replacement bus but the bus broke down. It was an absolute nightmare. We were in the studio, the other team already mic'ed up, and my team was still delayed. They were talking about replacing Emmanuel with another team; it was a real panic. They finally arrived, all hot, sweaty and bothered, and we went down minus 10 to 75 or something. The team was panicky, I was on edge, and I thought our journey would end there and then.' Happily for Bobby, the team rallied to reach the semi-finals.

The Answers

1   Paris
    (a) Alexandria
    (b) Euclid's *Elements*
    (c) Neoplatonism

2   *The Magic Flute*
    (a) Australia
    (b) Mexico
    (c) Indonesia

3   Quark
    (a) Clontarf
    (b) Sutherland
    (c) St Magnus

4   Lord John Russell
    (a) James Young Simpson
    (b) Phosgene
    (c) Ethanol

5   [Picture round]

6   Sigma
    (a) Ben Johnson
    (b) Handel (they were squabbling over who'd conduct the second half)
    (c) Galois

7   Magical Thinking (as in *The Year of Magical Thinking*)

8   Monza
    (a) Swedenborg
    (b) Immanuel Kant
    (c) Laplace

9   Poincare
    (a) Walter Scott
    (b) Charles Dickens
    (c) Dr Seuss

10 Bertrand Russell
    (a) Aung San Suu Kyi
    (b) Martin Rees
    (c) Grayson Perry

11 Dill
    (a) 1534, 1535 or 1536 and Henry VIII
    (b) 1554, 1555 or 1556 and Mary I
    (c) 1585, 1586 or 1587 and Elizabeth I

12 36 (16, 7, 8 and 5)

13 Christina
    (a) Amharic (AM)
    (b) Catalan (CA)
    (c) Kyrgyz (KY)

14 Moho
    (a) Buttercups
    (b) Heather
    (c) Rose

15 [Picture round]

16 Justified (Justified True Belief)
    (a) Bosons
    (b) Gluon
    (c) W+, W- and Z

17 Macbeth
    (a) Georges Perec
    (b) Albanian
    (c) Jacques Tati

18 'L' (Nepal, Senegal, Portugal and Brazil)
    (a) Santiago
    (b) Bolivia
    (c) Rio de Janeiro

19 'Cy' (Cymbeline and Cyrano de Begerac)
    (a) 'Mine' and 'fine.
    (b) 'Till' and 'sill'
    (c) 'Silt' and 'salt'

20 Dog

21 Ming
    (a) Hamburg
    (b) Nuremberg (or Nürnberg)
    (c) Berlin

22 Radon

Try Your Luck

Match

Your starter for ten:

1 Which historic castle includes the Chapel Royal of St Peter ad Vincula, within whose walls lie the remains of James Scott, Duke of Monmouth, Anne Boleyn and Lady Jane Grey?

Three questions on personality:
(a) What Greek-derived term denotes the nine-pointed diagram used by some to represent the spectrum of personality?
(b) Deriving from the Latin for an actor, what term is denoted by the letter 'H' in the abbreviation HPD, a personality disorder partly characterized by overly dramatic behaviour and feelings of discomfort when not the centre of attention?
(c) For what does the letter 'N' stand in NPD, a personality disorder sometimes known as 'megalomania'?

Your starter for ten:

2 Now an overseas department of France, which island was the birthplace of the Empress Josephine in 1763? Its chief town is Fort-de-France, and it lies about 120 kilometres south of Guadeloupe.

Your bonuses are on novelists. Each answer is a surname, and all three begin with the same two letters:
(a) Born in Austria in 1880, which author's works include a long, unfinished novel known in English as *The Man Without Qualities*?
(b) Born in Kolkata, which author's works include *The Lives of Others*, shortlisted for the Booker Prize in 2014?
(c) Born in Dublin in 1919, which author's numerous novels include *The Philosopher's Pupil*, *The Green Knight* and *The Bell*?

Your starter for ten:

3 The Shakespearean scholar Emma Smith states that which of

Shakespeare's plays is 'less a romantic comedy … than a satire on romantic comedy, in which boys ricochet between girls at random, revealing the shallowness of their impulses'? It concerns events surrounding the marriage of Theseus and Hippolyta.

Your bonuses are on physics and popular music. In each case, name the band whose name fits these scientific clues:
(a) A band whose first chart single in the USA was 'Radio Free Europe' in 1983; their three-letter name denotes a unit of radiation dosage equivalent to one-hundredth of a sievert?
(b) Taken in order, the letters representing total, orbital and spin angular momentum values in atoms spell out the name of which band, whose 2009 debut single was 'Beat Again'?
(c) Which term for energy converted per unit charge by a cell or generator is also the name of the band that had a hit in 1990 with 'Unbelievable'?

Your starter for ten:
4   Which Dutch-born Nobel chemistry laureate gives his name to a characteristic frequency of crystals, and to a related temperature and specific heat applying to solids at very low temperature?

Three questions on the art world and the First World War:
(a) Which poet, art critic and writer, whose death in 1918 was hastened by wounds sustained in conflict, championed the Cubist movement and coined the word 'surrealist'?
(b) Umberto Boccioni, who died after an accident in 1916 while serving in the Italian army, was a sculptor associated with which art movement that emphasized the dynamism and power of the machine?
(c) Killed in action in 1914, August Macke helped found which Expressionist group with Kandinsky and Franz Marc?

Your starter for ten:
5   What surname links all of these: a British poet and painter killed in April 1918; a widely used self-report instrument for evaluating self-esteem; and an American couple executed for spying in 1953 and mentioned at the start of Sylvia Plath's *The Bell Jar*?

Your bonuses are on poets and railways:
(a) 'And is no nook of English ground secure from rash assault?' Who wrote those words in a poem of protest on hearing of plans to extend the railway from Kendal to Windermere?
(b) 'The apparition of these faces in the crowd; / Petals on a wet, black bough'.

Entitled 'In a Station of the Metro', this two-line poem is the work of which poet, born in Idaho in 1885?

(c) 'Faster than fairies, faster than witches, / Bridges and houses, hedges and ditches'. Those words begin 'From a Railway Carriage', a work of 1885 by which Scottish poet?

Your starter for ten:

6   The InSight mission is a robotic lander managed by NASA that landed in 2018 at Elysium Planitia on which planet, whose deep interior it is designed to study?

Three questions on occupational surnames:

(a) What surname is that of a US film director noted for works in the horror and sci-fi genres, and has a meaning that is roughly equivalent to the Russian *plotnik*, the French *boissier*, or the German *Zimmermann*?

(b) What surname is that of the player who holds the goal-scoring record for the Ukraine national football team and has a similar meaning to the German *Schumacher*, 'shoemaker' or 'cobbler'?

(c) The winner of three Wimbledon titles, which German tennis player has a surname that is roughly the same in meaning as the French *fournier*?

Your starter for ten:

7   Mali and Kanem-Bornu were historical empires largely situated in what semi-arid zone between the Sahara desert and the more humid savannas? Its five-letter name is of Arabic origin.

Your bonuses are on plants recommended by the Woodland Trust for their ability to attract pollinating insects into a garden. In each case, name the plant from the description:

(a) A tall, hardy biennial with pink trumpet-shaped flowers; it contains a chemical used to treat heart failure and high blood pressure.

(b) What is the two-word common name of *Trifolium pratense*? Widely grown as a fodder crop, its distinctive brightly coloured flowers make it a popular ornamental plant.

(c) Finally, a vigorous woody climber with a sweet scent; its nectar-rich, tubular pink and cream flowers are used by dormice as a source of energy.

Your starter for ten:

8   Typically found in granite rock formations, which gemstone is a silicate and fluoride of aluminium, and has the value eight on the Mohs scale of hardness? It is the middle name of the poet William McGonagall.

Three questions on physics:
(a) In physics and chemistry, what letter is conventionally used to denote atomic number?
(b) Also conventionally labelled 'Z', what quantity measures the opposition of a circuit to the passage of current?
(c) In the standard model of particle physics, which fundamental force is carried in part by the 'Z boson'?

Your starter for ten:

9 After a local plant, the consumption of which was said to produce 'facial convulsions resembling horrible laughter', what island to the west of the Italian peninsula is the origin of a word meaning 'scornful' or 'mocking'?

Your bonuses are on feminist theorists. The named works were all written in French:
(a) Born in Belgium in 1930, who explored the construction of sexual difference in works such as *Speculum of the Other Woman* and *An Ethics of Sexual Difference*?
(b) Born in French Algeria, which theorist published *The Laugh of the Medusa* in 1975, followed by plays such as *Portrait of Dora*?
(c) During the 1980s, which Bulgarian-born French academic published *Powers of Horror: An Essay in Abjection* and *Black Sun: Depression and Melancholia*?

Your starter for ten:

10 I need the name of a planet here. The molecular formula for iodine monoxide is also the name of a moon orbiting which planet of the solar system?

Three questions on ferromagnetism:
(a) Ferromagnetic elements remain magnetized when an external field is removed; these include some lanthanides, and which three consecutive members of the 3d block – and I need all three?
(b) The Weiss theory of ferromagnetism says that materials can be divided into regions, each acting like an individual magnet. How are these small regions usually known?
(c) Born in 1859, which French Nobel laureate gives his name to the temperature at which a ferromagnetic substance loses its ferromagnetism?

Your starter for ten:

11 The title of a satirical film of 2006 by Mike Judge, what word was added to the Oxford English Dictionary in 2018 and refers to a society consisting of, or governed by, people considered to be stupid or ignorant?

Three questions on dictators of the Roman republic:
(a) Which Roman dictator twice ceded power in the 5th century BC to return to work on his farm?
(b) The victor of the first Roman civil war, which dictator of the 1st century BC assumed the name Felix in the belief that he was unusually lucky?
(c) Who was the last dictator of Rome?

Your starter for ten:

12 Including dresses designed for Princess Margaret and Margot Fonteyn, the V&A's 2019 exhibition *Designer of Dreams* charted the history and legacy of which French couturier, who died in 1957?

Three questions on musical chords:
(a) What term describes the note from which a chord is named, and which is often, although not always, the lowest note in the chord?
(b) What single word describes the shifting of the root to a position other than the lowest in the chord?
(c) A major chord with the top note raised one semitone is referred to by what term?

Your starter for ten:

13 Just over 4,000 metres in height, and sharing its name with the African country in which it is located, which active volcano lies close to the Gulf of Guinea and roughly midway between the Nigerian city of Calabar and the port of Douala?

Your bonuses are on words that were added to the official US Scrabble dictionary in 2018. In each case, give the word from the definition:
(a) Meaning 'little oranges' in Italian, the name given to balls of rice stuffed with a savoury filling and coated in breadcrumbs before being fried.
(b) A unit of currency in Azerbaijan. A five-letter word, it adds to the collection of about twenty playable words that begin with a 'q' but do not require a 'u'.
(c) A two-letter expression of disgust. Adding an initial consonant gives other words with meanings such as 'church seating' and 'a noise made by a cat'.

Your starter for ten:

14 Associated with Cumbria, what wind is often cited as the only named wind in Britain? Its short name is also a common noun with meanings including a piece of armour that covers the head, and the tiller of a ship.

Three questions on Christmas food:

(a) Meaning 'tunnel' in German, what cake-like bread coated in powdered sugar has an oblong shape intended to symbolize the baby Jesus in swaddling?

(b) Which German state capital city on the River Elbe is notably associated with the *Christstollen* and holds an annual *Stollen* festival?

(c) In 1491, the Pope issued a decree allowing Dresden's bakers to use what ingredient in their *Stollen*? Before that, the Church had banned its use during the fasting period of Advent.

Your starter for ten:

15 'The godfather of electronic music' and 'the father of disco' are terms that have been used to describe which Academy Award-winning music producer, born in Italy in 1940? He has worked with Daft Punk and David Bowie, and with Donna Summer on 'I Feel Love'.

Three questions on artists' models:

(a) Born in Wales in 1755, which actress sat for Gainsborough, Lawrence and Reynolds, the latter in a portrait depicting her as *The Tragic Muse*?

(b) Born 1828, who married John Ruskin and later John Everett Millais, posing for the latter in *The Order of Release*? She was the subject of a 2014 film written by Emma Thompson.

(c) Fernande Olivier, Eva Gouel, Irène Lagut and Sara Murphy were among the muses and models of which artist, who died in 1973?

Your starter for ten:

16 In rotational dynamics, the torque acting on a solid body is equal to the angular acceleration times what?

Three questions on snow and ice erosion:

(a) From the Latin for 'carrying away', what term is used for the superficial erosion of a glacier or floating ice and snow by melting, evaporation and other means?

(b) What word is used for the ablation process in which a mass of ice breaks away from a floating glacier or ice shelf to form an iceberg?

(c) From the Greek for 'descending', what name is given to wind formed when a pool of cold air blows down from a height? It is a cause of Antarctic snow erosion.

Your starter for ten:

17 Name two people, in addition to Hillary Clinton, who between 1999 and 2010 served as US secretary of state.

Three questions on cannibalism:

(a) In a legend said to have sprung from English anti-Scots sentiment, what was the surname of the Scottish cave-dwelling family who reputedly killed and ate more than a hundred people over a twenty-five year period?

(b) Associated with the Southern Gothic genre, which author's 1958 play *Suddenly, Last Summer* features an account of an apparent act of cannibalism?

(c) Released in 1991, which cult film directed by Jean-Pierre Jeunet and Marc Caro concerns a landlord who lures tenants into his building in order to butcher them as a cheap source of meat?

Your starter for ten:

18 Born in 1623, which French mathematician and philosopher made important contributions to probability theory, and shares his name with a computer programming language, the SI unit of pressure, and a philosophical argument for believing in God?

Three questions on affordable housing:

(a) The Y:Cube prefab and the Place pop-up village are housing solutions from the firm of which leading British architect? His less affordable projects have included the Pompidou Centre and the Millennium Dome.

(b) In 2018, Balkrishna Doshi won the Pritzker Prize for work including the Aranya development, an area of low-cost housing outside the city of Indore in which Indian state?

(c) Which collective won the Turner Prize in 2015 for its Granby Four Streets project, a community-led regeneration scheme in Liverpool's Toxteth?

Your starter for ten:

19 What phenomenon was captured for the first time in an image released in 2019, photographed by a network of eight telescopes across the world, taking simultaneous pictures, timed with atomic clocks, and showing an intensely bright ring of fire surrounding a dark circle?

Your bonuses are on terms that contain three consecutive identical letters, if spacing and hyphenation are ignored, such as the three 's's in 'cross section'. Identify the term in each case:

(a) First, a generic two-word term for a method of chemical analysis used to determine the relative abundance of isotopes by accelerating an ionized sample of the substance in question.

(b) A pedigree developed in a culture in laboratory conditions, which may proliferate to provide an indefinite supply of genetically identical biological units for experimentation.

(c) The fractional representation, in its lowest terms, of the number 0.375.

Your starter for ten:

20 Influenced by Impressionism, the Heidelberg School of artists was active in what country from the 1880s? Its leading figures included Frederick McCubbin and Tom Roberts, painters, respectively, of *The Pioneer* and *Shearing the Rams*.

Three questions on the nucleosome, the fundamental unit of DNA packaging in eukaryotic cells:
(a) The nucleosome consists of DNA wrapped around a core of eight proteins. Of uncertain etymology, what name is given to these proteins?
(b) While the length of the linker DNA separating nucleosomes can vary, the length of DNA that wraps around the core histones is largely constant. What is this length in base pairs? You can have 10 per cent either way.
(c) Due in part to the need for greater compaction, in vertebrates histones are replaced by protamines in the nuclei of what type of cell?

Your starter for ten:

21 The titles of a novel by Nikolai Cherny-Shevsky, the first book in Anthony Trollope's Palliser series and the first of Dorothy L. Sayers's Lord Peter Wimsey stories all contain what punctuation mark?

Three questions on aviation history:
(a) In June 1919, which British duo made the first non-stop transatlantic flight?
(b) Which Warwickshire-born engineer obtained a patent for a turbo-jet engine in 1930 and tested his first jet engine on the ground seven years later?
(c) Made by the De Havilland Company, what was the world's first commercial jet aircraft?

Your starter for ten:

22 Born in Kansas in 1920, which jazz musician is noted for his role in the development of bebop and his innovative use of eighth notes as the basic units of his phrases? Influenced by the saxophonists Lester Young and Buster Smith, his recordings include 'A Night in Tunisia' and 'Ornithology'.

Your bonuses are on foods traditionally eaten around Christmas. Give the name of the foodstuff that corresponds to the following:
(a) First, the biblical figure whose brothers were Shem and Japheth.
(b) The Irish rock band noted for songs including 'Linger' and 'Zombie'.
(c) Finally, the country of birth of the author Orhan Oamuk.

Your starter for ten:

23 In 19th-century Britain, William Butterfield and George Gilbert Scott were among the architects prominent in the revival of what style?

Your bonuses are on medical tests. For each, identify the test from the description:
(a) First, a test in which the fluid surrounding a foetus is sampled and analysed; it is used for the pre-natal diagnosis of chromosomal infections, and for sex determination.
(b) Also called a spinal tap, a procedure involving the direct withdrawal of cerebrospinal fluid by introducing a needle between vertebrae in the lower back; it can help to diagnose meningitis and cancer. I need a two-word term.
(c) A standard step in diagnosing tumours, a procedure in which cells or tissues are removed and examined, usually under a microscope.

Your starter for ten:

24 Iris Murdoch described what everyday concept as 'the extremely difficult realization that something other than oneself is real'? To Jean Anouilh, it was 'the gift of oneself', while Dr Johnson said it was 'the wisdom of the fool, and the folly of the wise'.

Your bonus questions are on 'antigrams', that is, anagrams whose meanings are the opposite, or near opposite, of that of the original expression. Examples include 'untied' and 'united':
(a) What single word is the antigram of the expression 'non-fire'?
(b) The three-word expression 'I limit arms' is the antigram of what single word?
(c) The expression 'I, not named' is the antigram of what word?

Your starter for ten:

25 By mass, what is the most abundant element of Earth's lithosphere and also Earth's hydrosphere, making up about 86 per cent of the latter?

Three questions on New Orleans in fiction:
(a) Running from 2010 to 2013, which television drama series by David Simon is set in New Orleans in the aftermath of Hurricane Katrina, with particular focus on the city's musicians?
(b) Which 2018 videogame sequel is set partly in the fictional city of Saint-Denis, an analogue of late 19th-century New Orleans?
(c) Which 2009 animated film tells the story of Tiana, a waitress in 1920s New Orleans who dreams of opening her own restaurant?

The Answers

1   Tower of London
    (a) Enneagram (from the Greek for 'nine')
    (b) Histrionic (personality disorder)
    (c) Narcissistic (personality disorder)

2   Martinique
    (a) (Robert) Musil
    (b) (Neel) Mukherjee
    (c) (Iris) Murdoch

3   *A Midsummer Night's Dream*
    (a) R.E.M.
    (b) JLS
    (c) EMF (electromotive force)

4   (Peter) Debye (1884–1966)
    (a) (Guillaume) Apollinaire
    (b) Futurism
    (c) (Die) Blaue Reiter / the Blue Rider

5   Rosenberg (Isaac; named after Morris; Julius and Ethel)
    (a) (William) Wordsworth ('On the Projected Kendal and Windermere Railway')
    (b) Ezra Pound
    (c) Robert Louis Stevenson

6   Mars (Interior Exploration using Seismic Investigations, Geodesy and Heat Transport)
    (a) Carpenter (John Carpenter)
    (b) Shevchenko (Andriy Shevchenko)
    (c) Becker (Boris Becker, meaning 'baker')

7   Sahel / Sahelian
    (a) Foxglove / *Digitalis purpurea*
    (b) Red clover
    (c) Honeysuckle / *Lonicera periclymenum*

8   Topaz
    (a) Z
    (b) Impedance
    (c) Weak (nuclear) force

9   Sardinia
    (a) (Luce) Irigaray
    (b) (Hélène) Cixous
    (c) (Julia) Kristeva

10   Jupiter (whose moon is Io)
      (a) Iron / cobalt / nickel (elements 26, 27, 28 in the periodic table)
      (b) (Magnetic) domains
      (c) (Pierre) Curie

11   Idiocracy
      (a) (Lucius Quinctius) Cincinnatus (c.519–430 BC)
      (b) (Lucius Cornelius) Sulla (Felix, 138–78 BC)
      (c) Julius Caesar (on whose death the office was abolished)

12   Christian Dior
      (a) Root
      (b) Inversion
      (c) Augmented (chord)

13   (Mount) Cameroon (Mount Kenya is more than 5,000 metres and is no longer an active
      volcano)
      (a) Arancini
      (b) Qapik
      (c) Ew

14   Helm (wind)
      (a) *Stollen* (accept *Weihnachtsstollen* or *Christstollen* as it is known during the festive season)
      (b) Dresden
      (c) Butter (previously only oil could be used, with less satisfactory results)

15   (Giorgio) Moroder
      (a) (Sarah) Siddons (née Kemble)
      (b) (Euphemia / 'Effie') Gray
      (c) (Pablo) Picasso

16   Moment of inertia (accept rotational inertia or angular mass)
      (a) Ablation (Latin: *ablat*)
      (b) Calving / calve
      (c) Katabatic (Greek: *katabatikos*)

17   (Madeleine) Albright / (Colin) Powell / (Condoleezza) Rice
      (a) Bean (i.e. Sawney Bean et al)
      (b) Tennessee Williams
      (c) *Delicatessen*

18   (Blaise) Pascal (1623–1662)
      (a) (Richard) Rogers
      (b) Madhya Pradesh
      (c) Assemble

19   (Supermassive) black hole
     (a) Mass spectrometry (or spectroscopy / spectrography)
     (b) Cell line (or lineage)
     (c) Three-eighths

20   Australia (after a settlement near Melbourne, now a suburb)
     (a) Histone (proteins) / histones
     (b) 146 (accept between 131 and 161; base pair is a fundamental unit of double-stranded nucleic acids)
     (c) Spermatid / sperm(atozoa)

21   Question mark (*What Is to Be Done?* / *Can You Forgive Her?* / *Whose Body?*)
     (a) (John) Alcock and (Arthur Whitten) Brown
     (b) (Sir Frank) Whittle
     (c) (The De Havilland DH106) Comet

22   Charlie Parker
     (a) Ham
     (b) (The) Cranberries
     (c) Turkey

23   Gothic (i.e. the Gothic Revival)
     (a) Amniocentesis / amniotic fluid (test) / 'amnio'
     (b) Lumbar puncture
     (c) Biopsy

24   Love (Murdoch's essay: 'The Sublime and the Good', 1959)
     (a) Inferno
     (b) Militarism
     (c) Nominated

25   Oxygen
     (a) *Treme*
     (b) *Red Dead Redemption 2* (accept *Red Dead 2*)
     (c) *The Princess and the Frog*

Closest Call
Reading University

VS

Imperial College London
(2022)

The early rounds of this series were filmed during coronavirus restrictions, but 126 universities colleges worked out how to organize online trials, remote practice sessions and virtual pub quizzes and applied to take part. The 28 best teams were rewarded with a trip to our studios where many of them met in person for the first time. Perspex screens divided contestants and teammates communicated via earpieces. Following 36 carefully sanitized matches, Imperial College took on Reading in what proved to be the joint-closest final to date.

Reading
Sylvian Jesudoss, originally from Thanjuvar, India, studying for a Marketing PhD
Margaret Ounsley from Reading, studying for a PhD in Poor Law History
Michael Hutchinson (captain) from Andover,
graduated with a PGCE and now teaching
Kira Bishop from Slough, studying Maths and Psychology

Imperial
Max Veng from Singapore, studying Biochemistry
Fatima Sherriff from Hitchin in Hertfordshire,
studying for a Masters in Science Communication
Michael Mays (captain) from near Montrose in Angus,
studying for a PhD in Computational Fluid Dynamics
Gilbert Jackson from Bury St. Edmunds, Suffolk, studying Chemistry

Your starter for ten:

1   I need the name of an early historian here. Who said: 'You know as well as we do that right is only in question between equals in power, while the strong do what they can and the weak suffer what they must'?

Your bonuses are on trees in English poetry. In each case, identify the poet who wrote the following lines. The three questions are in chronological order.
(a) How vainly men see themselves amaze, / To win the palm, the oak, or bays, / And their uncessant labors see / Crown'd from some single herb or tree
(b) Willows whiten, aspens quiver, / Little breezes dusk and shiver / Thro' the way that runs forever / By the Island in the river, / Flowing down to Camelot
(c) Loveliest of trees, the cherry now / Is hung with bloom along the bough / And stands about the woodland ride / Wearing white for Eastertide

Your starter for ten:

2   I need a specific two-word term. At the Tokyo Olympics, Kate French and Joseph Chong of Great Britain won the women's and men's individual gold medals in what sport, whose events include fencing, cross-country running and show-jumping?

Your bonuses are on modes in music:
(a) Which mode is identical to a normal major scale? It shares its name with the region of the Mediterranean Sea containing Ithaca and Corfu.
(b) Similar to that used in the theme to *The Simpsons*, which mode adds a sharpened fourth to the Ionian? This name also relates to an ancient region of Western Anatolia.
(c) Flattening the third and seventh tones of the Ionian gives which mode? It shares its name with one of Oscar Wilde's title characters.

Your starter for ten:

3   I need a five-letter term here. Wolfram MathWorld states that: 'Although the notion of this term is intuitively rather clear, the mathematical machinery used to deal with it can be surprisingly slippery.' Euclid himself gave the vague definition as 'that which has no part'. The source then refers to the mathematical—?
[The question was successfully interrupted]

Your bonuses are on the development of the periodic table:
(a) Firstly, born in Palermo in 1826, which Italian chemist developed the ideas of Avogadro and was influential in the atomic weight deliberations of the Karlsruhe Congress of 1860?

(b) Secondly, in 1864 the British chemist John Newlands developed what principle of element classification? Named by analogy with the seven intervals of the musical scale, it was named the law of what?

(c) In his periodic table of 1871, Mendeleev used what three-letter prefix before element names such as boron and aluminium to denote as yet undiscovered elements?

Your starter for ten:

4   [This was a picture round]

Your starter for ten:

5   Keying the words 'badass flag' into a search engine gives an image of the flag dating to the early 16th century of what European capital? The flag features three white St. Andrews' crosses resembling—?
[The question was successfully interrupted]

Your bonuses are on philosophy:

(a) *A Defence of Philosophic Doubt* is a work of 1879 by which future British prime minister, who also served as foreign secretary under Lloyd George?

(b) A founder of analytic philosophy, along with Russell and Wittgenstein, who wrote the 1925 essay *A Defence of Common Sense*?

(c) The work by Plato sometimes published as *The Defence of Socrates* is better known by what title, closer in form to the original Greek?

Your starter for ten:

6   Named after one of the three Greek Fates, which alkaloid is used in premedication to reduce bronchial and gastric secretions, as a mild anti-spasmodic drug and to dilate the pupils of the eyes?

Your bonuses are on New York drag slang as defined in the 1991 documentary *Paris Is Burning*. Give each term from the definition:

(a) Firstly, a single-word term defined by the designer and performer Dorian Corey as the real art of the insult. It usually means an exchange that's exaggeratedly savage and explicitly performative unlike its subtler form, 'throwing shade'?

(b) Secondly, an eight-letter word used to describe certain categories of drag ball performance, where, according to Corey, the aim is to be able to blend, to look as much as possible like your straight counterpart?

(c) Finally, a dance form defined by Corey as like 'taking two knives and cutting each other up, but through dance'?

Your starter for ten:

7   What capital letter of the Greek alphabet would be written if an unbroken line was drawn on the periodic table first from arsenic to nitrogen, then to fluorine and finally to bromine?

Your bonuses are on engineer Beatrice, or Tilly, Shilling:
(a) An accomplished motorcyclist, in 1934 Shilling earned a gold star for lapping at over 100mph on which former racing circuit near Weybridge in Surrey? It's now the site of an aviation and motor museum.
(b) As an engineer during the Second World War, Shilling's team notably solved a problem of engine cut-out on Spitfire and Hurricane fighter aircraft. After what bird of prey were these engines named?
(c) The team's solution was a modification to what engine component that blends air with fuel?

Your starter for ten:

8   [This was a music round; neither team could identify the 20th-century opera *Nixon in China*]

Your starter for ten:

9   I need the name and regnal number here: *The King Who Made Scotland* is the subtitle of Richard Oram's biography of which son of Malcolm Canmore, whose reign spanned those of Henry I and Stephen of England? [For the musical bonuses Imperial went on to identify just one of the historical figures from the arias from *Nixon in China*]

Your starter for ten:

10 Concerning psychological effects of colonialism, *Black Skin, White Masks* and *The Wretched of the Earth*—?
[The question was successfully interrupted]

Your bonuses are on the microbiologist Carl Woese:
(a) Woese was one of the first proponents of a theory of early evolutionary history in which ribonucleic acids proliferated prior to the evolution of DNA and proteins. What name is now given to this hypothesis?
(b) Woese is perhaps best known for proposing the three-domain system of life, separating the former prokaryote domain into which two domains?
(c) Woese's three-domain system was based on his phylogenetic analysis of the 16S subunit of which RNA-protein complex involved in the translation of messenger RNA?

Your starter for ten:

11 According to the Globe guide, a major theme of which play by Shakespeare is the insanity of desire? It states that the title promises carnival misrule, whilst what it delivers is grave and searching.

Your bonuses are on nude portraits:
(a) Described by the National Portrait Gallery as a bravura statement about the ability of women to paint hitherto taboo subjects, which British artist's works include a 1913 self-portrait of herself painting a nude female model?
(b) Which Italian Mannerist painter is widely regarded as the first female painter of female nudes in her 1613 work, *Minerva Undressing*?
(c) The first known example of a female nude self-portrait is a 1906 work by Paula Modersohn-Becker, a leading early figure in which art movement?

Your starter for ten:

12 I need a given name and a surname here: Which prominent advocate of women's rights was the wife of the second US president?

Your bonuses are on the kingdom of Prussia:
(a) In which present-day country is Konigsberg the former capital of East Prussia? The city was renamed after the Second World War.
(b) Built by the Brandenburger Company in the 1680s for trade in slaves and gold, Fort Gross Friedericksburg lies close to Sekondi-Takoradi in which West African country?
(c) In which country is the city of Neuchâtel or Neuenburg? It was under the nominal rule of the Prussian king until the mid-19th century.

Your starter for ten:

13 Derived from a Germanic word meaning 'skin' or 'covering', the word 'Sward' is often qualified by what colour, for example in the—?
[The question was successfully interrupted]

Your bonuses are on Islamic scholars mentioned in Chaucer's *Canterbury Tales*. In each case, name the person from the description:
(a) Firstly, born in 854, a Persian philosopher and writer on medicine he wrote a pioneering book on smallpox and measles.
(b) Secondly, a Persian physician and polymath born in Bukhara in about 980. His works include *The Canon of Medicine*.
(c) Finally, a 12th-century philosopher born in Cordoba and noted for his commentaries on Aristotle in Arabic, he is known as Ibn Rushd?

Your starter for ten:

14 [This was a picture round in which neither team could identify a mixed media self-portrait by Yinka Shonibare]

Your starter for ten:

15 Born in Ireland in 1819, which Irish-born scientist gives his name to all of these: the side band pattern in Raman spectroscopy, a theorem linking line and surface integrals and a law—?
[The question was successfully interrupted]

[The bonuses were pictures where Yinka Shonibare works engaged with specific works by other artists; Reading managed to name one]

Your starter for ten:

16 Thought to take its name from the practice of lighting fires for signalling, which upland area has Pen y Fan as its highest point?

Your bonuses are on planetary exploration:

(a) Scheduled for launch in 2027, *Dragonfly* is a planned NASA mission to send a quadcopter drone to explore which moon of the solar system, the only body other than Earth known to have liquids on its surface?
(b) Named after the large metallic asteroid that it will investigate, what mission is scheduled for launch in 2022?
(c) Finally, the Jupiter Icy Moons Explorer, or JUICE, will make flybys of three Jovian moons before going into a final orbit around which of them, the largest satellite of Jupiter?

Your starter for ten:

17 Combining the name of a star and a form of precipitation, what six-letter common name is given to carnivorous plants of the genus Drosera found in bogs and fens?
[Neither team correctly answered the question]

Your starter for ten:

18 I just need the surname here: *The Cantus Arcticus*, described as a concerto for birds and orchestra and the *Angel of the Light Symphony* are among the works of which composer, born in 1928 in Helsinki?

And the gong goes

At the gong, Reading had 115 points and Imperial won with 125 points having gone ahead on the last set of bonuses asked.

The presentation of the prize was made by the scientist Professor Sir Andre Geim. Of the final he said: 'Well, watching today helped me realize that the human brain is probably the strangest thing on this planet. When I was 25, I was also like a telephone book, answers popped up from my head, seemingly from nowhere. These days it takes me minutes, maybe sometimes hours. I need to mull over those questions and try to connect all those random neurons in my head trying to find those answers. I would be completely useless tonight for any of the teams. Absolutely impressive, both teams.'

The Answers

1 Thucydides
   (a) Andrew Marvell from 'Thoughts in a Garden'
   (b) Tennyson from 'The Lady of Shallot'
   (c) A.E. Housman

2 Modern Pentathlon
   (a) Ionian
   (b) Lydian
   (c) Dorian

3 Point
   (a) (Stanislao) Cannizzaro
   (b) Octaves
   (c) EKA

4 [Picture round]

5 Amsterdam
   (a) Arthur Balfour
   (b) G.E. Moore
   (c) *The Apology*

6 Atropine
   (a) Reading
   (b) Realness
   (c) Voguing

7 Pi
   (a) Brooklands
   (b) Merlin
   (c) Carburettor

8 [Music starter]

9 David I
   [Music bonuses]

10 Frantz Fanon
   (a) RNA World Hypothesis
   (b) Bacteria and archaea
   (c) Ribosome

11 *Twelfth Night*
   (a) Laura Knight

    (b) Lavinia Fontana
    (c) German Expressionism

12 Abigail Adams
    (a) Russia
    (b) Ghana
    (c) Switzerland

13 Green
    (a) Abu Bakr al-Razi
    (b) Ibn Sina (known as Avicenna in the West)
    (c) Averroes

14 [Picture starter]

15 (Sir George) Stokes
    [Picture bonuses]

16 Brecon Beacons
    (c) Titan
    (b) *Psyche* (in June 2022, this was postponed indefinitely)
    (a) Ganymede

17 Sundew

18 (Einojuhani) Rautavaara

Professional Embarrassment
The House of Commons

Journalists
(2003)

In June 2003, *University Challenge: The Professionals* saw a match-up of two occupations described on the programme by Jeremy as 'limbo dancing to become the lowest in public esteem'. On the politicians' team were Lembit Öpik (Lib Dem), Bill Cash (Conservative) and two representatives of Labour, Grimsby MP Austin Mitchell and Helen Clark, the then MP for Peterborough. The journalists were made up of staff from *The Times* and included Michael Gove, who, at the time, was an assistant editor.

House of Commons
Austin Mitchell, old Labour MP for Grimsby
Lembit Öpik, Liberal Democrat MP for Montgomeryshire
Helen Clark (captain), Labour MP for Peterborough
Bill Cash, Conservative MP for Stone

Journalists
Mark Henderson, Science Correspondent
Robert Hands, Sports Production Editor
Mary Ann Sieghart (captain), Assistant Editor and columnist
Michael Gove, Assistant Editor

Your starter for ten:

1 'Look, Tony, you've got a wife who earns a quarter of a million pounds a year, I've got a wife who spends a quarter of a million a year—'
[The question was successfully interrupted]

Your bonuses are on events of 1953:
(a) Who, in his inaugural address as US president, said, 'Whatever America wishes to bring to pass in the world, must first come to pass in the heart of America'?
(b) Having been actively involved in the Stalinist purges in the 1930s and 1940s, which Soviet chief of secret police was himself arrested at the Politburo meeting in July 1953 and charged with being a Western agent? He was executed secretly later in the year.
(c) Who was the winner of the 1953 Nobel Prize in Literature? He said of his only novel, 'I consistently urge my friends to abstain from reading it.' The novel's title was *Savrola*.

Your starter for ten:

2 Which wealthy American art collector lived in the Palazzo Venier dei Leoni—?
[The question was successfully interrupted]

Your bonuses are on benches:
(a) Which architect, born in London 1869, designed a bench for Gertrude Jekyll's gardens at Hestercombe in Somerset, the design having been much copied since?
(b) Solar powered and fitted with an internal MP3 player, a bench in memory of which rock musician was unveiled in Richmond Park in April 2002, a month after his death?
(c) What particular status has been granted to a bench in Bristol, enabling medical treatment to be given to homeless people in the area?

Your starter for ten:

3 What name connects unbleached linen used as a furniture covering with a first US navy submarine, a division of Lincolnshire, a former prime minister of New Zealand and the former keyboard player of *Squeeze*, who now fronts his own rhythm—?
[The question was successfully interrupted]

Your bonuses are on people named after white wine:

(a) Which film of 1944 is set in the 1860s and takes its title from a popular Victorian song? The title is also the nickname of the main character, a musical performer played by Tommy Trinder.

(b) Who is the author of *Hiding My Candy*, the autobiography of the Grand Empress of Savannah? She features in John Berendt's book, *Midnight in the Garden of Good and Evil*, and shares her name with a dry burgundy made from the Chardonnay grape.

(c) In the ITV's series *Footballers' Wives*, Chardonnay Lane married which character played by Gary Lucy in a ceremony described as 'so garish it made the Beckhams' look positively anaemic'?

Your starter for ten:

4 Which particle is this: in the free state it decays into a proton, an electron and antineutrino, it has a half-life of about 12 minutes, has zero net electric charge, a mass slightly greater than that of the proton and is a constituent of all atomic nuclei except than of normal hydrogen?
[Neither team answered the question correctly]

Your starter for ten:

5 Before decimalization of the British currency, if a customer had bought five items at 2 shillings and 7 pence each, how much change should she have received from a pound note?

Your bonuses are on being miserable:

(a) Which biblical figure's faith in Heaven remains constant despite his many misfortunes? He was supposedly comforted by three companions who instead aggravated his distress, prompting his words, 'Miserable comforters are ye all.'

(b) 'Heaven, as conventionally conceived, is a place so inane, so dull, so useless, so miserable that nobody has ever ventured to describe a day in Heaven but plenty have described a day at the seaside.' Which writer offered this opinion in the preface to his *Misalliance* of 1914?

(c) 'I was happy in the haze of a drunken hour, but heaven knows I'm miserable now.' Whose words were these in a song released in 1984?

Your starter for ten:

6 For your picture starter you will see a line from the chorus of a Kylie Minogue song. You need to tell me the song's title, and to make it a bit more interesting it is translated into Olde English: *Ic scule beon swa sælig, sælig, sælig, sælig.*

Your bonuses are three more examples of Kylie lyrics translated into Old English:
(a) *Tearas on minum bolstre*
(b) *Ic sodlice ne mæg þe drifan of minum heafode*
(c) *Betera se deofol the thu canst*

Your starter for ten:

7 Who is being described: born in 1802, she was encouraged by her brother James to become a writer on social and economic affairs, she espoused the abolishment movement on a visit to the USA and was a campaigner for women's rights, petitioning Parliament in 1867 to give votes to women?
[Neither team answered the question correctly]

Your starter for ten:

8 Celebrating its tenth birthday on 3 December 2002, which form of communication is estimated in the UK to average 2 million instances an hour?
[Again, no one answered the question correctly]

Your starter for ten:

9 *De Excidio et Conquestu Britanniae* is the work of which monk, born around 516 and considered to be the first British historian—?
[The question was successfully interrupted and the politicians finally had an answer correct and moved into plus figures]

Your bonuses are on optics (the branch of physics, that is)
(a) There are two conventions for assigning plus or minus signs for distances to the formulae involving lenses and mirrors. One is the Cartesian convention in which distances to the left of the optical centre are negative and those to the right are positive. What is the other?
(b) What is defined as the ratio of the focal length of a lens to the effective diameter of the lens?
(c) There are two principle forms of aberrational defect in the image produced by lenses, one is chromatic aberration due to the variation of the refracted index of glass with the wavelength of light. What is the other, produced by the curvature of the lens?

Your starter for ten:

10 From the Greek for 'unequal', what name is given in mathematics to a triangle of which no two sides are equal?
[Neither team answered the question correctly]

Your starter for ten:

11 Which word may come before 'horse' to mean a circus animal which performs its trick without a rider, before 'cap' for a type of mushroom and before 'hall' for a place where one may do as one pleases?

Your bonuses are on eponymous terms for personal language style:
(a) Whose name is used colloquially for a coded and careful use of language. Phrases such as 'Irrational exuberance has unduly escalated asset values' and 'a budgetary strategy that is consistent with a pre-emptive smoothing of the glide path for zero federal debt' have appeared in his speeches as US Federal Reserve Board chairman?
(b) Which character in *Alice in Wonderland* gives his name to an impression meaning the idiosyncratic use of language, in which the meaning of a word is determined by the speaker?
(c) Which former US vice president has given his name to a verb used colloquially to mean the construction of rambling and meaningless sentences containing large and unrelated words?

Your starter for ten:

12 [The next round was a music round. The House of Commons team correctly identified Beethoven from an excerpt from his Fifth Symphony; they went on guess one of three correct dates for Beethoven pieces]

Your starter for ten:

13 Which expression describing the human mind and its relation to the body, was coined by the philosopher Gilbert Ryle in *The Concept of Mind*, where he refers to the body in mechanical terms?
[Neither team answered correctly]

Your starter for ten:

14 Which genus of freshwater crustacean, often used as fish food, is named after the nymph of Greek mythology who was turned into a laurel bush to save her from the amorous advances of Apollo?

Your bonuses are on the Nobel Peace Prize:
(a) Which two women won the Nobel Peace Prize in 1976 for their work in the Women's Peace Movement in Northern Ireland?
(b) Secondly, since 1978 four women have won the Nobel Peace Prize. Name two for five points or four for ten.

Your starter for ten:

15 The title to which dukedom has been given to the second son of Henry IV, the younger brother to Edward VI who died mysteriously in the Tower of London, and to Edward VII's eldest son who died of pneumonia at Sandringham in 1892 and has been suspected by some of the Jack the Ripper murders?

Your bonuses are on artistic connections:
(a) In February 2003, which awards linked Dylan Thomas, the jazz musicians Artie Shaw and Bix Beiderbecke and the blues performer Charlie Patton?
(b) In January 2003, David Hockney, Antony Gormley, Gillian Wearing, Keith Tyson and the Chapman Brothers all had their work exhibited for the first time in what context?
(c) In September 2002, who took up a position previously held by Claudio Abbado, Hans von Bülow, Arthur Nikisch, Wilhelm Furtwängler and Herbert von Karajan?

Your starter for ten:

16 [This was a picture round; neither team identified the actress Louise Jamieson who played the *Doctor Who* companion Leela]

Your starter for ten:

17 Which novel of 1819 describes a jousting tournament at Ashby-de-la-Zouch in which the hero Wilfred defeats Sir Brian de Bois-Guilbert and Sir Reginald Front-de-Boeuf?
[The Journalists got the picture round and successfully identified one *Doctor Who* companion and the Doctor they accompanied]

Your starter for ten:

18 Which book of the Old Testament contains the Code of Holiness, listing regulations for eating, cleanliness, feast days and sacrifices—?

Your bonuses are on the human mind:
(a) Name the research psychologist, a professor at MIT, who published a book entitled *The Blank Slate: The Modern Denial of Human Nature* in 2002?
(b) The term 'blank slate', suggesting that the human mind at birth has no ideas, is an English version of what term taken from a Latin translation of Aristotle's *De Amina*?
(c) The metaphor of a white paper devoid of all characters appears in a discussion of innate ideas in a 1690 essay by which English empiricist philosopher?

Your starter for ten:

19 Which wading bird is known in some dialects as a 'clinker', a 'crooked bill' and a 'scooper', has an upward-curving beak and was selected as the logo for the Royal Society for the Protection of Birds?

Your bonuses are on utopias:
(a) The publication in Leuven in 1516 of Thomas More's *Utopia* was arranged by which Dutch scholar?
(b) *The Coast of Utopia*, comprising three plays *Voyage*, *Shipwreck* and *Salvage*, opened at the National Theatre in August 2002 and is the work of which playwright?
(c) *Utopia Limited*, subtitled *The Flowers of Progress*—

The gong goes

At the gong, the House of Commons had 25 points
and the Journalists won convincingly with 215 points.

Jeremy described the MPs' performance as 'frankly embarrassing', but in fairness he did say they were very sporting to take part. The Journalists went on to the semi-finals where they were narrowly defeated by the Royal Meteorological Society, who in turn lost the final to the Inland Revenue.

The Answers

1 John Prescott (arguing against a Cabinet pay freeze)
(a) (Dwight D.) Eisenhower
(b) (Lavrentiy) Beria
(c) Winston Churchill

2 Peggy Guggenheim
(a) (Sir Edwin) Lutyens
(b) Ian Dury
(c) Given its own postcode so they are not of no-fixed abode

3 Holland
(a) Champagne Charlie
(b) The Lady Chablis
(c) Kyle Pascoe

4 Neutron

5 7 shillings and 1 penny
(a) Job
(b) George Bernard Shaw
(c) Morrissey of The Smiths

6 'I Should Be So Lucky'
(a) 'Tears on My Pillow'
(b) '[I] Can't Get You Out of My Head'
(c) 'Better the Devil You Know'

7 Harriet Martineau

8 Text messages

9 Gildas
(a) Real is positive and virtual is negative
(b) The F number
(c) Spherical Aberration

10 Scalene

11 Liberty
(a) Alan Greenspan
(b) Humpty Dumpty
(c) Dan Quayle

12 [Music round]

13   The ghost in the machine

14   Daphnia
     (a) Betty Williams and Mairead Corrigan
     (a) Mother Teresa / Aung San Suu Kyi / Alva Myrdal / Rigoberta Menchú

15   Duke of Clarence
     (a) Grammy Awards (nominated for Best Historical Album category)
     (b) Covers for *G2* in *The Guardian*
     (c) Simon Rattle (conductor of Berlin Philharmonic Orchestra)

16   [Picture round]

17   *Ivanhoe*

18   Leviticus
     (a) Steven Pinker
     (b) *Tabula rasa*
     (c) John Locke

19   Avocet
     (a) Erasmus
     (b) Tom Stoppard

Publisher's Acknowledgements

The Publishers would like to thank Steve Tribe for his tireless efforts in putting this book together in extraordinary circumstances; Abigail Kemp for her enthusiasm and meticulous research in writing the additional material for the book; Clare Parody and Peter Gwyn, whose knowledge and guidance were crucial in getting all the material for the book together; and Shirley Patton for orchestrating everything from ITV's end.

Picture Credits